The Open University

MST326 Mathemat
and flui

Block 1

The cover image is of a two-dimensional Kármán vortex street (courtesy of the Institute of Computational Fluid Dynamics, Tokyo, Japan).

This publication forms part of an Open University course. Details of this and other Open University courses can be obtained from the Student Registration and Enquiry Service, The Open University, PO Box 197, Milton Keynes MK7 6BJ, United Kingdom: tel. +44 (0)845 300 6090, email general-enquiries@open.ac.uk

Alternatively, you may visit the Open University website at http://www.open.ac.uk where you can learn more about the wide range of courses and packs offered at all levels by The Open University.

To purchase a selection of Open University course materials visit http://www.ouw.co.uk, or contact Open University Worldwide, Walton Hall, Milton Keynes MK7 6AA, United Kingdom, for a brochure: tel. +44 (0)1908 858793, fax +44 (0)1908 858787, email ouw-customer-services@open.ac.uk

The Open University, Walton Hall, Milton Keynes, MK7 6AA.

First published 2009.

Edited, designed and typeset by The Open University, using the Open University TeX System.

Printed and bound in the United Kingdom by Henry Ling Limited, at the Dorset Press, Dorchester, DT11HD

ISBN 978 0 7492 2307 6

MIX
Paper from
responsible sources
FSC
www.fsc.org   FSC™ C013985

1.1

Contents

UNIT 1   Properties of a fluid

Study guide

Sections 1, 3, 4 and 5 should be read in the order in which they are presented. Section 2 features an audio activity, which can be carried out at any time during the study weeks for the first block of the course, although you are recommended to do it as part of *Unit 1*.

Sections 1 and 3 contain many ideas that may seem difficult to understand at this early stage in the course. You are advised to read through the sections, passing over any points that you find difficult. When studying Block 2, many of the ideas will become clearer, and a second look at these sections may then be beneficial.

In this unit, and throughout the course, you should take the magnitude of the acceleration due to gravity to be $9.81\,\mathrm{m\,s}^{-2}$, unless otherwise stated. You will find the solutions to the exercises near the end of the unit.

Where the icon shown on the right appears in the text, you are invited to turn to the *Media Guide* and access the non-textual resources referred to there.

Introduction

The study of fluids

It is natural to begin a course which has 'fluid mechanics' in its title with a description of the types of substance we are going to investigate and whose motions we are going to model. We begin by quoting a dictionary definition for the word 'fluid':

> **fluid 1**, *a*. Consisting of particles that move freely among themselves and yield to the slightest pressure; moving or changing readily, not solid or rigid or stable. **2**, *n*. Fluid substance (including gases and liquids).

This definition originally appeared in the *Concise Oxford Dictionary*.

This explanation contains the essential features that we need when trying to answer the question: 'What is a fluid?'. Although the word pressure is not used in the technical sense which we shall assign to it, the idea of yielding to the slightest pressure, that is, being easily deformed, is one of the defining properties of a fluid. Certainly, a fluid can be thought of as a substance that is not rigid, but there is no sharp dividing line between solids (rigid substances) and fluids. For instance, emulsion paint will become an elastic solid if left exposed to the air in its tin for some time, but if it is brushed onto a wall, it first runs and then sets and becomes solid. Thus we cannot say that paint is a fluid, without specifying or implying the exact conditions under which we are considering the paint. However, we shall be able to devise some simple guidelines which, under suitable conditions, allow us to classify most substances into one of three types: solids, liquids and gases. Liquids and gases are collectively called *fluids*. The two most common fluids are air and water. Air is an example of a gas, and water is an example of a liquid. The study of stationary and moving fluids is called *fluid mechanics*.

One of the earliest contributions to the subject was made by Archimedes (287–212 BC). He was concerned with studying fluids at rest, a branch of fluid mechanics called *fluid statics*. Archimedes' analysis of the buoyancy of submerged bodies resulted in the law which bears his name: the magnitude of the force exerted by a liquid on a body which is at rest and wholly or partly submerged in that liquid equals the weight of the liquid displaced by the body.

The study of fluids in motion is called *fluid dynamics*.

Although the Romans had a vague understanding of the relationship between flow and friction, there was no great development in fluid mechanics until the eighteenth century. Applying Newton's Laws of Motion to an element of a fluid, Leonhard Euler, in 1755, derived the basic differential equations governing the flow of a fluid; these are still known as *Euler's equations*. At about the same time, Daniel Bernoulli, in 1738, discovered some of the basic energy relationships that apply to a liquid.

See the *Media Guide* for historical information about the individuals referred to in the text.

The theories of Euler and Bernoulli were shown to have limited application by Jean-le-Rond d'Alembert (1717–1783). Using equations similar to those of Euler and Bernoulli, d'Alembert predicted that the force on a sphere placed in a flowing liquid should be zero — a situation that experimentation clearly showed to be false. Euler and Bernoulli had produced equations based on the assumption that there are no frictional forces within a fluid. This assumption may provide a good model for some flows, but for others the effects of friction or, as it is more often called, *viscosity*, are important.

A period of 70 years followed, in which the theories and the experimental results remained at variance. In the second quarter of the nineteenth century, another step forward was made by Louis Navier (in 1827) and Sir George Stokes (in 1845), who independently produced theories that included the forces on a fluid element due to viscosity. The associated equations of motion are called the *Navier–Stokes equations*. These equations are extremely difficult to solve in exact form and, in fact, analytical solutions have been found only for some rather simple flows, though existence theorems have been proved which show that it is worth looking for solutions. Usually, assumptions about the relative importance of the different terms in the equations have to be made; these lead to simplified equations whose solutions are approximate solutions of the Navier–Stokes equations. When considering flows in which viscosity can be neglected, the Navier–Stokes equations reduce to Euler's equations.

Not only are the Navier–Stokes equations difficult to solve but, even for the flow of liquid in a pipe, a problem for which the equations can be solved exactly, the prediction of the pressure drop along the pipe does not always agree with experimental evidence. This situation was rescued by Osborne Reynolds in 1883: he established experimentally that the flow of liquid in a pipe is of two types. For small velocities, the liquid moves smoothly in circular layers so that a coloured dye inserted in the liquid will produce straight lines. This is called *laminar flow*, and the equations of

Navier and Stokes provide a good model for laminar flows. However, for higher velocities, the flow becomes chaotic. Coloured dye inserted in the liquid produces a tangled array of lines. This is called *turbulent flow*, and some averaging of the Navier–Stokes equations is applied to take into account the randomness of the motion.

In 1904, Ludwig Prandtl modelled rapid flow around bodies by dividing the flow into two regions. In one region, at a distance from the body, the effects of viscosity can be neglected so that the equations are greatly simplified. In the other region, adjacent to the body, called a *boundary layer*, the effects of viscosity are very important and have to be included. This approach greatly simplifies problems of the flow around bodies in a fluid, in particular in the field of aerodynamics.

Over the past century, the subject of fluid mechanics has come a long way with many major contributors. However, the basic theories of Newton, Euler, Navier and Stokes still have wide application in many branches of science and engineering.

Since the advent of electronic computers in the mid-twentieth century, the field of *computational fluid dynamics* has developed. This involves the calculation of numerical solutions to the Navier–Stokes equations, and is now of major industrial importance.

In this course, an introduction to fluid mechanics and its application to real fluid flow is presented. For a given real problem, this will involve creating a mathematical model, by first making suitable assumptions and simplifications, then solving the resulting mathematical problem before interpreting and validating the results within the original real context.

The course introduces a selection of mathematical methods for the solution of such problems, which can also be applied beyond the field of fluid mechanics. Roughly speaking, Blocks 1 and 3 of the course deal with mathematical methods, while Blocks 2 and 4 concern fluid mechanics. However, *Unit 1* does not follow this pattern.

Scope of Unit 1

This unit sets the scene for the fluid mechanics component of the course, and will illustrate the need for mathematical methods. You should be familiar with the methods used in this unit from your previous studies.

Section 1 explains the essential differences between solids, liquids and gases, and introduces the ideas of *compressibility* (the ease with which a substance can be reduced in volume) and *viscosity* (its internal friction). The section concludes with further remarks about the scope of the course.

Section 2 gives you the opportunity to see many of the different features of a fluid in motion, by carrying out simple experiments with readily available household equipment. The aim of this section is to help you visualise the features of fluid flows that will be modelled in the course. You are not required to take any measurements or to make any predictions. The features to look for will be described on the audio.

For access to many other visual examples of fluid flows, see the *Media Guide*.

Section 3 begins the mathematical modelling process. Under certain assumptions, we model a fluid as a continuum: that is, the conceptual model has no holes or gaps (unlike a real fluid). This *continuum model* allows us to define various properties of a fluid, for example, density and pressure, at each point, and this feature is crucial to the formulation of the differential equations of motion which represent the flow of a fluid.

Sections 4 and 5 use the ideas of Section 3 to solve some problems
involving fluids at rest which are subject to the force due to gravity.
We shall make a careful study of two particular problems. The first of
these is to investigate the forces on canal lock gates due to the water in a
canal. The approach used here has important engineering applications; for
example, it can be applied to find the forces on a dam or tidal barrier.
The second problem is to develop a mathematical model of the Earth's
atmosphere. This problem illustrates the three main stages in the process
of mathematical modelling: formulation, solution and validation.

1   The nature of fluid mechanics

1.1   Solids and fluids

Our definition of the word *fluid* on page 4 gives two clues about where to
start when investigating the difference between solids and fluids; these are
the particles making up the substance, and the effect on the substance
when subject to certain forces. The properties of solids and fluids can be
explained in terms of the structure of, and the forces between, the
elementary particles (or molecules) from which the substance is formed.
However, a qualitative description can be obtained by considering the
effect of trying to set in motion a quantity of each type of substance.

Suppose that we take two glasses, with a sugar cube in one glass and a
quantity of water in the other. If we tilt the glass containing the sugar
cube, the cube will move around while retaining its shape, and as the glass
is tilted more, the sugar cube will come out of the glass in a lump. The
sugar cube behaves like a rigid solid object; it is difficult to deform its
shape. Now, the water behaves differently. If we tilt its glass, the water
will change its shape, and if the glass is tilted far enough, the water will
pour from the glass. The water is easily deformed and will *flow*, but the
sugar cube remains as a block. This gives an idea of the difference between
a solid and fluid, and so we might describe a fluid as follows: *a fluid is a
substance that flows.*

The last statement seems fine for water, and for oil and syrup at normal
room temperatures. We can think of water gushing out of a drainpipe, or
of blood travelling through our veins, as examples of flowing substances.
The water and blood are moving along quite smoothly and relatively
quickly so that the flowing motion is obvious. We tend to associate flow
with motion at speed. But now suppose that we replace the water in the
glass with thick treacle or grease, say. It is now not quite so obvious that
the treacle (or grease) will flow; it certainly changes its shape, but it does
so rather sluggishly. A mathematical meaning of the verb 'to flow' is 'to
deform continuously', thus implying a continuous movement of the
substance; but that movement may take place very slowly, as if, for
example, we pour thick treacle from a glass.

The most common definition of a fluid that can be found in textbooks, and which we shall adopt, is given below.

Definition

A **fluid** is a substance that deforms continuously when subjected to a shearing force, no matter how small that shearing force may be.

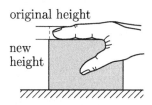

Figure 1.1

The term 'shearing force' can be explained in terms of a simple experiment. Suppose that we take a rectangular sponge and place it on a rough surface so that the sponge will not easily slide. If we press down uniformly on the sponge then it will, essentially, retain its rectangular vertical cross-section, but it will be reduced in height (see Figure 1.1), and so the volume of the sponge is reduced. The force being applied here is a *compressional force*.

If we apply a force which is tangential to the top surface, then the vertical face of the sponge will change shape as shown in Figure 1.2, the volume of the sponge being preserved. A force which produces a deformation like this is called a *shearing force*. The sponge takes up a new equilibrium position and the force tending to restore the sponge to its original shape is a horizontal force. When we remove the shearing force, the sponge regains its original shape.

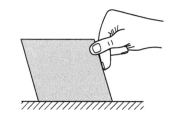

Figure 1.2

So, externally-applied shearing and compressional forces have different effects, as follows.

Compressional force	Shearing force
Tries to change the shape by changing the volume.	Tries to change the shape without changing the volume.

Now, if we could take a 'block of water' and apply a shearing force to it, then the water would be set in motion; that is, the water would flow along. It does not matter how small the force is, the water will always flow. The water cannot exert a restoring force to stop the motion and to produce a new equilibrium configuration, like that for the sponge. In other words, water is a fluid. A block of wood, on the other hand, would require a very large shearing force to change its shape significantly. The block of wood is an example of a *rigid solid.*

The description above gives an experimental way of distinguishing between solid- and fluid-like substances. Suppose that we place a substance between two parallel plates, such that the bottom plate is fixed and the top plate is free to move along (see Figure 1.3). If we apply a constant shearing force to the top plate, then the motion of the plate will tell us what kind of substance is present. The plate will exert a shearing force on the substance, and this shearing force will tend to deform the substance in a way similar to that described above for the sponge. If the plate moves with a steady velocity, no matter how small the magnitude of the force, then the substance can be modelled as a fluid. A fluid cannot withstand a shearing force without flowing.

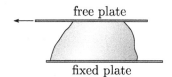

Figure 1.3

The difference between a solid and a fluid can be further understood if we look at a substance in terms of its molecular composition. Every substance is made up of molecules, and there is a force of attraction tending to bind the molecules together. When a solid experiences an externally applied force, like the shearing force described above, the force of cohesion between the molecules acts to resist any change of shape, or deformation. Furthermore, the molecules in a solid can change their relative positions by a small amount to counter the externally-applied force; for instance, an elastic spring can expand when a body is suspended from it.

In contrast, the molecules in a fluid are normally further apart than those of a solid, so that they do not have such a strong bond between them. The cohesive forces are small enough to allow a drift of the molecules relative to one another when an external force is applied.

Thus, a fluid cannot withstand shearing forces without deforming continuously as long as the force remains, whereas a solid is able to resist such forces.

The above defining properties of fluid and solid do not enable us to put all substances into one category or the other. In fact, there are some that appear to have properties of both a solid and a fluid. Putty, for instance, behaves like a solid for small shearing forces: a block of putty would be deformed a certain amount proportional to the force; but beyond a certain magnitude of force, the putty would flow like a fluid. Tar looks like a solid, is brittle to sudden blows, but flows over a period of days. You might think that flour could be modelled as a fluid, but a quantity of flour would not flow like a fluid because a finite force is required to overcome dry friction between adjacent particles of flour *before* a continuous deformation occurs.

Exercise 1.1

Which of the following substances are fluids?

> Air, oil, plastics, sand, water, golden syrup, ice, nitrogen, steel at room temperature.

Do not spend more than two minutes on this exercise.

1.2   Liquids and gases

Fluids can be classified into two types — liquids and gases. The distinction between liquids and gases may be illustrated as follows. If we pour a liquid into a container then it occupies a definite volume. A gas, on the other hand, may expand or contract to fill up any container in which it is placed. A volume of gas of 1 litre, say, can be squeezed into a container of volume $\frac{1}{2}$ litre by doubling the pressure on it; also, it will expand to fill a container of volume 2 litres, the pressure on it being halved. The same volume of water, though, will fill a container of volume 1 litre but not one of capacity 2 litres; and there is no way of squeezing 1 litre of water into a $\frac{1}{2}$-litre container.

In gases, the cohesive force between the molecules has little effect, and the movement of the molecules due to an externally applied force is very large. Molecules of a gas drift away until deflected by the boundary of a container. An important physical property of a fluid which describes the difference between a gas and a liquid is *compressibility*. The meaning of this term may be understood by considering what happens in a pump for bicycle tyres. At its simplest, the pump consists of a tube with a plunger that pushes the air out through a small hole. Figure 1.4 shows a section through such a pump. If there is air in the chamber, it is relatively easy to move the piston up and down. Suppose that you block the hole at the end of the chamber with a finger, and push down on the plunger. It is possible to move the plunger some distance before the air produces sufficient resistance to stop you. The air has taken up a smaller volume; you have been able to force the molecules closer together. Air is said to be *compressible*. Now suppose that the chamber is filled with water, and that

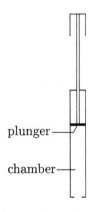

plunger

chamber

Figure 1.4

you try to push in the plunger. It is almost impossible to make the plunger move at all without applying a very large force (see Figure 1.5). Thus, in a model of this situation, we would treat the water as *incompressible*. If a fluid is incompressible, then the volume of the fluid cannot be reduced by applying a compressional force.

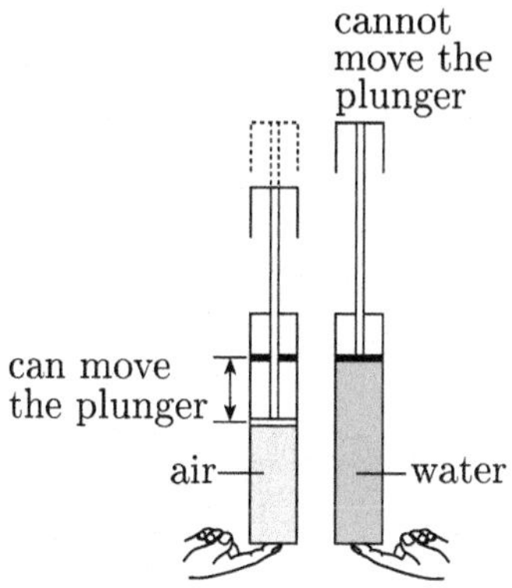

Gases are compressible, and liquids are almost incompressible. We say 'almost' because, if sound is to travel through a fluid, then the fluid must be compressible to at least a small extent. We know that sound can travel through (sea) water — for instance, it is the reason that sonar detection of submarines works — and so, when modelling sound waves in water, the slight compressibility of the water must be taken into account. For many purposes, however, liquids may be regarded as incompressible.

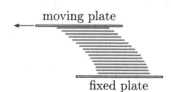

Figure 1.5

1.3 Viscosity

The manner in which air can be compressed into a given volume was explained with reference to the effect of applying an external compressional force to a volume of air in a bicycle pump. Thus, the compressible nature of a fluid can be investigated by externally applied *compressional forces*; that is, forces which tend to reduce the volume of a quantity of the fluid.

We next introduce a property of a fluid, namely *viscosity*, which is associated with *shearing forces*, that is, those externally applied forces which tend to make a substance flow. The property of a fluid that distinguishes it from a solid is its ability to flow when subject to shearing forces. Some fluids offer more resistance to shear than others. For instance, if we put golden syrup between the parallel plates in Figure 1.3 on page 11, then we would expect the top plate to move more sluggishly than if there were water between the plates. The syrup offers a much larger resistance to flow than does water, and we describe this concisely by saying that syrup is more *viscous* than water.

One model which explains this is based on the following analogy. Suppose that we put a pack of playing cards between the two plates; and suppose, further, that there is sufficient friction between the outer cards and the plates for each outer card to remain at rest relative to the plate it is touching. When a shearing force is applied to the top plate, the cards begin to move (see Figure 1.6). This motion can be modelled by slippage, each card sliding over the next. The ease with which the cards slide over each other depends on how much friction there is between them; for example, smooth new cards will slide more readily for a given shearing force than will grubby old cards.

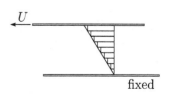

Figure 1.6

We can model the liquid between the plates in the same way, as a stack of thin layers or sheets. There is a frictional force between each pair of adjacent 'sheets of liquid', and for syrup this frictional force is much larger than for water. The ease with which one sheet of a fluid slides over a neighbouring sheet is associated with the viscosity of the fluid.

This simple idea of sliding sheets can be used to give a mathematical relationship between the shearing forces in a fluid and the velocity. Consider the flow of a liquid between two parallel plates, where one plate is held fixed and the other moves with constant speed U (see Figure 1.7). It may be observed experimentally that a fluid will 'stick' to a solid surface with which it is in contact; that is, there is no slippage of a fluid in contact with a solid. If the top plate is moving with speed U, then the liquid directly in contact with this plate will also have speed U. At the bottom plate, the liquid will be at rest, and so the speed of the liquid increases from the bottom plate to the top plate.

Figure 1.7

To keep the top plate moving at a constant speed, we have to apply a horizontal force on the plate to balance the viscous forces in the liquid which are opposing the plate motion. The viscous force is an internal friction force.

Each liquid 'sheet' tends to pull back the adjacent sheet above. It is found experimentally that if h is the distance between the plates then, to a good approximation, the magnitude of the retarding force per unit area on the top plate, τ say, is proportional to the ratio U/h; that is,

$$\tau = \frac{\mu U}{h},$$

This retarding force per unit area is also called the *shear stress* exerted on the plate by the liquid.

where μ, the constant of proportionality, is the *coefficient of viscosity*. The value of μ depends on the physical properties of the fluid. This relation was first formulated by Sir Isaac Newton and hence is known as *Newton's model of viscosity*. This mathematical model for the viscous forces in a fluid will be discussed more fully in *Units 7 and 8*.

Exercise 1.2

Consider the formula $\tau = \mu U/h$, in which τ is a force magnitude per unit area, U is a speed and h is a distance. In the SI system of units, what are the units of the coefficient of viscosity, μ?

Table 1.1 shows values of the coefficient of viscosity, μ, for various fluids at a temperature of 20°C. Note that, at this temperature, lubricating oil is nearly 100 times as viscous as water. We have to specify a temperature when discussing the viscosity of a fluid because it is temperature-dependent. For example, if you heat golden syrup, then it flows more easily; in fact, at 25°C the viscosity of golden syrup is $35 \, \text{kg} \, \text{m}^{-1} \text{s}^{-1}$, whereas at 35°C it is $10 \, \text{kg} \, \text{m}^{-1} \text{s}^{-1}$. The viscosity of a liquid diminishes with increases in temperature, whereas gases increase in viscosity as the temperature rises.

Table 1.1

Fluid	Coefficient of viscosity at 20°C (in $\text{kg} \, \text{m}^{-1} \text{s}^{-1}$)
air	0.018×10^{-3}
hydrogen	0.009×10^{-3}
lubricating oil	98.6×10^{-3}
mercury	1.55×10^{-3}
oxygen	0.020×10^{-3}
water	1.002×10^{-3}

A substance such as tar or syrup is very hard to shear; that is, it almost behaves like a solid. Such substances are very viscous, whereas water is only slightly viscous. So we think of the viscosity of a fluid as the reluctance of the fluid to move when acted on by a shearing force, or as the internal friction of the fluid.

Some substances have very small viscosities, and in many applications the viscous force is negligible when compared with other forces, so we form a model in such cases in which we assume that the viscosity is zero — such a fluid is said to be *inviscid*. A fluid which is both inviscid and incompressible is called an *ideal fluid*. Inviscid fluids and ideal fluids do not exist in reality; they are models. In many flow problems, water can be modelled as an ideal fluid.

In this course we begin our investigation of fluid flows, in *Units 5 and 6*, by taking a simple model of a fluid which neglects the effects of viscosity. The flow is said to be *ideal flow*. However, in *Units 7 and 8*, we develop a mathematical model which includes viscosity.

An ideal flow never really exists because there is always some viscosity present. However, under certain circumstances, ideal flow is an excellent model of a real flow. For instance, the flow of air over a car can be modelled by considering three regions (see Figure 1.8): a very thin region called the *boundary layer* in which viscosity is important; the region outside the boundary layer where the forces due to viscosity are negligible

Often, when studying the dynamics of particles and rigid bodies, we neglect friction, so this is a reasonable starting point in our approach to fluid dynamics.

when compared with other forces; and a third region behind the car called the *wake*, where the flow has separated from the surface of the car.

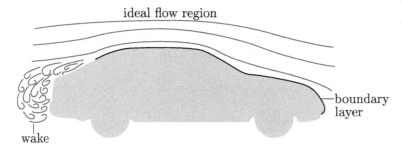

Figure 1.8

So the fluid flow is divided into various regions in which different modelling assumptions will be appropriate. The flow in the outer region can be taken as ideal flow, in which we use our simplest model without viscosity. In fact, this turns out to be a very good approximation to the real flow, so *there is value in investigating ideal flows.*

1.4 Flow visualisation

The exact motion of a moving fluid is not always easy to see. On a windy day, for instance, we cannot see the actual motion of the air but only its effect on clouds, trees, or leaves on the ground. The patterns produced by a moving fluid are often so complicated that we cannot analyse all of the details mathematically, and visual images are used to show the features of interest in a real flow.

Various methods of flow visualisation are used to give a pictorial representation of flows. Three of these methods are described below.

See the *Media Guide* for access to illustrations of flow visualisation methods.

The simplest procedure is to inject liquid dye into the flow of a liquid (without disturbing the flow). Dyes which are commonly used within water flows include potassium permanganate, gentian violet and methyl blue. Figure 1.9 shows a stream of dye injected into the swirling flow near a plughole. This type of feature in a fluid flow is called a *vortex*.

The flow of a gas can be visualised by the introduction of smoke into the flow. The smoke patterns clearly illustrate the subsequent flows. Figure 1.10 (overleaf) shows smoke introduced into the flow of air past a solid object. One of the difficulties of introducing smoke is that it may disturb the gas flow that we are trying to visualise. However, the method works well in wind tunnels specially designed for the purpose, provided that the wind speed is not too high.

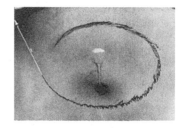

Figure 1.9

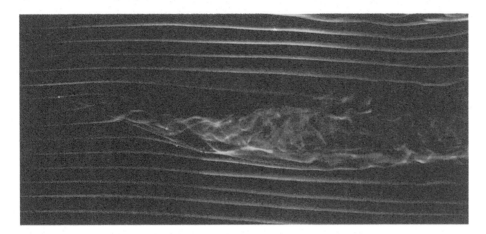

Figure 1.10

The third photograph, Figure 1.11, shows the complicated flow behind a circular cylinder placed in a stream of water. The visualisation method used in this experiment is a fine surface powder. The use of suspended particles is a common flow visualisation method. Of the various particles available, small polystyrene beads are particularly useful in water.

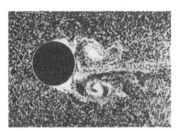

Figure 1.11

The type of flow visualisation method used depends on which features of the flow are being examined. The use of dye produces thin lines in the fluid called *streaklines*, whereas fine surface powder provides an overall picture of the structure of the flow.

Flows can be classified in many ways; we use terms such as turbulent, laminar, steady, unsteady. In *laminar flow*, the fluid flows in laminas, or layers, and dye injected into the flow will leave a thin line. In *turbulent flow*, the dye would soon become irregular and tangled up, thus showing the chaotic motion that exists. Figure 1.12 provides a simple example of laminar and turbulent flows in the smoke rising from a cigarette.

To start with, the smoke rises smoothly in *laminar flow*, but then the smoke begins to flow irregularly and the column widens into chaotic motion; the flow is now *turbulent*. The transition from the laminar flow to the turbulent one takes place over a narrow region.

Laminar flows are less likely in low-viscosity fluids or high-velocity flows. In such circumstances, laminar flow soon breaks down into turbulent flow. In this course, we shall for the most part consider mathematical models of laminar flows. However, *Unit 13* considers turbulent flows.

Figure 1.12

Steady flow occurs when the conditions at every point in the fluid are independent of time. What this means is that photographs taken of the flow at different times will look identical. Water being pumped along a pipe with a low constant velocity is an example of a steady flow; whereas, if the velocity is changing with time, then the flow will be *unsteady*. Note that turbulent flows are *not* steady, locally; however, mathematical models of such flows do treat them as steady, which is satisfactory provided that *average* velocities over a reasonable time interval remain constant.

Other classifications of flows will be discussed in later sections of this unit and in later units.

1.5 Scope of the course

We finish this section by giving three examples of applications of fluid mechanics, indicating where in the course we shall investigate some of the features that occur.

Figure 1.13 shows the flow from left to right of a liquid past a circular cylinder. The flow may be considered in three parts, as indicated in Figure 1.14 (and as already seen for a car in Figure 1.8):
(a) the smooth laminar flow in the region outside the boundary layer;
(b) the flow within the boundary layer (attached to the cylinder);
(c) the flow in the wake.

A simple model of the flow can be obtained by neglecting viscosity, and we should expect this to represent the flow in region (a) very well; but we should not expect it to be a good model for the flow in regions (b) and (c), since the boundary layer and wake are regions where viscous forces are not negligible. The zero viscosity model (investigated in Block 2) predicts the ideal flow pattern shown in Figure 1.15; it appears to give a good approximation for the flow outside the boundary layer. A mathematical model of the flow in the boundary layer and the wake, where viscous forces are not negligible, is far more complicated. The essential features in this region are the vortices. We shall discuss the motion of vortices in *Unit 7*, and suggest how they affect the forces on the cylinder due to the flow of the fluid. Boundary layers are considered further in *Unit 13*.

The study of waves is an important branch of fluid mechanics, and we shall introduce some of the ideas and terminology of wave phenomena in *Unit 12*. The ability of a fluid to deform under the action of very small forces can be seen easily in the following experiment. If you fill a bowl almost to the brim with water, and blow across it, the surface of the water deforms and small ripples are formed. Waves of this type are called *surface waves*. You will see in *Unit 12* that, in shallow water, the speed of these waves depends only on the water depth.

Waves are very common phenomena: for example, wind-generated waves on the sea, or bow waves generated by a ship. The designers of ships and fixed structures such as oil rigs have to consider the effects of the water waves that are likely to pound them. The continual battering by waves in the sea can have serious consequences for the lifespan of a structure.

Sound generated by musical instruments is transmitted to the listener by vibrations of the air. These vibrations are called *acoustic waves*. The properties of acoustic waves in air have some similarity to the behaviour of surface waves in water.

An introduction to the theory of water waves is given in *Unit 12*. The model used, which neglects viscosity, provides an adequate description of the surface waves on a fluid. However, the surface effects are influenced by the viscosity of the fluid; the damping of the waves is caused by viscous forces.

The neglect of viscosity in the formulation of the mathematical model to represent these real situations yields soluble mathematical problems. However, the effects of viscosity are evident in the real physical situations.

Viscosity is the central feature in the mathematical theory of *lubrication*. A film of lubricant (e.g. oil, water, grease) is used between moving surfaces to reduce the wear that would result if the surfaces were dry. Ideally, the fluid keeps the surfaces apart, and the friction that results is due only to the viscous forces in the fluid.

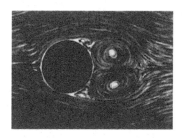

Figure 1.13 The flow past a circular cylinder

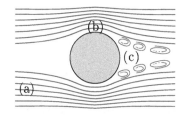

Figure 1.14 The flow past a cylinder in three parts

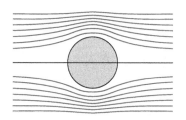

Figure 1.15 Ideal fluid flow

Every joint in the human body is lubricated by a natural fluid. If this fluid becomes ineffective, then physical ailments such as arthritis may result.

Every machine that has moving parts requires lubrication, so that a
knowledge of the theory of lubrication is important to the design engineer.
This is one of the most important applications of viscous flow theory.

A bearing in a machine is used to support large loads, and many types of
bearing have been devised. A simple type called a *slider bearing* is shown
in Figure 1.16. The inclined pad (the slider) supports a load and the lower
surface (the bearing) moves relative to the slider. The lubricating fluid lies
between the two surfaces. The surfaces are inclined to enable the fluid to
build up a high pressure which can be used to support very large loads.
The gap between the slider and bearing is small ($\simeq 2.5 \times 10^{-2}$ mm)
compared to the length of the slider ($\simeq 150$ mm).

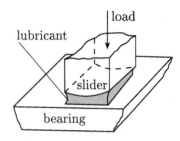

Figure 1.16   A slider bearing

These examples show the importance of knowing the important physical
features in a problem, and illustrate the potential limitations of the
mathematical model when solving a fluid mechanics problem.

Before attempting the following exercise, read the summary of this section
given in the *Handbook*.

End-of-section exercise

Exercise 1.3

(a) Classify the following statements as true or false.

  (i)   A fluid cannot remain at rest if a shearing force is applied.

  (ii) Shearing forces cause continuous distortion of fluids, which is not
        reversed once the force is removed.

  (iii) Gases are fluids.

  (iv) Liquids are not fluids.

  (v)   Gases and liquids are both fluids.

  (vi) A fluid may be either a gas or a liquid.

  (vii) A gas will expand to fill its container completely.

  (viii)A fluid is considered to be incompressible.

  (ix) The molecules of a fluid are more mobile than those of a solid.

(b) Explain the effect of compressional forces and shearing forces on a
    volume of liquid.

(c) In this section you have seen examples in which the flow of a fluid can
    be split into three regions (for the purpose of modelling): ideal flow
    region, wake and boundary layer. In which of these regions is viscosity
    omitted from the model? On what grounds is this step taken?

2 Some simple experiments (audio)

In this section you will have the opportunity to get your hands wet by doing some simple experiments which illustrate some of the features of fluid flow that will be described in this course. The apparatus for each experiment should be collected together according to the lists given, and the experiments should be carried out while listening to the audio. The presenter describes what features to look out for. Stop and start signals are not used during the experimental sessions, but long pauses have been left to give you time to observe what is happening.

Keep the audio going right through each session.

You do not need complicated equipment to observe fluid flow behaviour; important phenomena can be seen all around the house. For example, we ask you to begin in the bathroom.

Session 1   You will need the following:

(i)   a bath with approximately 10 centimetres of water in it;

(ii) a ruler;   (iii) a pencil;   (iv) some powder, e.g. talcum powder.

For this experimental session, you will need to be able to listen to your audio-player in the bathroom. If this is not possible, then you could either make a note of what to look out for, or carry out the experiments in a large bowl of water in the vicinity of your audio-player.

You will probably find a portable CD player most convenient. In any case, be aware of the danger of water in the presence of an electrical appliance.

When you are ready, start the audio at Track 1 of CD1.

At the end of this session, you may need some time to clean the bath!

Session 2   You will need to be able to create a column of smoke, for which you will need a sheltered place away from combustible materials and smoke alarms.

This experiment should not be performed in a room without ventilation. Make sure that any burning materials are fully extinguished when you have finished.

To do this, you could take an old plate or ashtray and burn something in it. You will have to experiment a bit to produce a good column of smoke. String works well if you set it alight and then blow out the flame so that it smoulders. Just blowing out a match also produces a column of smoke, but it is short-lived.

When you are ready, start the audio at Track 2 of CD1.

Session 3   You will need the following:

(i)   two sheets of A4 paper;   (ii) a cotton reel;   (iii) a postcard;

(iv) a drawing pin.

You can carry out this experimental session anywhere.

You will need to arrange the cotton reel, postcard and drawing pin as shown in Figure 2.1 below.

Figure 2.1

When you are ready, start the audio at Track 3 of CD1.

3   Formulating mathematical models

The process of mathematical modelling consists of three main stages. We take a problem set in the real world and first *formulate* it as a mathematical problem. The mathematical problem is then *solved* (where possible) and, finally, the solution is translated back into the original context so that the results produced by the model can be *validated* and interpreted to help solve the real problem.

Most real problems which involve fluid mechanics are very complex and involve the interplay of many physical effects. The art of mathematical modelling, in fluid mechanics as elsewhere, is to make simplifying assumptions so that the model includes the most important features of the problem and neglects others. Often we do not know just what is important until a model has been constructed and found inadequate. For example, in the theory of aerodynamics, a simple mathematical model neglecting viscosity does not predict any drag at all on an aerofoil in a flow of air, even though the effects of viscosity are rather small compared with engine thrust and gravitational forces. A better model is called for.

This course is not specifically about the process of mathematical modelling, but you will see mathematical modelling in action. We shall formulate real problems as mathematical problems; we shall use some of the methods in the course to solve these mathematical problems, and the solutions will be validated and the models criticised by comparison with real flows.

To make a start on the modelling formulation, we develop a mathematical framework in which to work by representing properties of the fluid by variables. The mathematical model will then take the form of relationships between these variables (e.g. differential equations).

You may find some of the ideas in this section difficult to understand at this early stage of the course. These concepts will become clearer as you study the units in Block 2. Also, see the *Media Guide* for appropriate references.

3.1   The continuum approach

All real fluids are composed of molecules, separated by empty regions. For example, at room temperature there are around 10^{20} air molecules in a thimble, the average distance apart being 3×10^{-9} m. Because fluid molecules are so numerous, and because they have a random time-dependent distribution in space, it is impossible to use their individual velocities to describe the flow of a fluid. So we seek a model for a fluid which ignores the molecular structure but in which fluid properties such as density (mass of molecules per unit volume) can be modelled accurately. In particular, in most applications under normal physical conditions, the gaps between molecules are many orders of magnitude smaller than the size of a characteristic length in a flow (e.g. the length of a car in the flow of air past the car), and ignoring the gaps in such applications is not significant. Indeed, to the naked eye, the fluids with which we are most familiar — air and water — do not appear to be comprised of molecules and gaps, and this leads us to describe fluids as 'continuous', i.e. having no gaps or holes. We take this as our fundamental assumption in formulating the mathematical model to describe the flow of a fluid. It amounts to taking a macroscopic view of the flow of a fluid rather than a microscopic one involving molecules.

Continuum hypothesis

We shall *assume* that a fluid is a perfectly continuous substance with no gaps or holes in it.

The mathematical model based on the continuum hypothesis is called the **continuum model**.

As indicated, this model is a good one for problems in which the physical dimensions of an object in a fluid or a fluid container are much larger than the distance between the molecules of the fluid, i.e. several orders of magnitude larger than 10^{-9} m. However, because of disregarding the molecular structure of a fluid in the continuum model, this approach does not completely represent reality; that is, there are situations in which the continuum model will fail. For example, at high altitudes, the number of air molecules per unit volume is small, and the average distance between molecules may be larger than the object whose motion is being investigated. However, such situations do not feature in this course; we shall consider only situations where the continuum model applies.

Now that we have a mathematical model of a fluid, we can define the properties of a fluid in terms of variables, and because the region is taken to be continuous, that is, it has no holes or gaps in it, we can apply the limiting processes of calculus to focus our attention on 'points' in this model of a fluid.

We begin by defining a property of a fluid called the *average density*, which specifies the mass of the fluid in a given 'small' volume, where 'small' means small in all linear dimensions. Such a volume will be called a **fluid element**. The following definition is typical of several that we shall make within the continuum model.

A fluid element is analogous to a volume element, as introduced in MST209 *Unit 25.*

Definition

Consider a fluid element B, with volume δV, contained wholly within the fluid, and suppose that the mass of fluid within B is δM.

The **average density** of the fluid within B is

$$\rho_B = \frac{\delta M}{\delta V}.$$

In SI units, mass and length are measured in kilograms and metres, respectively, so the units of average density are $\mathrm{kg\,m^{-3}}$.

Average density is a scalar quantity.

Now consider a particular point in a fluid, P say; we can imagine P to be in many different fluid elements of volume δV (see Figure 3.1). Each fluid element could contain a different mass of the fluid, so that the average density would depend on the fluid element we consider. In the model, our aim is to associate a unique density with each point P in a fluid. We do this by considering smaller and smaller fluid elements, with volumes $\delta V_1, \delta V_2, \ldots$, each containing the point P, thus smoothing out variation in ρ_B. *Within the continuum model*, we may assume that the fluid elements (no matter how small) always contain some fluid. So, as the volumes of successive elements $\delta V_1, \delta V_2, \ldots$ become smaller, the variation in average density of the fluid across the fluid element becomes smaller, so that the ratios $\delta M_1/\delta V_1, \delta M_2/\delta V_2, \ldots$ approach a constant value. Expressed mathematically, we say that in the limit as $\delta V \to 0$, the ratio $\delta M/\delta V$ tends to a unique value.

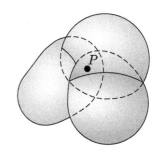

Figure 3.1

This process of taking the limit generalises to other properties.

Definition

Suppose that δV is the volume of an arbitrary fluid element containing the fixed point of interest, P say, and that δM is the mass of fluid within the fluid element. Taking smaller and smaller fluid elements, each containing P, the **density of the fluid at the point** P is the limit as $\delta V \to 0$ of $\delta M / \delta V$; we write

$$\rho = \lim_{\delta V \to 0} \frac{\delta M}{\delta V}$$

for this density (provided that the limit exists).

The SI units of density at a point are $\mathrm{kg\,m}^{-3}$, the limiting process having no effect on the units of δM or δV.

Like average density, density at a point is a scalar quantity.

In reality, there is no such thing as 'the density at point P', because the point P is either inside an atom, where the density is high, or in empty (inter-molecular) space where the density is zero. *In this definition, we are assigning a (point) density to the continuum model of the fluid and not to the real fluid.*

As an example of what happens in a *real* fluid as the fluid elements become smaller, consider the average density of a small element B of air, taken in the shape of a cube of side length a (in metres). If we calculate the average density of the air within the cube, that is, $\rho_B = m/a^3$, where m is the mass of air in the cube (in kg), the result varies with the size of the cube. Figure 3.2 shows this variation. Below about 10^{-8} metres, the average density fluctuates quite appreciably because there are relatively few molecules within the cube, and the average distance between the molecules is quite large on this scale. Between about 10^{-8} and 10^{-4} metres, the average density can be taken quite reasonably as a constant. Provided that the small volume has all linear measurements no smaller than about 10^{-8} metres, the assumption that the average density approaches a definite value is quite acceptable as a mathematical model of the real situation.

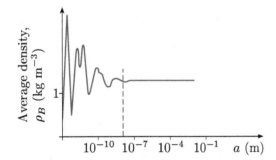

Figure 3.2   Average density of air

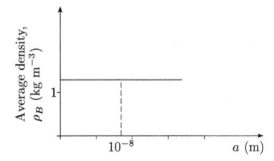

Figure 3.3   Average density for continuum model of air

Let α be the volume of a very small *sample volume*, with all linear dimensions no smaller than an order of 10^{-8} metres. Then the definition of (point) density could be written as

$$\rho = \lim_{\delta V \to \alpha} \frac{\delta M}{\delta V}.$$

The continuum model allows us to take limits as δV tends to zero, but we must remember that reality restricts the size of δV to the sample volume α. The continuum model assumes an average density graph like that shown in Figure 3.3. Notice that the variation below 10^{-8} metres, due to the molecular fluctuations, has disappeared in our 'smoothing process' of taking the limit to zero.

Table 3.1 shows the values of the density for various fluids at a temperature of 20°C (like viscosity, density is temperature-dependent). Notice that the densities of the gases are much smaller than those for the liquids. This is what a 'molecular view' of the fluids would tell us; the molecules of a gas are much further apart than for a liquid, and so, in a given fluid element, we should expect to find fewer of them, but moving much faster.

Table 3.1

Fluid	Density at 20°C ($\mathrm{kg\,m^{-3}}$)
air	1.20
hydrogen	0.084
mercury	13 546
oxygen	1.33
water	998

The density of a gas also depends on its pressure. The data in Table 3.1 are for a pressure of 1 atmosphere. (Subsection 3.2 introduces fluid pressure and its units of measurement.)

Before we can proceed to formulate the basic equations of fluid mechanics, we need to be able to label 'bits of the fluid'.

In particle dynamics we take, as our basic lump of matter, a *particle*, which is thought of as a concentration of matter that occurs at a single point in space. This is clearly a mathematical idealisation, but one that provides a framework on which to build and describe the motion of real objects. Newton's Laws of Motion applied to a particle provide the relationships between the position of the particle and the forces acting on it. Newton's laws are themselves a model, which agrees particularly well with reality in certain situations. In fluid mechanics we have, as our basic mathematical idealisation, the continuum hypothesis. However, we cannot write down a description of the flow of a fluid without resorting to a description of what happens at points in the fluid. So we adopt a particle approach like that in particle dynamics.

We define a **fluid particle** to be a concentration of fluid that occupies a single point in space. In the same way that a particle is a mathematical idealisation, so too is a fluid particle. By fluid particles we do *not* mean the molecules of a fluid.

Note that, although we use the term *fluid* particle, the concept exists within the continuum model, not in reality (for actual fluids). Sometimes the synonym *material point* is used.

In reality, we cannot consider properties of a fluid defined at a point; we can take fluid elements only as small as the sample volume. However, in the mathematical model, we can take the volume of a fluid element containing a point P to be as small as we like. In the limit as $\delta V \to 0$, we close in on the fluid particle at P, thus defining the properties of the fluid at P. For example, in this subsection we have defined the density of the fluid at P by considering the limit as $\delta V \to 0$ of the average density in the fluid element of volume δV.

The ideas introduced in this subsection are summarised in Table 3.2 below.

Table 3.2

	Real world	*Mathematical model*	
fluid	molecules, gaps between molecules	continuous matter, no gaps or holes	continuum
fluid element of volume δV	is 'small' and has any shape / average properties can be defined over volume δV		fluid element of volume δV
sample volume $\delta V \to \alpha$	has size	a point in space	fluid particle $\delta V \to 0$
	average properties of a fluid uniform throughout α (sometimes called *local* values)	can define properties of a fluid at a point (sometimes called *point* values)	

The link between the real world and the mathematical model is the fluid element. We shall use fluid elements of a definite size to define average values of the properties of a fluid and, by taking limits, we can define the properties at a point. Further (in later units), by considering the forces acting on the surface and throughout the volume of the fluid element, we shall be able to build up a mathematical theory to describe the motion of a fluid particle, and hence to arrive at a description of the flow of the fluid.

Exercise 3.1

Classify the following statements as true or false.

(a) In the continuum model, all the defined terms relate to molecules of the fluid.

(b) Molecules have no place in the continuum model.

(c) A fluid element contains many fluid particles.

(d) In the continuum model, fluid particles are considered to be points in the mathematical sense.

3.2   Pressure

The concept of *pressure* is of particular importance in fluid mechanics. When a ship floats, there is an upward force on it due to the water, which balances the weight of the ship. Also, it is important for an engineer designing a dam to know the force on the dam due to the water. The forces on the ship and on the dam can be calculated in terms of the pressure distribution in the water at the solid surface.

But what is 'pressure'? When a hole is made in a tank with vertical sides, containing water, the water will gush out (see Figure 3.4). Suppose that we put a flat metal plug over the hole to stop the water from flowing. The plug will remain at rest only if we apply an external force to it. It is reasonable to assume that the water exerts a force over that part of the plug which is in contact with the water. Now, since the water is at rest when the plug is in position, there are no shearing forces on the plug. The direction of the force at each point of the plug is perpendicular to the plane of the plug. Suppose that the area of the hole is A, and that the magnitude of the force on the plug is F; then the ratio F/A is called the average pressure on the plug due to the water in the tank. We use this idea to define the average pressure in a fluid.

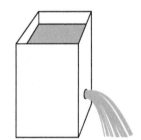

Figure 3.4

Definition

Let S be any flat surface element in a static fluid. Let S have area δA and let P be the point of S at which the resultant vector force $\delta \mathbf{F}$ on S (due to the fluid) acts, with direction normal to the plane of S (see Figure 3.5). Let δF be the magnitude of this force. We define the **average pressure** on S to be

$$p_S = \frac{\delta F}{\delta A}.$$

Briefly, average pressure is normal force magnitude per unit area.

The units of average pressure are the units of force divided by those of area; in SI units, $\mathrm{N\,m^{-2}}$. This unit is known as the *pascal* (Pa); that is, $1\,\mathrm{Pa} = 1\,\mathrm{N\,m^{-2}}$.

A surface element is the same as an area element, as used in MST209 *Unit 25*.

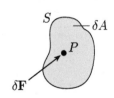

Figure 3.5

Note that the definition of average pressure applies to any flat surface element in the fluid. Furthermore, $\delta F/\delta A$ is a scalar quantity, because δF and δA, as defined, are magnitudes; that is, given any system of units, both δF and δA are fully specified by real numbers.

Pressure in a fluid can be explained in terms of molecular impacts. The molecules that make up a fluid are in random motion, and experience many collisions with each other and with any surface introduced into the fluid. Each collision results in a change in the linear momentum of the molecules (according to Newton's Second Law); that is, the force of the surface on a molecule of the fluid equals the rate of change in linear momentum of the molecule. The continual bombardment of the surface by the fluid molecules (see Figure 3.6) results in a force on the surface; by Newton's Third Law, the force on the molecule exerted by the surface equals in magnitude the force exerted on the surface by the molecule.

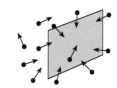

Figure 3.6

If we average the force on a small surface element over time, then we can derive a model for the surface force. Modelling the molecules as small spheres, we can imagine an impact like that of a snooker ball on the edge of a snooker table (see Figure 3.7). The force on the table during the impact is along the normal, because the momentum change of the ball is along the normal. Some of the component of linear momentum of the snooker ball along the normal direction is transmitted to the wall of the snooker table in the impact. In an analogous way, when the molecules collide with the surface, the direction of the force is perpendicular to the surface. Summing all the effects of the many collisions gives a force with direction along the normal to the surface, which is an assumption that we make in the definition of pressure.

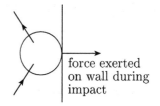

force exerted on wall during impact

Figure 3.7

Pressure, then, is associated with the normal component of the force pushing against a surface. There is a pressure at every point in a fluid, and it becomes apparent when a body is placed in the fluid and experiences forces. Pressure gives rise to a force distribution over any surface placed within a fluid.

In a static fluid, there is no component of the force on a surface other than the normal one. Where the fluid moves, there will also be a tangential component of force on the surface, due to viscosity (although certain models ignore this).

We now introduce the idealised concept of the pressure at a point in a static fluid, by means of a limiting argument similar to that for density at a point. (See pages 18 and 19 for the previous argument.) Consider, in the continuum model, the limit of the ratio $\delta F/\delta A$ as the surface S contracts to a point (within S), that is, as δA becomes smaller and smaller.

Definition

Suppose that δA is the area of an arbitrary flat surface element, S, within the fluid, containing the fixed point of interest, P say, and that δF is the normal component of surface force on S. Taking smaller and smaller surface elements, each containing P, the **pressure of the fluid at the point** P is the limit as $\delta A \to 0$ of $\delta F/\delta A$; we write

$$p = \lim_{\delta A \to 0} \frac{\delta F}{\delta A}$$

for this pressure (provided that the limit exists).

In the SI system, the units of pressure are $\mathrm{N\,m^{-2}}$ (Pa).

In this definition, we are assuming that the point P is contained in all possible surface elements of area δA, and that there is no special orientation for the surface. It does not matter how we orientate the surface S; provided the limit exists, there is a unique pressure associated with the point P. Since $\delta F/\delta A$ is a scalar quantity, the limit is also scalar, so that the pressure at a point P is (under our definition) given by a scalar field. We use the term *pressure distribution* to refer to pressure as defined by a scalar field.

In reality, the pressure at a point does not exist; it forms part of our continuum model. In the same way that our definition of density at a point (see page 22) requires the fluid element always to contain enough fluid molecules to form a sensible average, the definition of pressure at a point is such that the surface S is always adjacent to enough fluid molecules over which to average.

In the same way that we use density to relate mass and volume, the pressure distribution in a static fluid is used to express the force on a surface element placed in the fluid; when the pressure p at a point is given, the force $\delta \mathbf{F}$ on a surface element of area δA containing the point has magnitude

$$\delta F = p \, \delta A, \tag{3.1}$$

and direction along the normal to the plane of the surface element, as indicated in Figure 3.8 (where $\mathbf{n}$ is a unit vector in the normal direction).

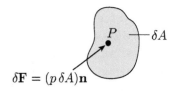

$$\delta \mathbf{F} = (p \, \delta A)\mathbf{n}$$

Figure 3.8

The fact that the definition selects no special orientation for the surface element S is expressed in the following law of physics.

Pascal's Law

The effect of the pressure at any point in a fluid at rest is the same in all directions.

This law can be verified experimentally. What it means is this: if you were a fluid particle, then no matter which way you faced in a static fluid, you would experience the same pressure effects.

The following exercise is a straightforward application of Equation (3.1).

Exercise 3.2

A bicycle pump, held horizontally, is filled with water and a force of 10 newtons is applied to the plunger (see Figure 3.9).

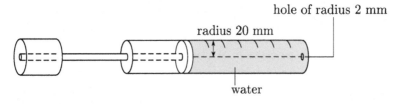

hole of radius 2 mm

radius 20 mm

water

Figure 3.9

If the radius of the chamber is 20 mm, determine the pressure (in Pa) exerted at each point of the water in contact with the plunger.

Recall that $1 \, \text{Pa} = 1 \, \text{N m}^{-2}$.

If this pressure is transmitted to all parts of the water, what magnitude of force do you have to exert on the small circular hole, of radius 2 mm, at the far end of the chamber, to keep the water in the chamber?

The following exercise gives an illustration of how the pressure in a fluid can be used to design a safety valve.

Exercise 3.3

A pressure cooker consists of a large pan with a sealing lid. A small amount of water is placed in the pan and vegetables are cooked in the steam produced by boiling the water. In the lid of the pan is a small safety valve; when the pressure of the steam exceeds the pressure outside the pan by a given amount, the steam can escape. The safety valve consists of a metal weight which is free to slide up and down on a smooth collar of diameter 3 mm. The steam pushes up the weight and escapes through a small hole in the collar (see Figure 3.10).

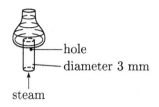

Figure 3.10

The excess pressure in the cooker that is required for ordinary day-to-day cooking is 10^5 Pa. What is the mass, m kg, of the metal weight which will rise and allow steam to escape through the hole when, but only when, the excess pressure exceeds 10^5 Pa? (Take $g = 9.81 \,\mathrm{m\,s^{-2}}$.)

Pressure is analogous to temperature, in that measurement of it can be expressed with reference to any datum level. There are two common datum levels: one is the *absolute zero* of pressure (this occurs in a complete vacuum), and the other is the *standard atmospheric pressure*, which has the value $1.013\,25 \times 10^5 \,\mathrm{N\,m^{-2}}$ with respect to absolute zero.

This value represents the mean air pressure at sea level on the latitude of Paris.

If the pressure in a fluid is expressed as the difference between its value and absolute zero, then it is called *absolute pressure*. When the pressure is expressed as the difference between its value and atmospheric pressure, it is called *gauge pressure*. So a zero gauge pressure is atmospheric pressure, and a zero absolute pressure corresponds to a vacuum. We shall deal usually in absolute pressures, and so omit the word 'absolute'.

More precisely, gauge pressure measurements are relative to the *local* atmospheric pressure, which will differ to some extent from the standard value given above (typically by up to $\pm 5\%$ at sea level).

The standard atmospheric pressure, $1.013\,25 \times 10^5 \,\mathrm{N\,m^{-2}}$ with respect to the absolute zero of pressure, is sometimes taken as a unit of pressure called 1 *atmosphere* (atm). So, a pressure given as 4.3 atm means a pressure of $4.3 \times 1.013\,25 \times 10^5 \,\mathrm{N\,m^{-2}}$. The SI unit of pressure, introduced earlier, is the **pascal**, written as Pa; that is, $1\,\mathrm{Pa} = 1\,\mathrm{N\,m^{-2}} = 1\,\mathrm{kg\,m^{-1}s^{-2}}$.

In Table 1.1 on page 14, coefficients of viscosity are given in units of $\mathrm{kg\,m^{-1}s^{-1}}$. These units can also be written as $\mathrm{Pa\,s}$, i.e. pascal seconds.

There are other units of pressure which may be familiar to you. For example, on weather maps the pressure is given in millibars, and in garages the pressure gauges on the air supply for car tyres may show in pounds force per square inch (psi). Table 3.3 shows various units of pressure and their relationships to the pascal.

Table 3.3

Unit	Conversion to pascals	Comments
$1\,\mathrm{N\,m^{-2}}$	1 pascal (Pa)	SI unit of pressure
1 atm	$1.013\,25 \times 10^5$ Pa	Used when comparing pressures to standard atmospheric pressure
1 bar	10^5 Pa	
1 millibar	10^2 Pa	Used on weather maps
1 psi	6.895×10^3 Pa	Imperial unit of pressure (14.7 psi = 1 atm)

Atmospheric pressure is also measured by its ability to displace a column of liquid (typically mercury). Hence you may encounter pressures in mmHg (millimetres of mercury, measuring the height of the column), where 760 mmHg = 1 atm.

Exercise 3.4

Convert a tyre pressure of 28 psi to pascals, and then to bars, and so check a car handbook which gives 28 psi as equivalent to 1.9 bar.

3.3   A perfect gas

In Section 1, you saw that the essential difference between a gas and a liquid lies in the extent to which they can be compressed. If an external force is applied to a gas, then the gas can readily be compressed into a smaller volume, whereas a quantity of liquid will greatly resist any attempt to reduce its volume. In the next section, you will see that the pressure in a liquid is due to its weight and to any external pressure that is applied to it. But it is not quite so obvious why a gas should exert a pressure. A simple experiment to show that air does exert a pressure is to push a glass tumbler upside down into a bowl of water. The water level in the glass tumbler is lower than that outside, because the pressure of the air inside the glass is greater than the air pressure outside the glass (see Figure 3.11).

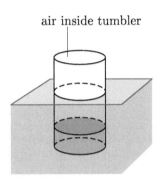

air inside tumbler

Figure 3.11

We can increase the pressure of the air in the tumbler by pushing the tumbler further into the water. The water will rise inside the tumbler, so that the volume occupied by the air is reduced. The mass of air inside the glass remains the same, so that the density of the air increases as its volume decreases. An *increase in pressure* of the air will *increase its density*. This experiment suggests that, for a gas, there is a physical law relating pressure p and density ρ; this law would be expressed as a functional relationship between p and ρ.

As well as pressure and density, another property of a gas that changes when we compress it is its *temperature*. For example, when a bicycle tyre is pumped up, the end of the pump becomes quite warm. We have used energy from our muscles to make the pump work, and a lot of that energy is transferred into heat energy, heating up the air going into the tyre. We have interpreted density and pressure in terms of the motions of the molecules making up a fluid. The temperature of a fluid is associated with the kinetic energy of the molecules. If we add energy to the fluid in such a way as to increase the average kinetic energy of random motion of the molecules (by stirring, for example), then the temperature of the fluid has increased. Temperature is a measure of the average kinetic energy of random motion of the molecules.

The pressure, density and temperature of a fluid are called *state variables*, and a relationship between them is called an *equation of state*. Real fluids are modelled by very complicated equations of state, and there is a whole branch of theoretical physics called *thermodynamics* that is concerned with the equations of state of a fluid.

In this course we shall adopt simple mathematical models for the equations of state of liquids and gases.

Equations of state for liquids and gases

(i) For a liquid, density ρ is taken to be a constant, ρ_0 say: $\rho = \rho_0$.

(ii) For a gas, the pressure p is given by $p = R\rho\Theta$, where R is the *specific gas constant* for the particular gas, Θ is the absolute temperature and ρ is the density. A gas satisfying this equation of state is often called a **perfect gas**, and so the equation is referred to as the *perfect gas law*.

Some texts write $R = k/m$, where k is *Boltzmann's constant* and m is the average mass of the gas molecules. We can then write $p = kN\Theta$, where N is the number density, i.e. the number of molecules per unit volume ($\rho = Nm$).

In the equation $p = R\rho\Theta$, the temperature Θ is measured in kelvins (K) and is known as the *absolute temperature*. The absolute temperature scale starts at $-273.15°\mathrm{C}$ (in degrees Celsius), so that $x°\mathrm{C} = (273.15 + x)\mathrm{K}$.

Exercise 3.5

At what absolute temperature does (a) water freeze, and (b) water boil?

Exercise 3.6

What are the SI units of the constant R in the equation of state for a perfect gas?

Exercise 3.7

$1\,\mathrm{kg}$ of hydrogen gas is confined in a volume of $0.1\,\mathrm{m}^3$ at $-40°\mathrm{C}$. If the pressure in the container is $9.6 \times 10^6\,\mathrm{Pa}$, what is the specific gas constant R for hydrogen? (Assume that hydrogen behaves as a perfect gas.)

The two equations of state in the box above are another part of our *mathematical models* for a liquid and a gas. As with all modelling assumptions, care must be taken when using them. For example, small vibrations of a liquid can result in the propagation of sound waves; in such a case, the equation of state $\rho = \rho_0$ is not a good model. To account for the existence of these waves, changes in density must be built into the model, even though these may be small compared with the density of the liquid when at rest (generally less than 1%).

In this course, we shall assume that the equation of state for a perfect gas is an adequate model for real gases. However, the model is only a first (sometimes rather good) approximation; high temperatures (at which the structure of the molecules changes), large densities or low temperatures (where gases come close to liquefying) lead to major departures from the perfect gas law. A more complicated equation of state is then required.

3.4 Forces in a continuum

To obtain a description of the motion of a fluid, we shall develop differential equations to represent the motion of the fluid particles. The approach we adopt is to consider an arbitrary fluid element, and equate the rate of change of momentum to the resultant force on the element (this is just Newton's Second Law). You will see this approach used in the next section, when the fluid is at rest, so that the momentum of the element is zero. Equations for a fluid in motion are developed in *Unit 5*.

To set the scene for our discussion of the forces that act on a fluid element, consider a small rectangular block of mass m sliding down an inclined plane AB (see Figure 3.12). We model the forces in this situation as follows. There are three (vector) forces acting on the block:

(i)   **W** is the weight of the block (force due to gravity); the magnitude of this force is mg, and its direction is vertically downwards.

(ii) **N** is the normal reaction; the direction of this force is normal (i.e. perpendicular) to the plane AB, and its magnitude must be just sufficient to prevent the block from sinking into the plane.

(iii) **F** is the force due to friction; its direction opposes the motion of the block and is parallel to the plane AB.

Now, suppose that we lift the block from the plane; then only one of these three forces acts on the block, namely, the force due to gravity. Wherever the block is taken, the force of gravity will act on it. This force always has magnitude mg and direction vertically downwards.

The normal reaction and frictional forces act on the block only when it is in contact with the plane. These forces are reactions produced between the lower surface of the block and the surface of the plane.

So the forces on the block can be classified into two different types of force. The normal reaction and frictional forces are called *surface forces*; they are present when we have two surfaces in contact. The force due to gravity is an example of a *body force*.

These ideas can be used to identify the forces on a fluid element in a fluid in motion. There are forces that can penetrate into the interior of a fluid — in terms of our model this means that they act on all the fluid particles within the fluid element. The force due to gravity is an example of such a force. In the same way that the force of gravity always acts on the block, this force acts on the fluid element wherever it moves within the fluid. There are other forces which have this penetrating property; for example, if a fluid in motion carries an electric charge, then each fluid particle experiences forces due to electric and magnetic fields.

Forces which act at every point in a fluid element are modelled by vector fields, and are called **body forces**. In this course, the only body force that we shall consider is that due to gravity.

The fluid element is also in contact with the rest of the fluid outside it. The molecular activity between neighbouring fluid elements (and between fluid elements and boundary surfaces) produces a net force per unit area at each point on the surface of the fluid element.

The magnitude of these forces decreases rapidly with distance, so that the force experienced by a fluid element is largely restricted to a thin layer of its surface. In the continuum model, we *assume* that these forces act only on the surface of the fluid element, and hence we call them **surface forces**.

The normal component of the surface force is associated with the pressure in the fluid, and the tangential component with the viscosity. In the

This subsection may appear rather abstract at this stage. You may find it helpful to read the material through, identifying the main ideas and terminology. Then return to this subsection when you have studied Section 4.

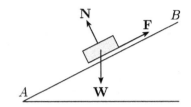

Figure 3.12

See MST209 *Unit 5.*

Body forces are often called *long-range* forces or *volume* forces.

Surface forces are often called *short-range* forces, to remind us that their magnitude decreases rapidly with distance, i.e. they act over a 'short range'.

analogy with the block sliding down a plane, the viscous forces act like the frictional force, i.e. opposing relative motion between the surfaces. If the fluid is modelled as inviscid, then the viscous forces are zero; this is similar to the modelling assumption often made in particle mechanics that the surfaces are 'smooth', meaning that there is no friction present.

There is an essential difference between the modelling of the body forces and the surface forces. The body forces are defined in terms of a force per unit mass, and we assume that this force does not change significantly within a fluid element. This assumption is reasonable because body forces originate outside the fluid, and decrease very slowly with an increase in distance between the interacting elements that cause the forces. The surface forces, however, are defined in terms of a force per unit area. The surface forces may alter rapidly on moving around the surface of the fluid element, and the mathematical representation of the surface forces must take these changes into account.

In the next section, we formulate the equations describing a fluid at rest which is subject to the force of gravity (a body force) and surface forces due to the pressure distribution in the fluid. In *Unit 5*, we shall use the same models for these forces to describe the motion of an inviscid fluid. In *Unit 8*, we shall formulate a model that takes into account also the viscous forces acting in a fluid.

Before attempting the following exercise, read the summary of this section given in the *Handbook*.

End-of-section exercise

Exercise 3.8

(a) What are the SI units of density?

(b) Granulated sugar will flow out of a container with a large hole in the bottom, in much the same way that water does. Is granulated sugar a fluid, according to the definition in Section 1 (see page 11)?

(c) By weighing a volume of the following substances, find their densities in $\mathrm{kg\,m}^{-3}$.

    (i) sugar;   (ii) salt;   (iii) milk.

(d) Classify the following statements as true or false.

    (i)   The force per unit area on a submerged object at a point on its surface, due to pressure, is directed normal to the surface at that point.

    (ii)   The pressure at a point in a fluid at rest depends on direction.

    (iii) Pressure is a scalar quantity.

    (iv) A perfect gas is incompressible.

    (v)   A perfect gas is inviscid.

    (vi) The pressure p, density ρ and absolute temperature Θ of a perfect gas satisfy the equation $p = R\rho\Theta$, where R is a constant.

4 Fluid statics 1: liquids

When studying particle mechanics, it is often convenient to begin by discussing the forces on a particle or body (object) at rest. The area of applied mathematics associated with bodies at rest is called *statics*. A study of statics allows us to investigate some of the forces that play an important part in dynamics, such as the normal reaction, the tension in strings, and the gravitational force on a body (or its weight). This investigation is simplified for a body at rest because, with no acceleration, the vector sum of the forces on the body is zero. In an analogous way, we begin our study of fluid mechanics by investigating the forces that exist in a fluid at rest. This is the science of *fluid statics*.

This is also called *hydrostatics*.

First, we shall study pressure and its variation in a fluid, and then pressure forces on boundary surfaces in the fluid. It was suggested in Section 1 that one simplification when modelling a fluid flow is to neglect (internal) friction, i.e. the forces due to viscosity. In fluid statics, there is no motion of the fluid, so there are no shearing forces between the layers of the fluid. Hence there are no viscous forces for a fluid at rest. The omission of viscous forces in this section is *not* a modelling simplification; all bodies at rest in a fluid experience only pressure forces acting on their surfaces and the gravitational force.

4.1 Pressure gradient due to gravity

In Section 3, the pressure at a point was defined by considering the average pressure on a flat surface element as the area of the surface element becomes smaller and smaller. You saw that the pressure at a point in a fluid is a scalar quantity.

In general, the value of the pressure at a point in a fluid will depend on where and when it is measured. In other words, pressure is a scalar function of position and time, and we write $p = p(x, y, z, t)$. In this subsection, we shall investigate how the pressure varies in a fluid at rest in a gravitational force field, and we shall obtain a differential equation which relates the pressure $p = p(x, y, z)$ and the acceleration due to gravity.

A fluid at rest experiences two types of force. There are the body (or long-range) forces, such as gravity, which act on every fluid element, and there are surface (or short-range) forces due to the contact of one fluid element with another or with a boundary. In this course, we assume that the only body force acting is that due to gravity.

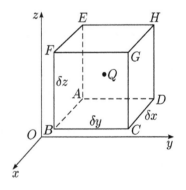

Figure 4.1

Consider a fluid element in the shape of a small block with rectangular faces (see Figure 4.1), oriented so that the edges AB, AD and AE are parallel to the fixed Cartesian coordinate axes Ox, Oy, Oz, respectively. Suppose that the edges of the block have lengths δx, δy and δz, and that the centre of the block, Q, has coordinates (x, y, z). The z-axis is chosen vertically upwards, so that the gravitational force is in the direction of $-\mathbf{k}$, where $\mathbf{i}$, $\mathbf{j}$ and $\mathbf{k}$ are the Cartesian unit vectors, directed along the x-, y- and z-axes, respectively.

Actually, it is not essential to choose Q as the centre of the fluid element; taking any point within the element will give the same final result.

Since the fluid is at rest, the 'block of fluid' can be considered as a body at rest, and hence the vector sum of the body force and surface forces on it is zero.

Throughout this section, the fluid is in static equilibrium, i.e. at rest.

(i) *The body force*: The density of the fluid, ρ, may change with position, but since the dimensions of the fluid element (the block) are small, we shall assume that ρ does not change within the element. The mass of the fluid within the block is

$$m = \rho\, \delta x\, \delta y\, \delta z,$$

and its weight is $-mg\,\mathbf{k}$, where g is the magnitude of the acceleration due to gravity. Hence the body force on the block, $\mathbf{F}_B$, is

$$\mathbf{F}_B = -(\rho\, \delta x\, \delta y\, \delta z)g\,\mathbf{k},$$

where ρ is the density of fluid in the block.

(ii) *The surface forces*: Since the dimensions of the block are small, we assume that the pressure over each of its faces is constant and equal to its value at the centre of the face. Consider the surface forces exerted *on* the block by the rest of the fluid.

On the top and bottom faces, let the forces be $\mathbf{F}_1$ and $\mathbf{F}_2$ (as shown in Figure 4.2), with magnitudes F_1 and F_2 respectively, and let p_1 and p_2 be the corresponding pressures. From the definition of average pressure on page 24, we have $p = \delta F/\delta A$. For face $EFGH$, we have $\delta F = F_1$, $p = p_1$ and $\delta A = \delta x\, \delta y$, so that

$$F_1 = p_1\, \delta x\, \delta y,$$

and likewise,

$$F_2 = p_2\, \delta x\, \delta y.$$

Now the forces $\mathbf{F}_1$ and $\mathbf{F}_2$ are in the directions of $-\mathbf{k}$ and $\mathbf{k}$, respectively, so that the vector sum of these two forces is the net surface force component vector in the $\mathbf{k}$-direction, which is

$$\mathbf{F}_1 + \mathbf{F}_2 = -(F_1 - F_2)\,\mathbf{k} = -(p_1 - p_2)\, \delta x\, \delta y\,\mathbf{k}.$$

Next consider the two faces $CDHG$ and $ABFE$, for which the surface forces are $\mathbf{F}_3$ and $\mathbf{F}_4$ (see Figure 4.3), with magnitudes F_3 and F_4 respectively. Following a similar argument to that above, the net surface force component vector in the $\mathbf{j}$-direction is

$$\mathbf{F}_3 + \mathbf{F}_4 = -(F_3 - F_4)\,\mathbf{j} = -(p_3 - p_4)\, \delta x\, \delta z\,\mathbf{j}.$$

Finally, for the two faces $BCGF$ and $ADHE$ (see Figure 4.4), the net surface force component vector in the $\mathbf{i}$-direction is

$$\mathbf{F}_5 + \mathbf{F}_6 = -(F_5 - F_6)\,\mathbf{i} = -(p_5 - p_6)\, \delta y\, \delta z\,\mathbf{i}.$$

Adding the surface forces on the six faces, we can write the net surface force exerted *on* the block by the fluid outside it, $\mathbf{F}_S$, as

$$\mathbf{F}_S = -(p_5 - p_6)\, \delta y\, \delta z\,\mathbf{i} - (p_3 - p_4)\, \delta x\, \delta z\,\mathbf{j} - (p_1 - p_2)\, \delta x\, \delta y\,\mathbf{k}.$$

(iii) *The resultant force*: Since the fluid is at rest, the vector sum of the body force, $\mathbf{F}_B$, and the net surface force, $\mathbf{F}_S$, is zero; that is,

$$\mathbf{F}_S + \mathbf{F}_B = \mathbf{0}.$$

The body force, $\mathbf{F}_B$, acts in the direction of $-\mathbf{k}$. Since $\mathbf{F}_S + \mathbf{F}_B = \mathbf{0}$, it follows that the components of $\mathbf{F}_S$ in the $\mathbf{i}$- and $\mathbf{j}$-directions are both zero, giving

$$p_3 = p_4 \qquad \text{and} \qquad p_5 = p_6.$$

Thus the only change in pressure is in the z-direction, so that

p is a function of z only; that is, $p = p(z)$.

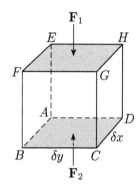

Figure 4.2

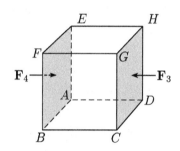

Figure 4.3

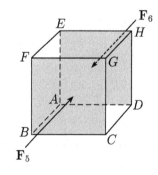

Figure 4.4

33

To determine how p changes, consider the values of the pressure at the top and bottom faces, p_1 and p_2. The pressure in the fluid at the centre of the top face $EFGH$ is p_1; hence

$$p_1 = p \left(z + \tfrac{1}{2}\delta z \right).$$

The pressure at the centre of the bottom face $ABCD$ is p_2; hence

$$p_2 = p \left(z - \tfrac{1}{2}\delta z \right).$$

Resolving $\mathbf{F}_S + \mathbf{F}_B = \mathbf{0}$ in the $\mathbf{k}$-direction gives

$$(p_1 - p_2)\, \delta x\, \delta y + \rho g\, \delta x\, \delta y\, \delta z = 0.$$

Substituting for p_1 and p_2, we have

$$\left[p \left(z + \tfrac{1}{2}\delta z \right) - p \left(z - \tfrac{1}{2}\delta z \right) \right] \delta x\, \delta y + \rho g\, \delta x\, \delta y\, \delta z = 0.$$

Dividing through by $\delta x\, \delta y\, \delta z$ $(\neq 0)$, we obtain

$$\frac{p \left(z + \tfrac{1}{2}\delta z \right) - p \left(z - \tfrac{1}{2}\delta z \right)}{\delta z} + \rho g = 0. \tag{4.1}$$

Note the approach used from here on; creating a derivative leads to an equation for a fluid particle rather than for a fluid element.

Now, to obtain an equation that describes the properties of the fluid at points in the fluid, we take the limit of the above equation as the block becomes smaller and smaller, converging to the point Q. In the limit as δx, δy and δz tend to 0, we have

$$\lim_{\delta x, \delta y, \delta z \to 0} \frac{p \left(z + \tfrac{1}{2}\delta z \right) - p \left(z - \tfrac{1}{2}\delta z \right)}{\delta z} = \frac{dp}{dz},$$

and so Equation (4.1) becomes $dp/dz + \rho g = 0$, which is equivalent to

$$\frac{dp}{dz} = -\rho g. \tag{4.2}$$

This first-order differential equation is the *basic equation of fluid statics*, where the only body force is due to a uniform gravitational field. If we had specific knowledge of how ρ, the density of the fluid, depends on z then, in principle, we could solve Equation (4.2) to find the pressure, p, at every point in the fluid. In fact, if $\rho = \rho(z)$, then

$$p = - \int \rho(z) g\, dz + c, \qquad \text{where } c \text{ is an arbitrary constant.}$$

Since (as deduced earlier) p is a function of z only, the pressure takes the same value at every point in a horizontal plane. This implies that any contours of constant pressure (called *isobars*) are at right angles to the direction of the body force (see Figure 4.5).

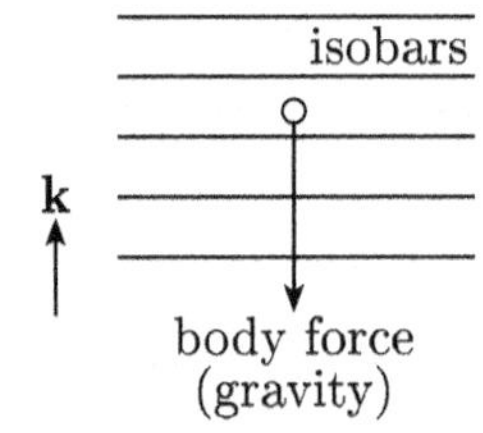

For the remainder of this section, we specialise to the case of liquids, for which we assume that ρ is constant. In Section 5, we shall solve Equation (4.2) for fluids of variable density (i.e. gases).

Figure 4.5

4.2 *Pressure distribution in a liquid due to gravity*

Let us assume that the density is constant, $\rho = \rho_0$ say. Equation (4.2) becomes $dp/dz = -\rho_0 g$, and integrating this with respect to z gives a formula for the pressure distribution in a liquid, as follows.

This is in line with the assumed equation of state for a liquid, given on page 29.

For a static fluid of constant density, the pressure is given by

$$p = -\rho_0 gz + c, \tag{4.3}$$

where z is measured vertically upwards, ρ_0 is the density of the fluid and c is a constant.

Thus, given any point (x, y, z), we can calculate $p(x, y, z) = p(z)$, the pressure at that point. The value of the constant c depends on the choice of origin for the coordinate system. This is like a potential energy with a datum level.

The derivation of Equation (4.2) indicates that there cannot be sudden jumps in the pressure within a fluid at rest. The same applies at any interface between two fluids (such as air and water); the pressure within either fluid must tend to the same value as any point on the interface is approached. In particular, for any liquid in an open container, the pressure at its upper surface is atmospheric pressure.

It was pointed out in Subsection 3.2 that pressure can be measured with respect to any datum level.

Example 4.1

Water is contained in an open vessel which stands on a horizontal surface. Assuming that the water can be modelled as an incompressible fluid, that it is static, and that the only body force is due to gravity, show that:

(a) the surface of the water is horizontal;

(b) the pressure at a depth h below the surface is given by $p = \alpha + \rho_0 gh$, where α is a constant and ρ_0 is the density of water. Interpret α for this physical situation.

Solution

(a) Suppose that the surface of the water is not horizontal, and consider two arbitrary points A and B on the surface of the water, at different heights z_A, z_B above the bottom (see Figure 4.6). If we choose the origin of coordinates at a point on the bottom of the vessel then, from Equation (4.3), the pressures p_A at A and p_B at B are given by

$$p_A = c - \rho_0 g z_A \quad \text{and} \quad p_B = c - \rho_0 g z_B,$$

for some constant c. Since $z_A \neq z_B$, we have $p_A \neq p_B$. As indicated above, there is no pressure discontinuity across the interface between two fluids, so that along the surface of the water the pressure is everywhere equal to atmospheric pressure (which can be taken to be constant over the surface). Thus $p_A = p_B = p_0$, where p_0 denotes the atmospheric pressure.

Here we use an approach similar to proof by contradiction.

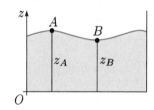

Figure 4.6

Hence we have a contradiction, and so deduce that $z_A = z_B$. This is true for all pairs of points on the surface of the water, so that this surface is horizontal, because the z-axis is directed vertically upwards.

(b) Suppose that the surface of the water in contact with the air has equation $z = z_0$; then a point Q at depth h in the water has z-coordinate given by $z = z_0 - h$ (see Figure 4.7). From Equation (4.3), the pressure at Q is therefore given by

$$p = c - \rho_0 g(z_0 - h)$$
$$= c - \rho_0 z_0 g + \rho_0 gh$$
$$= \alpha + \rho_0 gh,$$

where $\alpha = c - \rho_0 z_0 g$ is constant.

This applies even if the bottom of the vessel is not horizontal, provided that all heights are measured from a convenient horizontal level.

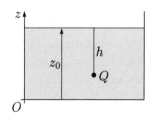

Figure 4.7

Now, when $h = 0$, the pressure is $p = p_0$ (atmospheric), so that the constant α is the value of the atmospheric pressure, and we can write

$$p = p_0 + \rho_0 g h. \quad \blacksquare$$

In Example 4.1(b), the pressure was expressed in terms of depth, h, rather than height, z, as in Equation (4.3). One reason for deriving this alternative expression is that, in practice, it is often easier to measure depth than height.

You can use the result of Example 4.1(b) in the following exercise, which also asks you to express a pressure in terms of depth.

Exercise 4.1

An open vessel standing on a horizontal table contains a layer of an incompressible fluid of density ρ_1, floating on top of a layer of incompressible fluid of density ρ_2 (see Figure 4.8). The surface between fluid 1 and the atmosphere is labelled S_1, and that between fluids 1 and 2 is labelled S_2. Both surfaces are horizontal.

Show that p_2, the pressure in fluid 2 at a point Q, which is depth h below the surface S_1, can be written as

$$p_2 = p_0 + \rho_1 g H + \rho_2 g (h - H) \quad (H \le h \le z_0),$$

where H is the depth of S_2 below S_1 and z_0 is the height of surface S_1 above the base of the vessel.

Do not spend more than ten minutes on this exercise.

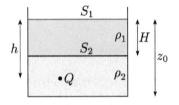

Figure 4.8

In Exercise 4.1, the surface S_2 was given to be horizontal. In fact, it can be shown that the boundary surface between any two layers of incompressible static fluids with different densities must be horizontal.

The boundary surface between two fluids is often called a *free surface*. Examples of free surfaces are S_1 and S_2 in Exercise 4.1.

The solution to Example 4.1(b) gives an important relationship between pressure and depth in an incompressible static fluid. This may be restated as follows.

> The pressure p at depth h below the free surface of an incompressible fluid at rest is given by
>
> $$p = P + \rho_0 g h, \tag{4.4}$$
>
> where ρ_0 is the (constant) fluid density and P, a constant, is the pressure at the free surface. If the free surface is exposed to the atmosphere, then $P = p_0$, the atmospheric pressure.

For fluid 2 in Exercise 4.1, we have $P = p_0 + \rho_1 g H$, $\rho_0 = \rho_2$ and h replaced by $h - H$ (depth below S_2).

Water can be modelled as such a fluid in many situations; for example, the pressure in the sea can be modelled by this formula.

Exercise 4.2

A spherical diving bell is rated to withstand a pressure difference on its walls of 1.5×10^6 Pa. It is lowered into sea with density $1028 \, \text{kg m}^{-3}$. Assuming that its internal pressure is equal to atmospheric pressure, p_0, and that the sea water can be modelled as an incompressible static fluid, how far below the surface can the diving bell be lowered before there is a danger of collapse? (Take $g = 9.81 \, \text{m s}^{-2}$.)

Exercise 4.3

A vessel whose bottom is horizontal contains mercury to a depth of 750 mm. Water to a depth of 500 mm floats on the mercury. Find the pressure difference (in pascals) between the water/air surface and the bottom of the vessel, stating any assumptions made about the water and mercury. (Take the densities of water and mercury to be $10^3 \, \text{kg m}^{-3}$ and $1.36 \times 10^4 \, \text{kg m}^{-3}$, respectively, and take $g = 9.81 \, \text{m s}^{-2}$.)

4.3 Force on a plane surface in a static liquid

When the only body force is due to gravity, the distribution of pressure in a fluid can be found by integrating the equation $dp/dz = -\rho g$ (Equation (4.2)). You have seen that if ρ is constant (ρ_0 say), then the pressure at depth h below a free surface is $p = P + \rho_0 g h$ (Equation (4.4)), and if the surface is exposed to the atmosphere, then $P = p_0$, the atmospheric pressure.

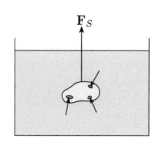

The pressure in a fluid exhibits itself when a solid body is inserted into the fluid. Each surface element of the body will experience a force due to the pressure in the fluid, and it is convenient to replace this distribution of forces by a net surface force, $\mathbf{F}_S$ (see Figure 4.9).

Consider a plane surface immersed in a liquid; the deeper the surface, the greater is the pressure due to the liquid, and hence the greater is the force exerted on the surface by the liquid. The following example illustrates this.

Figure 4.9   Net surface force, $\mathbf{F}_S$, on a body in a liquid

Example 4.2

A flat plate of area $A \, \text{m}^2$ is submerged to a depth of 100 m in an inland lake and kept horizontal. The density of the water is $1000 \, \text{kg m}^{-3}$. Find the increase in magnitude of the net force on the top surface of the plate if it is now lowered to a depth of 150 m. (Take $g = 9.81 \, \text{m s}^{-2}$.)

Solution

(Since a numerical solution is required, we are explicit about units from the outset.) Suppose that the top surface of the plate is at a depth h metres. At this depth, the pressure (in pascals) in the water is

$$p = p_0 + \rho_0 g h,$$

where p_0 is atmospheric pressure in pascals and ρ_0, g are also expressed in SI units. Since the plate is horizontal, the pressure is constant over the surface. The pressure is defined as 'normal force component per unit area' so that the net force on the top surface S of the plate has magnitude

$$F_S = pA = (p_0 + \rho_0 g h)A \quad \text{(in newtons)},$$

and direction vertically downwards (see Figure 4.10).

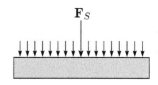

Figure 4.10   Net force on flat plate due to water pressure

At a depth of 100 m, the magnitude of the force is $F_1 = (p_0 + 100\rho_0 g)A$; at a depth of 150 m, the magnitude of the force is $F_2 = (p_0 + 150\rho_0 g)A$. The increase in the force magnitude is thus

$$F_2 - F_1 = 50\rho_0 g A \simeq 4.9 \times 10^5 A \quad \text{(in newtons).} \quad \blacksquare$$

You can think of this force difference in terms of the extra 'weight of water' resting on the flat plate. When the plate is lowered through 50 metres, there is an extra mass of water, equal to $(50 \times A \times \rho_0)$ kg, on top of the plate (see Figure 4.11), and the weight of this extra water is

$$50 \times A \times \rho_0 \times g \simeq 4.9 \times 10^5 A \qquad \text{(in newtons)}.$$

Using this argument, you might be tempted to think that there is no force on the surface of a *vertical* plate placed in the water. However, Pascal's Law says that, at a point in a static fluid, the pressure is the same in all directions. So on a vertical plate (see Figure 4.12), there is a force $\mathbf{F}$ of magnitude F on the surface AB due to the liquid. The plate does not move horizontally because there is an opposite force $-\mathbf{F}$, with equal magnitude F, on the surface CD. In the following example, we calculate the net surface force on one face of a vertical flat plate due to the pressure in a static liquid.

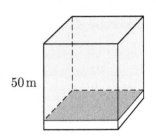

50 m

Figure 4.11

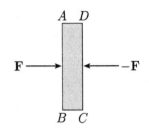

Figure 4.12

Example 4.3

A rectangular flat plate, with sides of length a and b, is submerged in a liquid of constant density ρ_0. Its face $ABCD$ is in a vertical plane, while the edge $ABFE$ is horizontal and at a depth h_0 below the surface of the liquid (see Figure 4.13). Find the net surface force on the face $ABCD$ of the plate.

Solution

For the horizontal plate in Example 4.2, the calculation of the net surface force magnitude on the plate is just the product of the area of the plate and the pressure. This is because the pressure is constant on a horizontal surface in a liquid. Now, on a vertical surface, the pressure due to the liquid increases with depth, so that the pressure distribution on the plate is not constant.

Let the corner A be the origin for Cartesian coordinates x and y, and consider an arbitrary surface element of area δA_i having centre Q with coordinates (x, y), as shown in Figure 4.14.

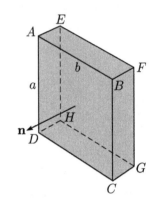

Figure 4.13

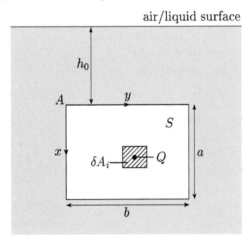

Figure 4.14

The force exerted on this surface element by the fluid has magnitude $p_i \delta A_i$, where p_i is the pressure at Q, and direction $-\mathbf{n}$, where $\mathbf{n}$ is a unit vector normal to the surface $ABCD$ of the plate and directed away from the surface (see Figure 4.13).

The net force $\mathbf{F}_S$ on the surface $ABCD$, denoted by S, is given by

$$\mathbf{F}_S = \lim_{\delta A_i \to 0} \sum_i p_i \delta A_i \, (-\mathbf{n})$$

(summing over surface elements covering the whole of S); that is, by

$$\mathbf{F}_S = -\mathbf{n} \int_S p \, dA.$$

Now, the point Q in the surface element is at depth $h_0 + x$ below the surface of the liquid, so that the pressure p at Q is given by

$$p = p_0 + \rho_0 g(h_0 + x).$$

It follows that

$$\mathbf{F}_S = -\mathbf{n} \int_S (p_0 + \rho_0 g(h_0 + x)) \, dA.$$

This area integral, over a rectangle of side lengths a and b, can be written in terms of two single integrals, one over y and the other over x. We have

Area integrals are introduced in MST209 *Unit 25*.

$$\mathbf{F}_S = -\mathbf{n} \int_0^a \left[\int_0^b (p_0 + \rho_0 g(h_0 + x)) \, dy \right] dx$$

$$= -\mathbf{n} \int_0^a (p_0 + \rho_0 g(h_0 + x)) \, b \, dx$$

$$= -b \left((p_0 + \rho_0 g h_0)a + \tfrac{1}{2}\rho_0 g a^2 \right) \mathbf{n}$$

$$= -ab \left(p_0 + \rho_0 g(h_0 + \tfrac{1}{2}a) \right) \mathbf{n}.$$

The product ab is just the area of the surface of the plate, and $p_0 + \rho_0 g(h_0 + \tfrac{1}{2}a)$ is the pressure in the liquid half-way down the plate. Thus, we can write the net surface force on a vertical face of a rectangular flat plate of area A as

$$\mathbf{F}_S = -p_G A \, \mathbf{n},$$

where p_G is the pressure in the liquid at the mid-point of the plate. ◼

We have found the magnitude and direction of the net surface force on the plate, but it remains to find where it acts. This will be addressed shortly.

Exercise 4.4

A uniform solid cube, with side of length a, is lowered into water of constant density ρ_0. Two faces of the cube are horizontal, and the position of its centre of mass, Q, is at a depth h_0 $(> \tfrac{1}{2}a)$ below the water surface.

(a) Find the net surface forces on each of the six faces of the cube.

(b) Show that the total force on the cube due to the surface forces has magnitude $a^3 \rho_0 g$ and points in the vertically upward direction.

The result from Exercise 4.4 is a special case of the following principle.

Archimedes' Principle

If a body is at rest, wholly or partly immersed in a liquid, then the resultant force due to the pressure distribution over the body is directed vertically upwards and has magnitude equal to the weight of liquid displaced by the body.

The resultant upward force on the body due to the pressure in a liquid is often called the *buoyancy force*.

In Exercise 4.4, the volume of liquid displaced is a^3 (the volume of the cube), so the corresponding weight of liquid is $a^3 \rho_0 g$, which is independent of the depth, h_0. If the cube were not wholly submerged, then the integrations would have to be done in two parts, for the surfaces beneath the water and for those above. In this case, the result is that the total force on the cube due to the surface forces has magnitude $a^2 b \rho_0 g$, where b is the depth of cube immersed in the liquid (see Figure 4.15). This force magnitude is again equal to the weight of liquid displaced.

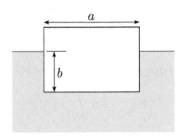

Figure 4.15

If the weight $\mathbf{W}$ of the cube itself is greater in magnitude than the vertically upward force due to the surface forces, $\mathbf{F}_S$, then the cube will sink to the bottom of the vessel containing the water. On the other hand, if $\mathbf{F}_S$ is greater in magnitude than the weight of the cube, then the cube will rise to the surface and float (see Figure 4.16). So Archimedes' Principle can be used to provide a simple criterion for a body to float.

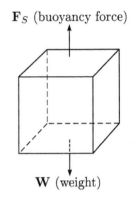

Figure 4.16 The forces on a cube immersed in a fluid

Centre of pressure

We have evaluated the force exerted on a flat plate immersed in a liquid, due to the pressure in the liquid. The *magnitude* of the force is given by $\int_S p \, dA$. Since the plate is flat, all the forces on the surface elements are perpendicular to it, so the *direction* of the net surface force on the plate is perpendicular to the plate. Hence we know the magnitude of the net surface force and its direction, but we do not know its point of application, which is called the *centre of pressure*. This point has the property that the net *torque* on the surface about the point, due to the torques on all surface elements, is equal to zero.

For the vertical plate in Example 4.3, the position of the centre of pressure is *not* at its centre of mass. To understand why this is so, consider the plate divided into surface elements which are horizontal strips, as shown in Figure 4.17. For a strip XY, the pressure in the liquid is constant, because the strip is horizontal. The point of application of the surface force on this strip, due to the liquid, is at the centre of the strip, that is, on the axis of symmetry AA'. Now, this result is true for all of the strips, so the centre of pressure for the plate will also lie on the axis AA'.

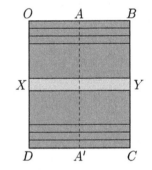

Figure 4.17

The pressure in the liquid increases with depth, so the force on a strip towards the bottom of the plate is larger than the force on a strip near the top. This increase in magnitude of the surface forces means that there is a net torque about the centre of mass, and hence the net surface force must have a point of application on the lower half of the plate, as shown in Figure 4.18. (The centre of mass of the plate is at its geometric centre.)

We could extend the results for the net surface force and the centre of pressure to plates which are non-rectangular in shape. This would involve evaluating surface integrals with non-constant limits. The essential steps are the same as for rectangular plates, the only difference being in actually evaluating the surface integrals. Since we are concerned with the principles of fluid statics here, we shall not consider non-rectangular plates.

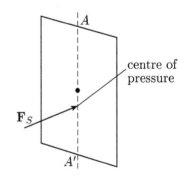

Figure 4.18

4.4 A case study: canal lock gates

We now use some of the ideas introduced in this section to describe an application of fluid statics. The variation of pressure in a liquid is of particular importance to the engineer when designing structures such as dams or sluice gates in a canal or river, which retain water at different levels. The pressure distribution can give rise to large forces, and structures must be designed to be strong enough to resist these forces. In this subsection, we take as a case study the forces exerted on lock gates in a canal due to the water pressure.

The canal builders of the eighteenth and nineteenth centuries had to solve many problems. To keep the route of a canal reasonably straight, they had to build aqueducts, cuttings, tunnels and locks. The purpose of a lock is to allow the canal to climb uphill: the canal is built in a series of short stretches, called pounds, and successive pounds are connected by a lock.

Figure 4.19   Lock gates

A boat travelling up the canal starts at the lower level, with the water in the lock at the same level as the canal water. The boat enters the lock and the lock gates are closed behind it. The lock is filled with water by opening sluice gates in the other pair of lock gates (see Figure 4.19). When the level of water in the lock is the same as that in the top pound, the lock gates can be opened, and the boat leaves the lock. Lock gates in a canal separate water at heights which can differ by up to 3 metres.

Figure 4.20 shows the essential features of a canal lock. In this picture there are two pairs of lock gates. They are held tightly closed by the force exerted on them due to the pressure in the water. Only when the level of water in the lock is the same as that in the lower pound (or the top pound) can the bottom gates (or top gates) be opened.

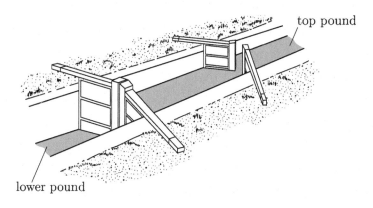

Figure 4.20   A canal lock with two pairs of lock gates

Using the methods of Subsection 4.3, we can calculate the magnitude of the force on each side of one of the gates due to the water.

Suppose that the height of water is H on side 1 of a gate and h on side 2 of the gate, as shown in Figure 4.21, and that the breadth of the gate is b. Let the portion of lock gate which is above the water on side 1 be of height c.

Consider a coordinate system Oxz in the plane of the gate, and a surface element of area δA containing the point Q with coordinates (x, z), as shown in Figure 4.22. (Here O is taken as a lower corner of the gate, Ox is horizontal and Oz is vertical.) Since the depth of Q below the water level is $H - z$, the pressure on side 1 of the lock gate is

$$p_1 = \begin{cases} p_0 + \rho_0 g(H - z) & (0 \le z \le H), \\ p_0 & (H \le z \le H + c), \end{cases}$$

where p_0 is atmospheric pressure and ρ_0 is the (constant) density of water.

Then the force $\mathbf{F}_1$, on side 1 of the gate (S_1), has magnitude

$$F_1 = \int_{S_1} p_1 \, dA$$

$$= \int_0^H \int_0^b [p_0 + \rho_0 g(H - z)] \, dx \, dz + \int_H^{H+c} \int_0^b p_0 \, dx \, dz$$

$$= \int_0^H b \, [p_0 + \rho_0 g(H - z)] \, dz + \int_H^{H+c} b p_0 \, dz$$

$$= b \left(p_0 H + \rho_0 g H^2 - \tfrac{1}{2}\rho_0 g H^2 \right) + b p_0 c$$

$$= \tfrac{1}{2}\rho_0 g b H^2 + b p_0 (H + c).$$

The pressure on side 2 of the gate is the atmospheric pressure, p_0, above the water (that is, for $h \le z < H + c$), and is also due to the water for $0 \le z \le h$. Since the depth below the surface of the water of a point Q with coordinates (x, z) is $h - z$, the pressure on side 2 of the gate is given by

$$p_2 = \begin{cases} p_0 + \rho_0 g(h - z) & (0 \le z \le h), \\ p_0 & (h \le z \le H + c). \end{cases}$$

By an argument analogous to that above for side 1, the force $\mathbf{F}_2$ on side 2 has magnitude

$$F_2 = \tfrac{1}{2}\rho_0 g b h^2 + b p_0 (H + c).$$

The net surface force on the gate, $\mathbf{F}_S = \mathbf{F}_1 + \mathbf{F}_2$, has magnitude

$$F_S = F_1 - F_2 = \tfrac{1}{2}\rho_0 g b (H^2 - h^2), \tag{4.5}$$

and its direction is from side 1 to side 2, as expected (see Figure 4.23). It is this force, exerted on the gates by the water in the lock, that keeps them closed.

For a typical canal, $b = 3\,\text{m}$, $h = 2\,\text{m}$ and $H = 5\,\text{m}$, so that the net force on a canal lock gate with these dimensions is about $3 \times 10^5\,\text{N}$. This is a substantial force. Since an apple weighs about 1 newton, it is roughly the weight of 300 000 apples; or, putting it another way, it is the weight of a 30 000 kg (30 tonne) lorry!

The force produced by the water in a full lock is quite sufficient to hold the lock closed without any mechanical device. In fact, even a very small difference in water levels will make it almost impossible to open the lock gates. However, when the water levels are exactly equal, the lock gates can be opened, since the net force due to the pressure is then zero.

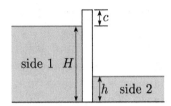

Figure 4.21 A lock gate with water at different levels

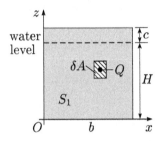

Figure 4.22 Side 1 of the gate

Note that p_1 is given by two different rules, according to the range in which z lies. Hence the integral for F_1 is split into two parts, each requiring its appropriate formula for p_1.

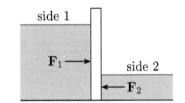

Figure 4.23

Even when the levels are the same, some force is required to open the gates, due to resistance at the socket.

Exercise 4.5

If the level of water in a lock is 0.01 metres above the level outside the lock, and the depth of water in the canal is 2 metres (that is, $h = 2\,\mathrm{m}$ and $H = 2.01\,\mathrm{m}$), what net force magnitude due to water pressure is acting on one of the lock gates, of width 3 metres? (Take the density of water to be $1000\,\mathrm{kg\,m^{-3}}$ and $g = 9.81\,\mathrm{m\,s^{-2}}$.)

The solution to this exercise shows that, for even a small difference in water levels (0.01 m), there is a significant force magnitude (590 N) on each lock gate holding it closed. Now, a lock gate may be opened by pushing on the end of an arm, about 5 metres long, that is joined to the gate (see Figure 4.24, which shows the view from above). The point of application of the net force on the gate due to the water lies on its axis of symmetry, that is, on the line $x = \frac{1}{2}b$. (The coordinate system was set up in Figure 4.22.)

590 N is approximately the weight of a 60 kg body.

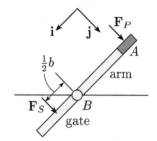

Figure 4.24

The force $\mathbf{F}_P = F_P\,\mathbf{j}$, exerted by the person at A, produces a torque about the pivot point B (on the same horizontal level as A) of

$$-AB\,\mathbf{i} \times F_P\,\mathbf{j} = -AB \times F_P\,\mathbf{k}.$$

The net surface force $\mathbf{F}_S = F_S\,\mathbf{j}$, exerted on the gate by the water, produces a torque about B whose $\mathbf{k}$-component vector is

$$\tfrac{1}{2}b\,\mathbf{i} \times F_S\,\mathbf{j} = \tfrac{1}{2}bF_S\,\mathbf{k}.$$

Ignoring resistance at the socket, the gate will be on the point of opening when the sum of these two $\mathbf{k}$-components is zero, that is, when

$$-AB \times F_P + \tfrac{1}{2}bF_S = 0, \qquad \text{or} \qquad F_P = \frac{bF_S}{2 \times AB}.$$

Using the solution to Exercise 4.5 and a lock gate arm length of 5 metres, we can calculate the force magnitude needed to open a lock gate when the water levels differ by 0.01 m to be, approximately,

$$F_P = \frac{3 \times 590}{2 \times 5}\,\mathrm{N} = 177\,\mathrm{N}.$$

This force, approximately the weight of an 18 kg body, is required to open one lock gate when the water levels differ by only 1 centimetre ($= 0.01$ m). The deeper the water on either side of the gate, or the greater the difference in water levels, then the greater is the force magnitude F_P. For example, consider lock gates for which $H = 5.01\,\mathrm{m}$ and $h = 5\,\mathrm{m}$. This leads to a net surface force on one of the gates of approximately 1473 N, and the force required to open the gate is then about 442 N. This is roughly $2\frac{1}{2}$ times the force (177 N) required to open a lock gate with $H = 2.01\,\mathrm{m}$ and $h = 2\,\mathrm{m}$, as considered above.

To see this, put
$$H^2 - h^2 = (H + h)(H - h)$$
in Equation (4.5).

If instead we increase the difference in height to 0.05 m (5 cm), so that $H = 2.05\,\mathrm{m}$ and $h = 2\,\mathrm{m}$, then the force required to open the gate is 894 N, roughly five times what is required when the gap is 0.01 m.

This case study has shown that large surface forces exist on structures that retain water at different levels. For the lock gates, the net surface force depends on the width of the gate and hence on the width of the lock. The locks considered above are wide enough to require a pair of lock gates at each end of the lock.

A different design of lock is shown in Figure 4.25. Here, there is one lock gate at each end instead of two. A lock gate with this design is used in narrower canals. Beyond a certain width, the gate cannot sustain the large net surface force produced by the water pressure distribution.

Figure 4.25

Before attempting the following exercise, read the summary of this section given in the *Handbook*.

End-of-section exercise

Exercise 4.6

(a) Classify the following statements as true or false.

  (i)   Pressure in a static fluid is the same at all points.

  (ii) Pressure in a static fluid is the same at all points in a given horizontal plane.

  (iii) In dealing with a fluid at rest, the basic modelling assumption is that viscous forces are negligible.

  (iv) The pressure at a point in a liquid of constant density at rest varies linearly with the depth of the point below the surface.

  (v)   The centre of pressure on a submerged vertical surface is at the centre of mass of the submerged surface.

  (vi) The centre of pressure can be at the centre of mass of a surface.

(b) (i) What is the pressure distribution in a solution of brine (salt water) that has *variable* density $\rho = a + bh$, where h is the depth below the free surface (the brine/atmosphere boundary) and a, b are constants?

  (ii) A square plate of side length 10 metres is submerged in the brine, so that the top edge of the plate lies on the free surface and the faces of the plate are vertical. Find the total force on one face of the plate due to the pressure in the fluid, if $a = 1000\,\mathrm{kg\,m^{-3}}$ and $b = 12\,\mathrm{kg\,m^{-4}}$. (Take the atmospheric pressure to be $p_0 = 1.01 \times 10^5\,\mathrm{Pa}$.)

5   Fluid statics 2: modelling the atmosphere

In Section 4, we found the pressure distribution in a constant-density fluid (modelling a liquid) at rest, and investigated the surface forces on rigid bodies that are immersed in such fluids. In this section, we shall model the atmosphere as a static fluid. The basic equation of fluid statics,

$$\frac{dp}{dz} = -\rho g,$$

This is Equation (4.2) on page 34.

forms part of the model. For the other part, we shall require an equation of state for the atmosphere. You are asked to begin with an exercise which assumes that the atmosphere has a *constant* density.

Exercise 5.1

Model the atmosphere as a static fluid of density $\rho_0 = 1.225 \, \text{kg m}^{-3}$. If the pressure at sea level is $p_0 = 1.013 \times 10^5 \, \text{Pa}$, at what height is the pressure $\frac{1}{10} p_0$? (Assume that g is constant and equal to $9.81 \, \text{m s}^{-2}$.)

The relationship between pressure and height for a constant-density fluid under constant gravity is $p = -\rho_0 g z + c$, as in Equation (4.3).

The solution to this exercise would suggest that the pressure in the atmosphere decreases linearly with height, and that at a height of 7.6 kilometres the pressure is one tenth of its value at sea level.

What evidence is there to check the validity of this constant-density model? If you were to climb a mountain, you would experience both a lower pressure and lower air density. At the top of Mount Everest, for example, the pressure and density in the air are approximately one third of their values at sea level. So the constant-density model is immediately suspect: qualitatively, the prediction that the pressure decreases is correct, but quantitatively, the prediction is not good. In fact, the constant-density model predicts zero pressure at a height of about 8.4 km, which is below the height of Everest.

Mount Everest is 8796 metres above sea level, higher than 7600 m, at which the constant-density model gives $p = \frac{1}{10} p_0$.

This height is given by $p_0/(\rho_0 g)$, taking the values in Exercise 5.1.

The actual variations of pressure and density in the atmosphere are found experimentally, by using weather balloons or from satellite observations. The distributions of pressure and density with height are shown in Figures 5.1 and 5.2. Also shown in the figures are the pressure and density graphs for the constant-density model used in Exercise 5.1.

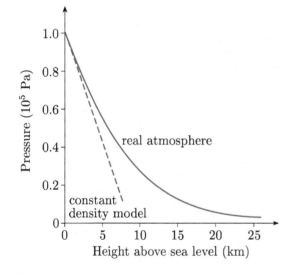

Figure 5.1

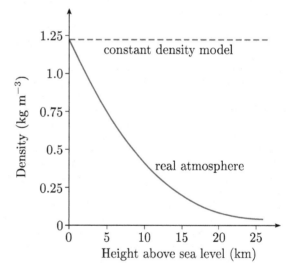

Figure 5.2

The pressure at points at any horizontal level in the atmosphere is less than for points on a lower level. However, the pressure decrease is not uniform as it is for a liquid, because the density of the atmosphere is not constant. Liquids are considered to be incompressible, and we often assume that the density is the same at all levels. This is not true for the atmosphere, and we cannot ignore its compressibility in any sensible model of the *whole* atmosphere. So far, we have ignored the temperature distribution in the atmosphere. The next subsection introduces temperature into the discussion.

5.1   An isothermal atmosphere

Consider a model of the atmosphere as a perfect gas for which the equation of state is (as in Subsection 3.3)

$$p = R\rho\Theta,$$

where R is the specific gas constant for air, ρ is air density and Θ is the absolute temperature. To use this equation, we need to know something about the temperature distribution in the atmosphere.

Isothermal means 'at the same temperature'.

For many problems involving gases, the assumption of the perfect gas law is sufficiently in agreement with the properties of real gases. For problems in which the temperature does not change, this law says that the pressure at a point in a fluid is proportional to the density at that point, which may also be stated as follows.

See Subsection 3.3.

Boyle's Law

For a gas at constant temperature,

$$\frac{p}{\rho} = \text{constant}.$$

This relation was first discovered experimentally by the physicist Robert Boyle, who was a contemporary of Newton. You can see that Boyle's law is a special case of the general perfect gas law.

A process in which the pressure and density of a gas change without alteration to the temperature is called an **isothermal process**. In an isothermal process, the conditions in the gas are changing sufficiently slowly for the heat energy created to be dissipated through the walls of the vessel containing the gas (so leaving the gas at the same constant temperature).

As a revision to the constant-density model, let us assume that the atmosphere is isothermal; that is, $\Theta = \Theta_0$, a constant. Then we have (from Boyle's law)

$$\frac{p}{\rho} = \text{constant} = \frac{p_0}{\rho_0},$$

where p_0 and ρ_0 are, respectively, the pressure and density of the atmosphere at some datum level, usually sea level, where they can be measured. For example, at sea level and at a temperature of 15°C (288.15 K), p_0 and ρ_0 take the values 1.013×10^5 Pa and 1.225 kg m^{-3}, respectively.

Note that, from these values, it is possible to calculate the specific gas constant for air, as

$$R = \frac{p}{\rho\Theta} = \frac{1.013 \times 10^5}{1.225 \times 288.15}$$
$$\simeq 287 \quad \text{(in SI units)}.$$

Example 5.1

Model the atmosphere as a perfect gas under isothermal conditions, and find the pressure at a point 20 km above the sea. (Take the values of pressure and density at sea level as given above, and assume that g is constant and equal to 9.81 m s^{-2}.)

Solution

The equation defining the rate of change of pressure with height z (above sea level) is

$$\frac{dp}{dz} = -\rho g,$$

and the isothermal relation between p and ρ is

$$p = \frac{p_0}{\rho_0}\rho.$$

This is Equation (4.2) on page 34.

Hence, on substituting for ρ into the first equation, we have

$$\frac{dp}{dz} = -\frac{\rho_0 g}{p_0}p = -\frac{p}{H}, \qquad \text{where } H = \frac{p_0}{\rho_0 g} \text{ is constant.}$$

(You will see shortly that H is a height of particular significance.) This can be written as

$$\frac{1}{p}\frac{dp}{dz} = -\frac{1}{H},$$

or as

$$\frac{d}{dz}(\ln p) = -\frac{1}{H}.$$

This is a first-order differential equation which can be solved using separation of variables. Since the equation is linear, it could also be solved by the integrating factor method.

The natural logarithm ln may also be written as $\log_e$.

Integration gives

$$\ln p = -\frac{z}{H} + c, \qquad \text{where } c \text{ is an arbitrary constant.}$$

When $z = 0$, we have $p = p_0$, and so $c = \ln p_0$. Thus

$$\ln\left(\frac{p}{p_0}\right) = -\frac{z}{H} = -\frac{\rho_0 g}{p_0}z.$$

Hence the pressure at any height z is given by

$$p = p_0 \exp\left(-\frac{\rho_0 g}{p_0}z\right).$$

Using $p_0 = 1.013 \times 10^5\,\text{Pa}$, $\rho_0 = 1.225\,\text{kg m}^{-3}$, $g = 9.81\,\text{m s}^{-2}$ and $z = 2 \times 10^4\,\text{m}$ (20 km), we obtain

$$p = 1.013 \times 10^5 \exp\left(-\frac{1.225 \times 9.81}{1.013 \times 10^5} \times 2 \times 10^4\right)$$

$$\simeq 9.44 \times 10^3\,\text{Pa.} \quad \blacksquare$$

The solution to this example shows that, for an isothermal atmosphere, the pressure decreases exponentially with increase in height above the Earth's surface.

If the atmosphere were modelled as a constant-density fluid of height H and density ρ_0, with a vacuum above, then the pressure p_0 at sea level would be given by $p_0 = \rho_0 g H$; and, using the values of p_0, ρ_0 and g given above, the value of H is 8.4 km. The ratio $H = p_0/(\rho_0 g)$, which also occurs in the solution for the isothermal atmosphere, is called the *height of the constant-density atmosphere*, and we can write the pressure distribution for the isothermal model as

$$p = p_0 e^{-z/H}.$$

This value of H was also arrived at on page 45.

Figure 5.3 (overleaf) shows the pressure distributions for an isothermal atmosphere, for a constant-density atmosphere and for the real atmosphere.

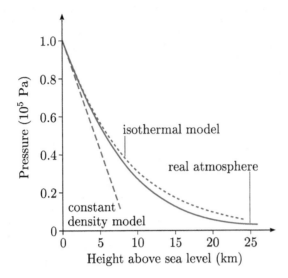

Figure 5.3

This figure suggests that the constant density and isothermal models both provide a very good fit in the lower atmosphere, for 0–1 km. Up to about 5 km, the isothermal model is good; but for 5 km upwards, there is a discrepancy between the real and predicted values. Above 2 km, the constant-density model must be abandoned.

Exercise 5.2

What is the density distribution for the isothermal model?

What evidence is there to check the validity of the isothermal model? The assumption of a constant temperature in the atmosphere does not agree with the experience of climbing, which demonstrates a decrease of temperature with increasing altitude. Figure 5.4 shows a typical temperature distribution between sea level and a height of 25 km.

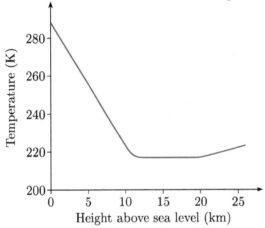

Figure 5.4 The temperature distribution in the real atmosphere

In the lower atmosphere, up to about 11 km (the *troposphere*), there is a steady decrease of temperature with height, so the isothermal model breaks down in this region. However, in the *stratosphere*, that is, for heights from about 11 to 20 km, the temperature has a constant value of approximately −56°C (217 K), and so for this region an isothermal model is a good one.

Exercise 5.3

Assume that the temperature distribution in the lower atmosphere, up to
11 km (that is, $0 \leq z \leq 1.1 \times 10^4$ m) is given by

$$\Theta = 288.15 - 0.0065z \quad \text{(in kelvins)}.$$

The constant gravity, static, perfect gas model of atmosphere is given by

$$\frac{dp}{dz} = -\rho g \quad \text{and} \quad p = R\rho\Theta.$$

Show that, for the lower atmosphere,

$$\frac{1}{p}\frac{dp}{dz} = -\frac{g}{R(288.15 - 0.0065z)}.$$

Solve this equation to find $p(z)$, and hence find the pressure and density in
the atmosphere at a height of 11 km. (Take atmospheric pressure at sea
level as $p_0 = 1.013 \times 10^5$ Pa. For air, the specific gas constant R is 287 in
SI units.)

This is a standard model for troposphere temperature. It represents a temperature decrease of 6.5 K for each km increase in height.

Exercise 5.4

Consider now the upper atmosphere, between 11 km and 20 km (that is,
1.1×10^4 m $< z \leq 2 \times 10^4$ m). Using the temperature distribution given in
Exercise 5.3, find the temperature, Θ_1, at a height of 11 km.

Model the upper atmosphere as being isothermal with this temperature,
and take the value of pressure at $z = 1.1 \times 10^4$ m as obtained in
Exercise 5.3. Show that the differential equation for the pressure
distribution $p(z)$ in this case is

$$\frac{1}{p}\frac{dp}{dz} = -\frac{g}{R\Theta_1}.$$

Solve this equation to find $p(z)$, and hence find the pressure at height
16 km. How does this value compare with the real value from Figure 5.3?

If we put together the pressure distributions obtained in the solutions to
these two exercises, then we have a model which compares very favourably
with the real atmosphere, as shown in Figure 5.5 (overleaf). The figure
shows the pressure distribution for a model based on the perfect gas law,
$p = R\rho\Theta$, where

$$\Theta = \begin{cases} 288.15 - 0.0065z & (0 \leq z \leq 1.1 \times 10^4 \text{ m}), \\ 216.65 & (1.1 \times 10^4 \text{ m} < z \leq 2 \times 10^4 \text{ m}). \end{cases}$$

This model has a linear temperature gradient in the lower atmosphere and is isothermal in the upper atmosphere.

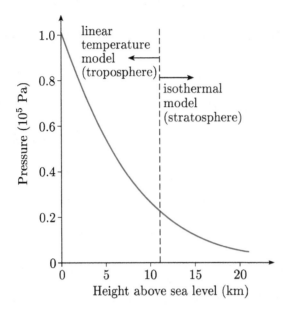

Figure 5.5

5.2 Discussion

It is perhaps rather surprising that a static model turns out to describe the atmosphere so accurately. In fact, the equation of fluid statics,

$$\frac{dp}{dz} = -\rho g$$

(which may also be written as $dp/dz + \rho g = 0$), is only an approximation to the vertical momentum equation that describes the motion of an inviscid fluid. This momentum equation is

$$\rho \frac{du_3}{dt} + \frac{dp}{dz} + \rho g = 0,$$

where u_3 is the vertical component of velocity of a fluid particle. For the atmosphere of the Earth, the term involving the vertical acceleration, $\rho \, du_3/dt$, is usually very small in comparison with the body force, ρg, and surface forces, dp/dz.

This is one of Euler's equations, to be developed in *Unit 5.*

However, to describe the pressure distribution in a turbulent atmosphere, such as in the higher altitudes of the atmosphere of Venus for instance, the static model would not be suitable because the vertical acceleration du_3/dt is large.

We began, in Exercise 5.1, with a constant-density model. This assumption of an incompressible fluid is a good description of the density distribution of many liquids, but is poor in all planetary atmospheres where the density decreases approximately exponentially with height. A combination of a linear temperature distribution below 11 km and isothermal conditions above 11 km gives a reasonably accurate formula for the pressure distribution in the Earth's atmosphere.

But what about the temperature distribution itself? How good is the isothermal/linear model? To appreciate that it is no easy matter to model the temperature distribution in the atmosphere, we must look briefly at what causes the temperature to change.

The controlling influence on most of the dynamics of the Earth's atmosphere, and its temperature distribution, is solar radiation. Around 70% of the solar radiation that is incident on the Earth is absorbed, mainly by the Earth's surface, but a small amount is absorbed by the atmosphere. (The other 30% is reflected directly back into space.) As a warm body, the Earth radiates heat, and the absorption of this secondary radiation largely determines the vertical temperature distribution. Typically, 90% of this secondary radiation from the Earth's surface is reabsorbed, largely by water vapour in the lowest few kilometres near the surface. (This contrasts with Mars, for example, where 90% of the surface radiation passes straight into space.)

The Earth's atmosphere acts as a very complex 'heat engine', trying to redistribute the air in order to warm the cooler latitudes (the poles) and cool the hotter latitudes. This dynamical activity changes the vertical temperature distribution. Thus the Earth's atmosphere is, in reality, a mixture of gases (oxygen, nitrogen, etc.) in very complicated motion. By using a model of the temperature distribution based on experimental data (as we have done), we can deduce the pressure and density distributions using a static model. But to obtain a model describing the temperature distribution would require a more complicated dynamical theory than we can discuss in this course.

Before attempting the following exercise, read the summary of this section given in the *Handbook*.

End-of-section exercise

Exercise 5.5

(a) What temperature distribution is required for a constant-density atmosphere? (Assume that the perfect gas law holds.)

(b) The atmosphere can be modelled as a perfect gas, for which the relation between pressure, p, and density, ρ, as the altitude increases is given by $p = k\rho^{\gamma}$, where k and γ are constants. Show that the relation between temperature, Θ, and altitude, z, for such an atmosphere is given by

$$\Theta = \Theta_0 - \left(\frac{(\gamma - 1)g}{\gamma R} \right) z,$$

where Θ_0 is the temperature at $z = 0$ and R is the specific gas constant for air.

What value of γ gives a good representation of the temperature distribution in the real atmosphere? (Take $R = 287$ in SI units.)

Outcomes

After studying this unit you should be able to:

- explain what distinguishes a fluid from a solid, and a liquid from a gas;
- explain how pressure is associated with compressional forces and viscosity with shearing forces;
- explain how the continuum model relates to the real world, and how it leads to definitions of density and pressure at any point in a fluid;
- understand, and apply where appropriate, each of Pascal's Law, Archimedes' Principle, and the equations of state for liquids and gases;
- apply the basic equation of fluid statics to obtain the pressure distribution in a liquid of given density, or to find the surface forces on a submerged object of simple shape;
- apply the basic equation of fluid statics and perfect gas law to obtain expressions for the pressure, density or temperature in a planetary atmosphere.

Acknowledgements

Grateful acknowledgement is made to the following for permission to reproduce photographs in this text:

Figures 1.9 and 1.11: *NCFMF Book of Film Notes*, 1974, The MIT Press with Education Development Center Inc;

Figure 1.10: Cranfield Institute of Technology;

Figure 1.13: *Journal of the Royal Aeronautical Society*, vol. 31, The Royal Aeronautical Society;

Figure 4.19: Ian Rotea/Flickr Photo Sharing;

Figure 4.25: Wendy Seltzer/Flickr Photo Sharing.

Every effort has been made to contact copyright holders. If any have been inadvertently overlooked the publishers will be pleased to make the necessary arrangements at the first opportunity.

Solutions to the exercises

Section 1

Solution 1.1

The following are fluids: air, oil, water, golden syrup, nitrogen.

Solution 1.2

From $\tau = \mu U/h$, the units of μ are given by
$$\frac{(\text{units of } \tau) \times (\text{units of } h)}{\text{units of } U}.$$
The units of τ, U and h are $\mathrm{N\,m^{-2}}$, $\mathrm{m\,s^{-1}}$ and m, respectively, so that the units of μ are
$$\frac{(\mathrm{N\,m^{-2}})\mathrm{m}}{\mathrm{m\,s^{-1}}} = \mathrm{N\,m^{-2}s}.$$
Alternatively, putting $1\,\mathrm{N} = 1\,\mathrm{kg\,m\,s^{-2}}$, we can also write the units of μ as $\mathrm{kg\,m^{-1}s^{-1}}$.

Solution 1.3

(a) (i) true (the defining property of a fluid);

(ii) true;   (iii) true;   (iv) false;

(v) true;   (vi) true;   (vii) true;

(viii) false for gases, which can be compressed easily;

(ix) true.

(b) Compressional forces attempt to compress the liquid into a smaller volume; but, because of the almost incompressible nature of a liquid, there is very little change in volume. Shearing forces cause the liquid to flow; the resistance to motion depends on the viscosity.

(c) Viscosity is assumed to be zero in the ideal flow region, because viscous forces are negligible here when compared with other forces. In the other two regions, viscosity is important.

Section 3

Solution 3.1

(a) false;   (b) true

(c) true (for the continuum model; in the real world fluid particles do not exist);   (d) true.

Solution 3.2

The area of water on which the piston pushes is
$$\pi \times \left(\frac{20}{1000}\right)^2 \mathrm{m^2}.$$
The pressure exerted on the water is
$$p = \frac{10}{\pi \times (0.02)^2} \simeq 7958\,\mathrm{Pa}.$$

If this pressure is transmitted to all parts of the water, then the magnitude of the force exerted to keep the water in the pump chamber is given by
$$F = p \times \text{area of hole}$$
$$\simeq 7958 \times \pi \times (0.002)^2\,\mathrm{N},$$
so that $F = 0.1\,\mathrm{N}$.

Solution 3.3

If the metal weight of mass m kg is about to rise when the excess pressure is 10^5 Pa, then the upward force due to the pressure must just balance mg newtons, the weight of the metal; that is,
$$10^5 \times \pi \times (0.0015)^2 = m \times 9.81,$$
so that
$$m = \frac{10^5 \times \pi \times (0.0015)^2}{9.81} = 0.072\,\mathrm{kg} \quad \text{(to 3 d.p.)}.$$

Solution 3.4

Since $1\ \mathrm{psi} = 6.895 \times 10^3$ Pa, we have
$$28\ \mathrm{psi} = 28 \times 6.895 \times 10^3\,\mathrm{Pa}$$
$$\simeq 1.93 \times 10^5\,\mathrm{Pa}$$
$$\simeq 1.93\,\mathrm{bar}.$$
The car handbook gives the value correct to 2 s.f.

Solution 3.5

(a) Water freezes at $0°\mathrm{C}$, which is $273.15\,\mathrm{K}$.

(b) Water boils at $100°\mathrm{C}$, which is $373.15\,\mathrm{K}$.

Solution 3.6

From $p = R\rho\Theta$, the units of R are given by
$$\frac{\text{units of } p}{(\text{units of } \rho) \times (\text{units of } \Theta)}.$$
Thus, the units of R are
$$\frac{\mathrm{N\,m^{-2}}}{\mathrm{kg\,m^{-3} \times K}} = \frac{\mathrm{kg\,m\,s^{-2}m^{-2}}}{\mathrm{kg\,m^{-3}K}} = \mathrm{m^2\,s^{-2}\,K^{-1}}.$$
(Alternatively, you may have obtained $\mathrm{m^2\,s^{-2}\,°C^{-1}}$ if you used degrees Celsius instead of kelvins. However, the kelvin is the SI unit for temperature. Another alternative is $\mathrm{J\,kg^{-1}K^{-1}}$.)

Solution 3.7

The density of the hydrogen at $-40°\mathrm{C}$ is $1/0.1 = 10\,\mathrm{kg\,m^{-3}}$. The absolute temperature of the hydrogen is
$$(273.15 - 40)\,\mathrm{K} = 233.15\,\mathrm{K}.$$
The pressure of the hydrogen is 9.6×10^6 Pa.

The perfect gas law, $p = R\rho\Theta$, gives (to 2 d.p.)
$$R = \frac{9.6 \times 10^6}{10 \times 233.15} \simeq 4.12 \times 10^3\,\mathrm{m^2\,s^{-2}\,K^{-1}}.$$

Solution 3.8

(a) The SI units of density are $\mathrm{kg\,m^{-3}}$.

(b) Sugar is not a fluid because a finite force is required to overcome 'dry friction' before sugar 'flows'. For example, once sugar falls onto a surface, it does not flow but remains in a pile.

(c) Our results (using kitchen equipment) were:

(i) granulated sugar: $10^3\,\mathrm{kg\,m^{-3}}$

(ii) cooking salt: $1.35 \times 10^3\,\mathrm{kg\,m^{-3}}$

(iii) milk: $0.96 \times 10^3\,\mathrm{kg\,m^{-3}}$.

(d) (i) true;   **(ii)** false;   **(iii)** true;
(iv) false;   **(v)** false;   **(vi)** true.

Section 4

Solution 4.1

Suppose that the point Q is height z above the base of the vessel; then, according to Equation (4.3) on page 35, we have

$$p_2 = c - \rho_2 g z \qquad (0 \le z \le z_0 - H).$$

Now

$$z = z_0 - h \qquad (0 \le h \le z_0),$$

and so

$$\begin{aligned} p_2 &= c - \rho_2 g(z_0 - h) \\ &= c - \rho_2 g z_0 + \rho_2 g h \qquad (H \le h \le z_0). \end{aligned} \qquad \text{(S.1)}$$

At any point M on the surface S_2, the pressure is, from Example 4.1(b),

$$p_M = p_0 + \rho_1 g H. \qquad \text{(S.2)}$$

When $h = H$, the pressure is $p_2 = p_M$ (due to continuity of pressure at the interface). Hence, from Equations (S.1) and (S.2), we obtain

$$c - \rho_2 g z_0 + \rho_2 g H = p_0 + \rho_1 g H,$$

giving

$$c - \rho_2 g z_0 = p_0 + \rho_1 g H - \rho_2 g H.$$

Thus, from Equation (S.1), at point Q the pressure is given by

$$p_2 = p_0 + \rho_1 g H + \rho_2 g(h - H) \qquad (H \le h \le z_0).$$

Solution 4.2

If p is the pressure in the sea water, then the pressure difference across the walls of the diving bell is $p - p_0$.

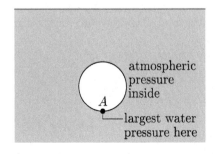
atmospheric pressure inside

A

largest water pressure here

The maximum pressure on the bell will be at its lowest point, A (because pressure increases with depth). Let the water pressure there be $p = p_A$. For the bell not to collapse, we require (in SI units)

$$p_A - p_0 \le 1.5 \times 10^6.$$

Now, $p_A = p_0 + \rho_0 g h_A$, where $\rho_0 = 1028\,\mathrm{kg\,m^{-3}}$, $g = 9.81\,\mathrm{m\,s^{-2}}$ and h_A (in m) is the depth of A. Thus

$$p_A - p_0 = 1028 \times 9.81 \times h_A \le 1.5 \times 10^6.$$

Hence

$$h_A \le \frac{1.5 \times 10^6}{1028 \times 9.81} \simeq 148.7,$$

so the bottom of the diving bell can be lowered to a depth of 148.7 m (if no safety margin is allowed).

Solution 4.3

Assume that the water and mercury are homogeneous, incompressible liquids that do not mix.

Let A be a point on the water/air surface, B a point on the mercury/water surface, and C a point at the bottom of the vessel.

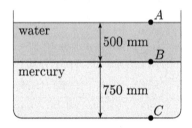

Using Equation (4.4) on page 36, the pressures at A, B and C are:

$$p_A = \text{atmospheric pressure} = p_0;$$

$$p_B = p_A + \rho_0 g h_{AB},$$

where ρ_0 is the water density and h_{AB} is the depth of B below A;

$$p_C = p_B + \rho_M g h_{BC},$$

where ρ_M is the mercury density and h_{BC} is the depth of C below B.

Combining these expressions gives (in SI units)

$$\begin{aligned} p_C &= p_0 + \rho_0 g h_{AB} + \rho_M g h_{BC} \\ &= p_0 + (10^3 \times 9.81 \times \tfrac{1}{2}) + (1.36 \times 10^4 \times 9.81 \times \tfrac{3}{4}) \\ &\simeq p_0 + 1.05 \times 10^5. \end{aligned}$$

Hence the pressure difference between the bottom (C) and the water/air surface is $p_C - p_0 \simeq 1.05 \times 10^5\,\mathrm{Pa}$.

Solution 4.4

(a) Choose directions for the Cartesian unit vectors as shown below.

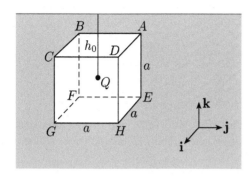

The force on the top face, $ABCD$, is

$$\mathbf{F}_1 = -a^2\left(p_0 + \rho_0 g(h_0 - \tfrac{1}{2}a)\right)\mathbf{k}.$$

The force on the bottom face, $EFGH$, is

$$\mathbf{F}_2 = a^2\left(p_0 + \rho_0 g(h_0 + \tfrac{1}{2}a)\right)\mathbf{k}.$$

For the four vertical faces, the magnitude of each force is equal to $(p_0 + \rho_0 g h_0)a^2$ (from Example 4.3).

For $CDHG$: $\mathbf{F}_3 = -(p_0 + \rho_0 g h_0)a^2\,\mathbf{i}.$
For $AEFB$: $\mathbf{F}_4 = (p_0 + \rho_0 g h_0)a^2\,\mathbf{i}.$
For $DHEA$: $\mathbf{F}_5 = -(p_0 + \rho_0 g h_0)a^2\,\mathbf{j}.$
For $BCGF$: $\mathbf{F}_6 = (p_0 + \rho_0 g h_0)a^2\,\mathbf{j}.$

(b) The resultant force on cube due to these forces is

$$\mathbf{F}_1 + \mathbf{F}_2 + \mathbf{F}_3 + \mathbf{F}_4 + \mathbf{F}_5 + \mathbf{F}_6 = a^3 \rho_0 g\,\mathbf{k},$$

which is vertically upwards.

Solution 4.5

Here $H = 2.01\,\mathrm{m}$, $h = 2\,\mathrm{m}$, $\rho_0 = 10^3\,\mathrm{kg\,m^{-3}}$ and $b = 3\,\mathrm{m}$ so that, from Equation (4.5) on page 42,

$$F_S = \tfrac{1}{2} \times 10^3 \times 9.81 \times 3 \times (2.01^2 - 2^2) \simeq 590\,\mathrm{N}.$$

Solution 4.6

(a) (i) false; (ii) true; (iii) false;
(iv) true; (v) false;
(vi) true, if the surface is horizontal.

(b) (i) From Equation (4.2) on page 34, we have

$$\frac{dp}{dz} = -\rho g = -(a + bh)g,$$

where z is measured upward from some reference point O. Now the height z and depth h of any point are related by $z + h = z_0$, where z_0 is the height of the surface above O (see Figure 4.7 on page 35). Hence $h = z_0 - z$, and so $dh/dz = -1$. By the Chain Rule,

$$\frac{dp}{dz} = \frac{dp}{dh}\frac{dh}{dz} = -\frac{dp}{dh},$$

and so we have

$$\frac{dp}{dh} = (a + bh)g.$$

Integration gives

$$p = \left(ah + \tfrac{1}{2}bh^2\right)g + p_0,$$

where p_0 is the atmospheric pressure.

(ii) Adopt the coordinate system shown below, in which x takes the place of h.

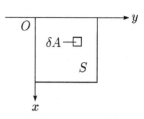

The surface force magnitude on a surface element of area δA is $p\,\delta A$. The total surface force (in newtons) on one face of the plate has magnitude

$$\int_S p\,dA = \int_S \left((ah + \tfrac{1}{2}bh^2)\,g + p_0\right)dA$$

$$= \int_0^{10}\int_0^{10}\left((1000x + 6x^2)\times 9.81 + 1.01 \times 10^5\right)dy\,dx$$

$$= 10\int_0^{10}\left((1000x + 6x^2)\times 9.81 + 1.01 \times 10^5\right)dx$$

$$= 10\left[(500x^2 + 2x^3)\times 9.81 + 1.01 \times 10^5 x\right]_0^{10}$$

$$= 10(4.905 \times 10^5 + 19.62 \times 10^3 + 1.01 \times 10^6)$$

$$\simeq 1.52 \times 10^7\,\mathrm{N}.$$

Section 5

Solution 5.1

Using the constant-density model, we have

$$p = p_0 - \rho_0 g z,$$

where z denotes height above sea level. Hence $p = \tfrac{1}{10}p_0$ for a height

$$z = \frac{9p_0}{10\rho_0 g} \simeq 7600\,\mathrm{m} \qquad \text{(i.e. 7.6 km)}.$$

Solution 5.2

If $p = p_0\rho/\rho_0$ (from Boyle's law) and $p = p_0 e^{-z/H}$ (from page 47), then

$$\rho = \rho_0 e^{-z/H}.$$

The density also decreases exponentially for an isothermal atmosphere.

Solution 5.3

The given equations are

$$\frac{dp}{dz} = -\rho g, \qquad p = R\rho\Theta, \qquad \Theta = \Theta_0 - kz,$$

where $\Theta_0 = 288.15$ and $k = 0.0065$. Thus

$$\frac{dp}{dz} = -\frac{gp}{R(\Theta_0 - kz)},$$

which can be written as

$$\frac{1}{p}\frac{dp}{dz} = -\frac{g}{R(\Theta_0 - kz)} = -\frac{g}{R(288.15 - 0.0065z)}.$$

Integrating, we have (since $\Theta_0 - kz > 0$)

$$\ln p = \frac{g}{Rk}\ln(\Theta_0 - kz) + c.$$

The condition $p = p_0$ when $z = 0$ gives
$$c = \ln p_0 - \frac{g}{Rk}\ln \Theta_0,$$
so that
$$\ln\left(\frac{p}{p_0}\right) = \frac{g}{Rk}\ln\left(\frac{\Theta_0 - kz}{\Theta_0}\right).$$
Thus
$$p = p_0\left(\frac{\Theta_0 - kz}{\Theta_0}\right)^{g/(Rk)}$$
$$= p_0\left(\frac{288.15 - 0.0065z}{288.15}\right)^{g/(0.0065R)},$$
where $p_0 = 1.013 \times 10^5$ Pa and $R = 287$. When $z = 1.1 \times 10^4$ m (height of 11 km), the pressure is
$$p \simeq 2.26 \times 10^4 \text{ Pa}.$$
The density at height 11 km is
$$\rho = \frac{p}{R\Theta}$$
$$= \frac{2.26 \times 10^4}{287 \times (288.15 - 0.0065 \times 1.1 \times 10^4)} \simeq 0.36 \text{ kg m}^{-3}.$$

Solution 5.4

The temperature at height 11 km is
$$\Theta_1 = 288.15 - 0.0065 \times 1.1 \times 10^4 = 216.65 \text{ K}.$$
The isothermal model with $\Theta = \Theta_1$ has pressure and density distributions satisfying
$$\frac{dp}{dz} = -\rho g, \quad p = R\rho\Theta_1 \quad (1.1\times 10^4 \text{ m} < z \leq 2\times 10^4 \text{ m}).$$
Eliminating ρ, we have
$$\frac{1}{p}\frac{dp}{dz} = -\frac{g}{R\Theta_1}.$$
Integration gives
$$\ln p = -\frac{g}{R\Theta_1}z + c;$$
that is,
$$p = A\exp\left(-\frac{gz}{R\Theta_1}\right), \quad \text{where } A = e^c.$$
When $z = 1.1 \times 10^4$ m, we have $p = 2.26 \times 10^4$ Pa, so that $A = 1.28 \times 10^5$ Pa, giving
$$p = 1.28 \times 10^5 \exp\left(-\frac{gz}{R\Theta_1}\right).$$
At height 16 km, the pressure is
$$p = 1.28 \times 10^5 \exp\left(-\frac{g \times 1.6 \times 10^4}{R\Theta_1}\right)$$
$$\simeq 1.03 \times 10^4 \text{ Pa}.$$
According to Figure 5.3 on page 48, for the real atmosphere, $p \simeq 10^4$ Pa at height 16 km, so that the calculated value here is quite close to the real value.

Solution 5.5

(a) If the density is constant, ρ_0 say, then
$$p = p_0 - \rho_0 gz.$$
The temperature distribution is given by
$$\Theta = \frac{p}{R\rho_0} = \frac{p_0 - \rho_0 gz}{R\rho_0} = \frac{p_0}{R\rho_0} - \frac{gz}{R}$$
$$= \Theta_0 - \frac{g}{R}z.$$

This is a linear function of z, but with $R = 287$ (in SI units) we have $g/R = 0.034$ K m^{-1}, which is somewhat larger than the value for the real atmosphere $(0.0065 \text{ K m}^{-1})$.

(b) The model consists of three parts:
$$\frac{dp}{dz} = -\rho g \quad \text{(fluid statics equation);} \tag{S.3}$$
$$p = R\rho\Theta \quad \text{(perfect gas law);} \tag{S.4}$$
$$p = k\rho^\gamma \quad \text{(pressure/density law).} \tag{S.5}$$
Equations (S.3) and (S.5) will give p (or ρ) as a function of z, and then Equation (S.4) will give Θ. We have
$$\frac{dp}{dz} = -\rho g = -\frac{gp^{1/\gamma}}{k^{1/\gamma}},$$
or
$$\frac{1}{p^{1/\gamma}}\frac{dp}{dz} = -\frac{g}{k^{1/\gamma}}.$$
Integrating gives
$$\frac{p^{(-1/\gamma)+1}}{-(1/\gamma)+1} = -\frac{g}{k^{1/\gamma}}z + c,$$
where
$$c = \frac{p_0^{(-1/\gamma)+1}}{-(1/\gamma)+1}.$$
Rearranging gives
$$p^{(\gamma-1)/\gamma} = p_0^{(\gamma-1)/\gamma} - \frac{(\gamma-1)gz}{\gamma k^{1/\gamma}}. \tag{S.6}$$
From Equation (S.4), we have
$$\Theta = \frac{p}{R\rho} = \frac{k^{1/\gamma}p}{Rp^{1/\gamma}}$$
$$= \frac{k^{1/\gamma}}{R}p^{1-(1/\gamma)} = \frac{k^{1/\gamma}}{R}p^{(\gamma-1)/\gamma}.$$
From Equation (S.6), this gives
$$\Theta = \frac{k^{1/\gamma}}{R}\left(p_0^{(\gamma-1)/\gamma} - \frac{(\gamma-1)gz}{\gamma k^{1/\gamma}}\right)$$
$$= \Theta_0 - \left(\frac{(\gamma-1)g}{\gamma R}\right)z.$$
In the real (lower) atmosphere, $(\gamma-1)g/(\gamma R) = 0.0065$, so that $\gamma = 1.235$ gives a good representation for Θ.

UNIT 2 Ordinary differential equations

Study guide

It is assumed in this text that you know a certain amount about the solution of first-order differential equations and linear constant-coefficient second-order differential equations. In particular, you should be relatively familiar with the contents of MST209 *Units 2* and *3*. You can, if necessary, brush up on your familiarity with this area by working through Section 1 of the *Revision Booklet*. Knowledge of MS221 *Chapter C3* would also be helpful (alternatively, see the appendices in this unit).

The sections of this unit can be studied in sequence, but Sections 4 and 5 are largely independent of the contents of Sections 1–3, and Section 2 can be studied at any stage.

There is an audio activity associated with Subsection 3.2.

You may find this unit rather long. Of the five sections, the most important for later developments are Sections 1, 3 and 4, and you may therefore wish to concentrate your study time on these.

Introduction

Unit 1 introduced many of the basic concepts concerning fluids and fluid motion. This initial survey of the subject area touched on several phenomena that are susceptible to mathematical modelling, and we shall be investigating models for these phenomena in due course. Before doing so, however, it is necessary to extend the available range of mathematical techniques. This is what we shall concentrate on for the remainder of Block 1 (*Units 2–4*). Most of the methods included here are used in subsequent units, but they are also of interest in their own right and find frequent application in fields other than fluid mechanics.

This unit deals with the solution of ordinary differential equations, a topic that should already be somewhat familiar to you. Ordinary differential equations may be used to describe the pathlines or streamlines of a fluid flow, but they also arise in the course of solving some of the partial differential equations that occur in fluid mechanics problems.

Pathlines and streamlines were introduced via the *Media Guide* during your study of *Unit 1*.

As an example of this second type, consider the steady flow of an incompressible viscous fluid within a long straight pipe of uniform circular cross-section (see Figure 0.1). The incompressibility and steadiness of the flow imply that its speed, u, is independent of distance along the pipe. The physical situation is symmetric around the pipe's central axis, so that u will depend only on r, the radial distance from this axis. It can be shown

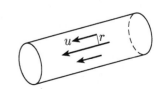

Figure 0.1

that the appropriate partial differential equation reduces to

$$r^2 u''(r) + r u'(r) = -kr^2, \tag{0.1}$$

where k is a positive constant which depends on the uniform pressure gradient, the density and the viscosity of the fluid.

This is a consequence of the Navier–Stokes equation for viscous flow, a partial differential equation which you will meet in *Unit 8*.

This is an example of a *Cauchy–Euler differential equation*, the general form of which is

$$ax^2 y''(x) + bxy'(x) + cy(x) = f(x),$$

where a, b, c are constants and f is a continuous function. In each term on the left-hand side, the power of x is equal to the order of the derivative.

Section 1 explains how to find the general solution of any homogeneous second-order Cauchy–Euler equation, and extends the method to solve certain other differential equations. Section 2 shows how partial knowledge of the solutions of a second-order differential equation can be used as a lever to obtain the general solution, both in the homogeneous and inhomogeneous cases.

Section 3 is concerned with *boundary-value problems*, in which we seek the particular solution of a differential equation which satisfies certain *boundary conditions*. If the differential equation models a physical process, then the boundary conditions usually arise naturally from the circumstances in which that process takes place.

Suppose, for example, that the pipe described above is of radius a. Then we should be interested in the solution of Equation (0.1) on the interval $0 < r < a$, and it would be necessary to specify boundary conditions on u at $r = 0$ and at $r = a$ in order to find a particular solution. At $r = a$, the appropriate condition follows from the assumption (according well with observation) that the speed of a viscous flow tends towards zero as a stationary physical boundary is approached.

This is called the *no-slip condition* for viscous flow.

The mathematical expression of this assumption is

$$u(a) = 0.$$

We do not have the same correspondence between a physical and a mathematical boundary at $r = 0$, since this is just the centre of the pipe. In order to find a particular solution for $u(r)$, it is sufficient to require that the speed should be bounded in the limit as r tends to zero. Any real flow must certainly satisfy this condition!

In Section 3 we examine the basic types of boundary-value problem which occur in practice. A feature of such problems is that they do not always have solutions, and that if a solution exists then there may be more than one of them. For example, consider the motion of standing shallow water waves in a flat-bottomed channel of length L, where the equilibrium water depth is h (see Figure 0.2).

In this respect, boundary-value problems differ from initial-value problems, for which in many cases unique solutions exist. For example, Theorem 3.1 of MST209 *Unit 3* guarantees unique solutions for one class of problem.

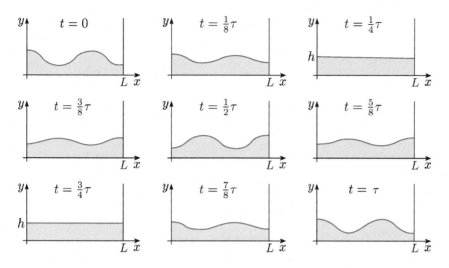

Figure 0.2   The motion of a standing shallow water wave over one oscillation of period τ

The water depth $y(x, t)$ at position x and time t is found to be of the form

$$y(x, t) = h + C \cos(\sqrt{\lambda gh}\, t + c)\, u(x),$$

where the function $u(x)$ satisfies the boundary-value problem

$$u''(x) + \lambda u(x) = 0, \qquad u'(0) = u'(L) = 0. \tag{0.2}$$

Now $u(x) = 0$ is a solution to this problem for any value of λ. There are also non-zero solutions if and only if λ takes one of the values $n^2\pi^2/L^2$, where n is an integer. This corresponds to the physical fact that, for given values of h and L, standing wave motions can occur only for certain frequencies of oscillation.

A problem such as that given by Equations (0.2) is called an *eigenvalue problem*. The values of the undetermined constant λ for which non-zero solutions exist are known as the *eigenvalues*, and the corresponding non-zero solutions $u(x)$ are called *eigenfunctions*. This is the subject of Subsection 3.2.

Section 4 introduces another method that can be used either to find an expression for the general solution of a differential equation or to solve an initial-value problem. It involves assuming a solution which has the form of an infinite series, the terms of which are multiples of powers of x, and reducing the problem to that of solving a recurrence relation for the coefficients in the series. This is a valuable approach where no solution in terms of elementary functions can be found. However, it has some limitations, since it is not obvious that the series will converge to a limit at all points where the solution is sought. Section 5 investigates when such a series can be expected to give valid results.

Shallow water waves are investigated in *Unit 12*. A *standing wave* has the property that certain points on the surface remain at their equilibrium position throughout the motion. (In Figure 0.2 this is true of the surface points at $x = \frac{1}{6}L$, $x = \frac{1}{2}L$ and $x = \frac{5}{6}L$.) Such points are called *nodes*.

The constants C and c are determined, respectively, by the amplitude and phase of the standing wave ($c = 0$ is chosen in Figure 0.2).

The integer n is equal to the number of nodes. Hence in Figure 0.2 we have $n = 3$, $\lambda = 9\pi^2/L^2$ and

$$\tau = 2\pi/\sqrt{\lambda gh} = \tfrac{2}{3}L/\sqrt{gh}.$$

1 Change of independent variable

You may recall that certain integrals can be evaluated using the method of Integration by Substitution, which involves a change of variable in the integrand. The method depends on the Chain Rule for differentiating a composite function, which states that

if $u = g(x)$, where $x = h(t)$,

Here g and h are differentiable functions.

then

$$\frac{du}{dt} = \frac{dx}{dt}\frac{du}{dx}. \tag{1.1}$$

In this section you will see that a change of independent variable can sometimes be used in a similar way to solve differential equations. In particular, Cauchy–Euler equations may be solved by this approach.

1.1 Cauchy–Euler equations

A second-order **Cauchy–Euler equation** is a differential equation of the form

$$ax^2\frac{d^2y}{dx^2} + bx\frac{dy}{dx} + cy = f(x),$$

where a, b, c are constants (with $a \neq 0$) and f is a continuous function.

This definition generalises in a natural way to nth-order Cauchy–Euler equations, in which the coefficient of the mth derivative is a multiple of x^m for each $m \leq n$.

Consider first the homogeneous second-order Cauchy–Euler equation,

$$ax^2\frac{d^2y}{dx^2} + bx\frac{dy}{dx} + cy = 0 \qquad (x > 0). \tag{1.2}$$

The range excludes $x = 0$, for a reason to be explained shortly.

We shall show that the general solution of this equation can be found by making the change of variable

$$x = e^t. \tag{1.3}$$

Our object then is to rewrite Equation (1.2) in terms of t, y, dy/dt and d^2y/dt^2. Since

$$\frac{dx}{dt} = e^t = x,$$

the Chain Rule formula (1.1) becomes

$$\frac{du}{dt} = x\frac{du}{dx}, \tag{1.4}$$

and putting $u = y$ gives

$$\frac{dy}{dt} = x\frac{dy}{dx}. \tag{1.5}$$

Also, putting $u = dy/dt$ in Equation (1.4) gives

$$\frac{d}{dt}\left(\frac{dy}{dt}\right) = x\frac{d}{dx}\left(\frac{dy}{dt}\right),$$

or, using Equation (1.5) on the right-hand side,

$$\frac{d^2y}{dt^2} = x\frac{d}{dx}\left(x\frac{dy}{dx}\right).$$

From the Product Rule for differentiation, this becomes

$$\frac{d^2y}{dt^2} = x\frac{dy}{dx} + x^2\frac{d^2y}{dx^2},$$

and employing Equation (1.5) again gives

$$x^2\frac{d^2y}{dx^2} = \frac{d^2y}{dt^2} - \frac{dy}{dt}.$$
(1.6)

Equations (1.5) and (1.6) permit us to rewrite Equation (1.2) as

$$a\frac{d^2y}{dt^2} + (b-a)\frac{dy}{dt} + cy = 0.$$
(1.7)

So by substituting $x = e^t$ and using the Chain Rule, we have converted the Cauchy–Euler equation (1.2), which has variable coefficients, into a differential equation with constant coefficients. The method for solving the constant-coefficient equation (1.7) should be familiar to you. It depends on finding the roots of the auxiliary equation

$$a\lambda^2 + (b-a)\lambda + c = 0,$$
(1.8)

which is obtained by substituting $y = e^{\lambda t}$ into Equation (1.7). But we have $e^{\lambda t} = (e^t)^\lambda = x^\lambda$, so Equation (1.8) can also be obtained directly by substituting $y = x^\lambda$ into the Cauchy–Euler equation (1.2). Because of this, Equation (1.8) is called the **indicial equation** of Equation (1.2).

Suppose that Equation (1.8) has two distinct real roots, $\lambda = \lambda_1$ and $\lambda = \lambda_2$. Then the general solution of Equation (1.7) is

$$\begin{aligned}y &= Ae^{\lambda_1 t} + Be^{\lambda_2 t}\\ &= A(e^t)^{\lambda_1} + B(e^t)^{\lambda_2},\end{aligned}$$

where A, B are arbitrary constants, so that the general solution of Equation (1.2) is

$$y = Ax^{\lambda_1} + Bx^{\lambda_2}.$$

If initial conditions are given, then the particular solution of the Cauchy–Euler equation which satisfies these initial conditions can be found in the usual way.

See Procedure 1.1 in MST209 Unit 3, or Subsection 1.4 of the Revision Booklet.

As you will see in Example 1.1 below, this is how Equation (1.8) is usually derived in practice.

Example 1.1

Find the general solution of the differential equation

$$3x^2\frac{d^2y}{dx^2} - 2x\frac{dy}{dx} - 2y = 0 \qquad (x > 0).$$

Find also the particular solution for which $y = 0$, $dy/dx = 1$ when $x = 1$.

The initial conditions here can also be written as
$$y(1) = 0, \quad y'(1) = 1.$$

Solution

If $y = x^\lambda$, then $dy/dx = \lambda x^{\lambda-1}$ and $d^2y/dx^2 = \lambda(\lambda-1)x^{\lambda-2}$. So putting $y = x^\lambda$ into the given differential equation leads to

$$3\lambda(\lambda-1)x^\lambda - 2\lambda x^\lambda - 2x^\lambda = 0.$$

Dividing through by x^λ produces the indicial equation

$$3\lambda^2 - 5\lambda - 2 = 0, \qquad \text{or} \qquad (3\lambda+1)(\lambda-2) = 0,$$

with roots $\lambda = -\frac{1}{3}$ and $\lambda = 2$.

The general solution of the differential equation is therefore

$$y = Ax^{-1/3} + Bx^2,$$

where A, B are arbitrary constants. The derivative of this is

$$\frac{dy}{dx} = -\tfrac{1}{3}Ax^{-4/3} + 2Bx.$$

The given initial conditions then lead to the equations

$$0 = A + B,$$
$$1 = -\tfrac{1}{3}A + 2B,$$

with solution $A = -\tfrac{3}{7}$, $B = \tfrac{3}{7}$. The required particular solution is

$$y = \tfrac{3}{7}(x^2 - x^{-1/3}). \quad \blacksquare$$

Above, we dealt with the case for which Equation (1.8) has distinct real roots. More generally, the general solution of Equation (1.7) is

(i) $y = Ae^{\lambda_1 t} + Be^{\lambda_2 t}$, if Equation (1.8) has two distinct real roots, $\lambda = \lambda_1$ and $\lambda = \lambda_2$;

(ii) $y = (A + Bt)e^{\alpha t}$, if Equation (1.8) has equal roots, $\lambda = \alpha$;

(iii) $y = e^{\alpha t}[A\cos(\beta t) + B\sin(\beta t)]$, if Equation (1.8) has complex conjugate roots, $\lambda = \alpha \pm i\beta$.

The corresponding general solution of Equation (1.2) is obtained by changing back to the original variable x, where $t = \ln x$ from Equation (1.3). This leads to the following procedure for solving Equation (1.2).

The solution of an initial-value problem may be checked by substituting it back into the differential equation and initial conditions.

In each case, A and B are arbitrary constants.

Procedure 1.1   Solving Cauchy–Euler equations

To solve the homogeneous second-order Cauchy–Euler equation

$$ax^2\frac{d^2y}{dx^2} + bx\frac{dy}{dx} + cy = 0 \quad (x > 0),$$

proceed as follows.

(a) Put $y = x^\lambda$ to obtain a quadratic equation in λ, called the indicial equation.

(b) Solve the indicial equation.

(c) Write down the general solution of the Cauchy–Euler equation:

(i) if the indicial equation has two distinct real roots, $\lambda = \lambda_1$ and $\lambda = \lambda_2$, then the general solution is

$$y = Ax^{\lambda_1} + Bx^{\lambda_2};$$

(ii) if the indicial equation has equal roots, $\lambda = \alpha$, then the general solution is

$$y = (A + B\ln x)x^\alpha;$$

(iii) if the indicial equation has complex roots, $\lambda = \alpha + i\beta$ and $\lambda = \alpha - i\beta$, then the general solution is

$$y = x^\alpha[A\cos(\beta\ln x) + B\sin(\beta\ln x)].$$

In each case, A and B are arbitrary constants.

The general solution for $x < 0$ is obtained on replacing x by $|x|$ throughout Step (c). The change of variable required to derive the solution in this case is $x = -e^t$.

Exercise 1.1

For each of the following differential equations, find the general solution and also the particular solution for which $y = 1$, $dy/dx = -2$ when $x = 1$. (Take $x > 0$ throughout.)

(a) $2x^2 \dfrac{d^2y}{dx^2} + 11x \dfrac{dy}{dx} - 5y = 0$

(b) $x^2 \dfrac{d^2y}{dx^2} + 3x \dfrac{dy}{dx} + 10y = 0$

(c) $9x^2 \dfrac{d^2y}{dx^2} - 3x \dfrac{dy}{dx} + 4y = 0$

(d) $x^2 \dfrac{d^2y}{dx^2} + x \dfrac{dy}{dx} + 7y = 0$

(e) $5x^2 \dfrac{d^2y}{dx^2} + 3x \dfrac{dy}{dx} = 0$

The change of variable $x = e^t$, which was used to derive Procedure 1.1, can also be applied to the inhomogeneous Cauchy–Euler equation,

$$ax^2 \frac{d^2y}{dx^2} + bx \frac{dy}{dx} + cy = f(x) \qquad (x > 0).$$

Equations (1.5) and (1.6) transform this into

$$a \frac{d^2y}{dt^2} + (b - a) \frac{dy}{dt} + cy = f(e^t),$$

whose general solution may be sought by standard methods if $f(e^t)$ is of an appropriate form.

See Procedures 2.1–2.3 in MST209 *Unit 3*, or Subsection 1.4 of the *Revision Booklet*.

We conclude this subsection by pointing out one property of Cauchy–Euler equations which is not possessed by constant-coefficient equations. A linear second-order differential equation

$$p(x) \frac{d^2y}{dx^2} + q(x) \frac{dy}{dx} + r(x)y = f(x)$$

By the definition of 'linear', p, q, r and f are continuous functions (see Subsection 1.1 of MST209 *Unit 3*).

is said to have a **singular point** at $x = x_0$ if $p(x_0) = 0$. For a Cauchy–Euler equation, $p(x) = ax^2$, and so $x = 0$ is the only singular point.

A constant-coefficient equation has no singular points, since in this case p is a constant function.

In general, there may be no solutions to a differential equation in an interval which contains a singular point, and if such solutions do exist it will not usually be possible to find one which satisfies arbitrarily given initial conditions for y and dy/dx at some point in the interval. This explains why we have been careful to put $x > 0$ (or $x < 0$) when the aim has been to find the solution of a Cauchy–Euler equation.

Example 1.2

The Cauchy–Euler equation

$$x^2 \frac{d^2y}{dx^2} + 4x \frac{dy}{dx} + 2y = 0 \quad (x > 0)$$

has general solution

$$y = Ax^{-1} + Bx^{-2}.$$

The indicial equation is $\lambda^2 + 3\lambda + 2 = 0$, with roots $\lambda = -1$ and $\lambda = -2$.

Which solutions are bounded and tend to a limiting value as $x \to 0$?

Solution

Both x^{-1} and x^{-2} are unbounded as $x \to 0$. Hence the only solution which is bounded in this limit is $y = 0$ (choosing $A = B = 0$). ■

If $x > 0$, then $\lim\limits_{x \to 0} x^n = 0$ for $n > 0$, but this limit does not exist for $n < 0$.

Exercise 1.2

The general solutions of the Cauchy–Euler equations in Example 1.1 and Exercise 1.1(a) are respectively

(a) $y = Ax^{-1/3} + Bx^2$,

(b) $y = Ax^{1/2} + Bx^{-5}$,

both defined for $x > 0$. Which solutions of each of these Cauchy–Euler equations are bounded and tend to a limiting value as $x \to 0$?

Types of behaviour similar to those exhibited by solutions of Cauchy–Euler equations can be observed near the singular points of other linear differential equations.

1.2 Extending the method

You have seen how the change of independent variable from x to t, where $x = e^t$, can be used to solve Cauchy–Euler equations. We next demonstrate how the same method can be applied to certain other differential equations. In each case, we start by taking $x = h(t)$ for some suitable function h, and then write down the corresponding Chain Rule.

Example 1.3

Use the change of variable

$$x = \tan t \qquad \left(-\tfrac{1}{2}\pi < t < \tfrac{1}{2}\pi\right)$$

to find the general solution of the differential equation

$$(1 + x^2)^2 \frac{d^2 y}{dx^2} + (1 + x^2)(2x + 1)\frac{dy}{dx} - 6y = 0.$$

Solution

If $x = \tan t$, then

$$\frac{dx}{dt} = \sec^2 t = 1 + \tan^2 t = 1 + x^2.$$

Therefore, the Chain Rule formula (1.1) becomes

$$\frac{du}{dt} = (1 + x^2)\frac{du}{dx}, \tag{1.9}$$

so that (putting $u = y$)

$$\frac{dy}{dt} = (1 + x^2)\frac{dy}{dx}, \tag{1.10}$$

and (putting $u = dy/dt$ in Equation (1.9), and then using Equation (1.10))

$$\frac{d^2 y}{dt^2} = \frac{d}{dt}\left(\frac{dy}{dt}\right) = (1 + x^2)\frac{d}{dx}\left[(1 + x^2)\frac{dy}{dx}\right]$$

$$= (1 + x^2)\left[2x\frac{dy}{dx} + (1 + x^2)\frac{d^2 y}{dx^2}\right]$$

$$= (1 + x^2)2x\frac{dy}{dx} + (1 + x^2)^2\frac{d^2 y}{dx^2}.$$

The differential equation becomes

$$\frac{d^2 y}{dt^2} + \frac{dy}{dt} - 6y = 0,$$

which has general solution

$$y = Ae^{2t} + Be^{-3t}.$$

Hence the solution of the original equation is

$$y = Ae^{2\arctan x} + Be^{-3\arctan x}. \quad \blacksquare$$

To ensure that the method gives a valid solution to a second-order equation, h must be a one–one twice differentiable function whose inverse, h^{-1}, is also twice differentiable. These conditions are satisfied for the particular changes of variable considered here and for the given domains.

You will not be expected to *find* an appropriate change of variable, except in very simple cases, but you should be able to transform a differential equation when the change of variable is given.

Exercise 1.3

(a) Use a suitable change of variable and a result from Exercise 1.1(a) to find the general solution of the differential equation

$$2(x - \mu)^2 \frac{d^2y}{dx^2} + 11(x - \mu)\frac{dy}{dx} - 5y = 0 \qquad (x > \mu),$$

where μ is a constant.

(b) Use the change of variable

$$x = \cos t \qquad (0 < t < \pi)$$

to find the general solution of the differential equation

$$(1 - x^2)\frac{d^2y}{dx^2} - x\frac{dy}{dx} + \lambda y = 0 \qquad (-1 < x < 1),$$

where λ is a positive constant.

This is known as *Chebyshev's equation*.

Note that the change of variable $x = t + \mu$ employed in Exercise 1.3(a) can be used to solve any second-order equation of the form

$$a(x - \mu)^2 \frac{d^2y}{dx^2} + b(x - \mu)\frac{dy}{dx} + cy = 0 \qquad (x > \mu),$$

where μ is a constant. In fact, the general solution of this equation is obtained on replacing x by $x - \mu$ throughout Procedure 1.1.

End-of-section exercises

Exercise 1.4

Find the general solution of each of the following differential equations.

(a) $t^2 \dfrac{d^2u}{dt^2} - 3t\dfrac{du}{dt} + 4u = 0 \qquad (t > 0)$

(b) $(x - 3)^2 \dfrac{d^2y}{dx^2} + 5(x - 3)\dfrac{dy}{dx} + 5y = 0 \qquad (x > 3)$

In part (a), the independent variable is t and the dependent variable is u.

Exercise 1.5

Use the change of variable

$$x = \cosh t \qquad (t > 0)$$

to find the general solution of the equation

$$(1 - x^2)\frac{d^2y}{dx^2} - x\frac{dy}{dx} + \lambda y = 0 \qquad (x > 1),$$

where λ is a positive constant.

This exercise concerns Chebyshev's equation again, but here we have $x > 1$ rather than $-1 < x < 1$ as in Exercise 1.3(b), so a different change of variable is required. The hyperbolic functions cosh and sinh are introduced in MS221 *Chapter C3*. See also Appendix 1 in this unit.

2 Change of dependent variable

For a differential equation that involves y, dy/dx and perhaps d^2y/dx^2, the independent variable is x and the dependent variable is y. We seek a solution function $y(x)$ that expresses the dependent variable in terms of the independent variable. In Section 1, all of the changes of variable considered were changes of the independent variable. We now consider some applications of the idea that the dependent variable also can be changed.

This could enable a non-linear differential equation to be 'linearised', by use of a change of dependent variable that requires another use of the Chain Rule. However, we shall concentrate here on simpler changes of variable, applied to linear equations, that require use of the Product Rule. In Subsection 2.1, you will see how the general solution of certain equations may be found after a single particular solution has been identified. Subsection 2.2 turns to the question of finding particular integrals for inhomogeneous equations.

In order to cut down the amount of algebra involved, we use in this section the 'prime' notation for derivatives, writing $y'(x)$ or just y' for dy/dx, $y''(x)$ or y'' for d^2y/dx^2, and so on.

2.1 Reduction of order

It is sometimes the case that one solution of a second-order linear homogeneous differential equation is much easier to recognise than another, independent, solution. In such a circumstance, the method of *reduction of order* permits an independent solution, and hence also the general solution, to be found. This is best demonstrated by an example.

In this context, two solutions are *independent* (or more precisely, *linearly independent*) if neither is a constant multiple of the other.

Example 2.1

The differential equation
$$x^2(1-x)y''(x) - 2xy'(x) + 2y(x) = 0 \qquad (0 < x < 1)$$
has a solution $y_1(x) = x$ (as can rapidly be checked). By seeking an independent solution of the form $y(x) = x\,u(x)$, where $u(x)$ is to be determined, find the general solution of the differential equation.

This is neither a constant-coefficient equation nor a Cauchy–Euler equation, so the procedures developed for these cases do not apply.

Solution

In abbreviated form, we take $y = xu$. Then, by the Product Rule, we have
$$y' = u + xu' \qquad \text{and} \qquad y'' = 2u' + xu''. \tag{2.1}$$
Since y is to be a solution of the differential equation, we have
$$x^2(1-x)y'' - 2xy' + 2y = 0.$$
From Equations (2.1), this can be expressed in terms of u and its derivatives as
$$x^2(1-x)(2u' + xu'') - 2x(u + xu') + 2(xu) = 0,$$
that is,
$$x^3(1-x)u'' + \left(2x^2(1-x) - 2x^2\right)u' = 0, \quad \text{or} \quad (1-x)u'' - 2u' = 0.$$
Note that the terms involving u (as opposed to u' and u'') have cancelled out.

On putting $v(x) = u'(x)$, we have a first-order differential equation for $v(x)$, namely,

$$(1 - x)v' - 2v = 0.$$

Either separation of variables or the integrating factor method can be applied to show that this has general solution

$$v(x) = \frac{A}{(1 - x)^2}, \qquad \text{where } A \text{ is an arbitrary constant.}$$

This is worth checking.

Since $u'(x) = v(x)$, we then find that

$$u(x) = \int \frac{A}{(1 - x)^2}\, dx = \frac{A}{1 - x} + B,$$

where B is another arbitrary constant. Thus the general solution of the original differential equation is

$$y(x) = x\, u(x) = \frac{Ax}{1 - x} + Bx.$$

The second term on the right-hand side corresponds to the particular solution $y_1(x) = x$ that was known from the outset, while the $x/(1 - x)$ term is an independent solution that has been found. ■

To generalise from this example, suppose that $y_1(x)$ is a known solution of the linear homogeneous second-order differential equation

$$p(x)\, y''(x) + q(x)\, y'(x) + r(x)\, y(x) = 0,$$

or more briefly,

$$py'' + qy' + ry = 0. \tag{2.2}$$

We seek an independent solution of the form $y(x) = u(x)\, y_1(x)$, that is, $y = u\, y_1$, where u is to be found. By the Product Rule, we have

$$y' = u\, y_1' + u'\, y_1 \qquad \text{and} \qquad y'' = u\, y_1'' + 2u'\, y_1' + u''\, y_1. \tag{2.3}$$

Now $y(x)$ is to be a solution of Equation (2.2). Taking Equations (2.3) into account, this means that

$$p(u\, y_1'' + 2u'\, y_1' + u''\, y_1) + q(u\, y_1' + u'\, y_1) + r(u\, y_1) = 0,$$

which can be rearranged as

$$(py_1)u'' + (2py_1' + qy_1)u' + (py_1'' + qy_1' + ry_1)u = 0. \tag{2.4}$$

However, $y_1(x)$ is a (known) solution of the differential equation, and hence satisfies Equation (2.2). It follows that the coefficient of the u term in Equation (2.4) must be zero, leaving

$$(py_1)u'' + (2py_1' + qy_1)u' = 0.$$

Putting $v(x) = u'(x)$ and rearranging, we have

$$v' + \left(\frac{2y_1'}{y_1} + \frac{q}{p} \right) v = 0, \tag{2.5}$$

We assume that $p(x) \neq 0$ and $y_1(x) \neq 0$.

an equation which can be solved by either separation of variables or the integrating factor method. Once this has been done, we can integrate to obtain $u(x)$ from $v(x)$, then multiply $u(x)$ by $y_1(x)$ to obtain the general solution $y(x)$.

The method outlined here is known as **reduction of order** because, starting from a second-order equation for $y(x)$, we reduce the problem to that of solving a first-order equation for $v(x)$. However, this can be achieved only if one solution is known beforehand. The procedure is summarised on the next page.

Procedure 2.1   Reduction of order

To solve the linear homogeneous second-order differential equation

$$p(x)\, y''(x) + q(x)\, y'(x) + r(x)\, y(x) = 0,$$

for which one solution $y_1(x)$ is already known, proceed as follows.

(a) Assume a solution of the form $y(x) = u(x)\, y_1(x)$, where $u(x)$ is to be found.

(b) By substituting this form into the differential equation, obtain a first-order equation for $v(x) = u'(x)$, namely,

$$v' + \left(\frac{2y_1'}{y_1} + \frac{q}{p}\right) v = 0. \tag{2.5}$$

(c) Solve this equation for $v(x)$, integrate to find $u(x)$, and hence obtain the general solution $y(x) = u(x)\, y_1(x)$.

Exercise 2.1

(a) Show that $y_1(x) = x^2$ is a solution of the differential equation

$$x^2 y''(x) - x(3x + 4)y'(x) + 6(x + 1)y(x) = 0.$$

(b) Use the method of reduction of order to find the general solution of this differential equation.

Exercise 2.2

(a) Show that $y_1(x) = e^{-2x}$ is a solution of the differential equation

$$xy''(x) + 2(x - 1)y'(x) - 4y(x) = 0.$$

(b) Use the method of reduction of order to find the general solution of this differential equation.

It is possible in a similar way to apply reduction of order to find the general solution of an *inhomogeneous* differential equation,

$$p(x)\, y''(x) + q(x)\, y'(x) + r(x)\, y(x) = f(x),$$

given one solution $y_1(x)$ to the corresponding *homogeneous* equation. In fact, this leads to a version of Equation (2.5) with $f/(py_1)$ rather than 0 on the right-hand side. However, rather than demonstrate this, you will see in the next subsection a slightly different approach to solving inhomogeneous equations.

2.2   Variation of parameters

In this subsection, we introduce a method for finding a particular integral for an inhomogeneous linear differential equation, of the form

$$p(x)\, y''(x) + q(x)\, y'(x) + r(x)\, y(x) = f(x). \tag{2.6}$$

As indicated at the end of the previous subsection, the method of reduction of order could be used for this purpose, given one known solution $y_1(x)$ to the associated homogeneous equation. However, it is often the case, when seeking a particular integral, that the general solution of the homogeneous equation is already known; if this is so, then the method of *variation of parameters*, described in this subsection, has advantages over reduction of order.

We therefore assume that the general solution of the associated homogeneous equation is known, and that $y_1(x)$, $y_2(x)$ are two independent solutions of this equation. In other words, reverting to abbreviated notation, we have

$$py_1'' + qy_1' + ry_1 = 0 \qquad \text{and} \qquad py_2'' + qy_2' + ry_2 = 0. \tag{2.7}$$

For the inhomogeneous equation (2.6), we now assume a solution of the form

$$y(x) = u_1(x)\,y_1(x) + u_2(x)\,y_2(x), \quad \text{that is,} \quad y = u_1 y_1 + u_2 y_2. \tag{2.8}$$

We also assume (and the most compelling rationale for this step is that it simplifies matters considerably) that the unknown functions u_1 and u_2 satisfy the further condition

$$u_1' y_1 + u_2' y_2 = 0. \tag{2.9}$$

Applying the Product Rule to Equation (2.8), and noting the effect of Equation (2.9), gives

$$y' = u_1' y_1 + u_1 y_1' + u_2' y_2 + u_2 y_2' = u_1 y_1' + u_2 y_2' \tag{2.10}$$

and

$$y'' = u_1' y_1' + u_1 y_1'' + u_2' y_2' + u_2 y_2''. \tag{2.11}$$

The next step is to substitute the expressions for y, y' and y'' into Equation (2.6). From Equations (2.8), (2.10) and (2.11), we have

$$p(u_1' y_1' + u_1 y_1'' + u_2' y_2' + u_2 y_2'') + q(u_1 y_1' + u_2 y_2') + r(u_1 y_1 + u_2 y_2) = f,$$

which can be rearranged as

$$p(u_1' y_1' + u_2' y_2') + (py_1'' + qy_1' + ry_1)u_1 + (py_2'' + qy_2' + ry_2)u_2 = f. \tag{2.12}$$

From Equations (2.7), the coefficients of both the u_1 and u_2 terms in Equation (2.12) must be zero. We conclude that

$$p(u_1' y_1' + u_2' y_2') = f, \qquad \text{or} \qquad u_1' y_1' + u_2' y_2' = f/p. \tag{2.13}$$

Recalling the extra condition (2.9), we now have a pair of simultaneous linear equations for u_1' and u_2', namely,

$$u_1' y_1 + u_2' y_2 = 0, \tag{2.9}$$
$$u_1' y_1' + u_2' y_2' = f/p. \tag{2.13}$$

Writing this as a matrix equation, we have

$$\begin{bmatrix} y_1 & y_2 \\ y_1' & y_2' \end{bmatrix} \begin{bmatrix} u_1' \\ u_2' \end{bmatrix} = \begin{bmatrix} 0 \\ f/p \end{bmatrix}.$$

Inverting the 2×2 matrix of coefficients in the usual way, we find that

$$\begin{bmatrix} u_1' \\ u_2' \end{bmatrix} = \frac{1}{W(y_1, y_2)} \begin{bmatrix} y_2' & -y_2 \\ -y_1' & y_1 \end{bmatrix} \begin{bmatrix} 0 \\ f/p \end{bmatrix},$$

where

$$W(y_1, y_2) = y_1 y_2' - y_2 y_1' \tag{2.14}$$

is the determinant of the 2×2 matrix. The last matrix equation is equivalent to

$$u_1' = -\frac{y_2 f}{W p}, \qquad u_2' = \frac{y_1 f}{W p}. \tag{2.15}$$

As you may recall, the general solution of the associated homogeneous equation is known as the complementary function. In terms of the functions $y_1(x)$ and $y_2(x)$ referred to here, the complementary function is
$$Ay_1(x) + By_2(x).$$

The choice in Equation (2.8) is less constraining than putting $y = uy_1$, as with reduction of order; hence the ability to specify the further constraint (2.9).

We assume that $p(x) \neq 0$.

See MST209 *Unit 9* or MST121 *Chapter B2*.

Here $W(y_1, y_2)$ is known as the *Wronskian* of y_1 and y_2. Provided that y_1, y_2 are independent solutions (as assumed), their Wronskian is non-zero, so that the pair of equations for u_1', u_2' do have a solution.

All of f, p, y_1 and y_2 are known functions, and W is obtainable via Equation (2.14). We need then to integrate each of Equations (2.15) to find expressions for u_1 and u_2, before returning to the assumed form (2.8) for the solution y.

This procedure, known as **variation of parameters**, is summarised below and then illustrated by an example.

The 'parameters' whose variation is referred to in this phrase are u_1 and u_2.

Procedure 2.2   *Variation of parameters*

To solve the linear inhomogeneous second-order differential equation

$$p(x)\,y''(x) + q(x)\,y'(x) + r(x)\,y(x) = f(x), \qquad (2.6)$$

for which independent solutions $y_1(x)$, $y_2(x)$ to the associated homogeneous equation are known, proceed as follows.

(a) Assume a solution of the form $y(x) = u_1(x)\,y_1(x) + u_2(x)\,y_2(x)$, where $u_1(x)$, $u_2(x)$ are to be found, with the further condition

$$u_1' y_1 + u_2' y_2 = 0. \qquad (2.9)$$

(b) Calculate the expression

$$W(y_1, y_2) = y_1 y_2' - y_2 y_1'. \qquad (2.14)$$

(c) By substituting the form for y, assumed in Step (a), into the differential equation, and applying Equation (2.9), obtain a pair of equations for u_1' and u_2' , namely,

$$u_1' = -\frac{y_2 f}{Wp}, \qquad u_2' = \frac{y_1 f}{Wp}. \qquad (2.15)$$

(d) Solve these equations by integration, and hence obtain the general solution $y(x) = u_1(x)\,y_1(x) + u_2(x)\,y_2(x)$.

Example 2.2

Find the general solution of the differential equation

$$y''(x) + y(x) = \tan x \qquad (-\tfrac{1}{2}\pi < x < \tfrac{1}{2}\pi).$$

Solution

The associated homogeneous equation, $y'' + y = 0$, has general solution $A\cos x + B\sin x$, so take

$$y_1(x) = \cos x, \qquad y_2(x) = \sin x,$$

and assume a solution to the given equation of the form $y = u_1 y_1 + u_2 y_2$, subject to Equation (2.9). From Equation (2.14), we have

$$W(y_1, y_2) = y_1 y_2' - y_2 y_1' = (\cos x)(\cos x) - (\sin x)(-\sin x) = 1.$$

Hence from Equations (2.15), with $p(x) = 1$ and $f(x) = \tan x$, we have

$$u_1 = -\int \frac{y_2 f}{Wp}\,dx = -\int \sin x \tan x \, dx$$

$$= -\int \frac{\sin^2 x}{\cos x}\,dx = -\int \frac{1 - \cos^2 x}{\cos x}\,dx = -\int \sec x \, dx + \int \cos x \, dx$$

$$= -\ln(\sec x + \tan x) + \sin x + A,$$

and

$$u_2 = \int \frac{y_1 f}{Wp}\,dx = \int \cos x \tan x \, dx = \int \sin x \, dx = -\cos x + B.$$

While this equation has constant coefficients, a particular integral cannot be found using the method of undetermined coefficients. In MST209 *Unit 3*, the latter method was described for cases in which the right-hand side is a polynomial, exponential or sinusoidal function.

Note that there is a list of standard integrals in the *Handbook*.

Hence the general solution of the given differential equation is

$$y = u_1 y_1 + u_2 y_2$$
$$= (- \ln(\sec x + \tan x) + \sin x + A) \cos x + (- \cos x + B) \sin x$$
$$= A \cos x + B \sin x - \cos x \ln(\sec x + \tan x). \quad \blacksquare$$

Exercise 2.3

Using variation of parameters, find the general solution of the differential
equation

$$y''(x) + 4y(x) = \sec(2x) \qquad (-\tfrac{1}{4}\pi < x < \tfrac{1}{4}\pi).$$

Exercise 2.4

Find the general solution of the differential equation

$$x^2(1-x)y''(x) - 2xy'(x) + 2y(x) = x^3 \qquad (0 < x < 1),$$

given that (as found in Example 2.1) the general solution of the associated
homogeneous equation is

$$\frac{Ax}{1-x} + Bx.$$

End-of-section exercises

Exercise 2.5

The differential equation

$$(1-x^2)y''(x) - 2xy'(x) + 2y(x) = 0 \qquad (-1 < x < 1)$$

has one solution $y_1(x) = x$. Use the method of reduction of order to find
the general solution of this differential equation.

Hint: Note that $\dfrac{2}{x^2(1-x^2)} = \dfrac{2}{x^2} + \dfrac{1}{1+x} + \dfrac{1}{1-x}$ for $x \neq 0$ and $x \neq \pm 1$.

This is *Legendre's equation* of
order 1.

Exercise 2.6

(a) Find the general solution of the homogeneous differential equation

$$y''(x) - 2y'(x) + y(x) = 0.$$

(b) Use variation of parameters and your answer to part (a) to find the
general solution of the differential equation

$$y''(x) - 2y'(x) + y(x) = \frac{e^x}{1+x^2}.$$

3 Boundary-value problems

In this section we continue as in Section 2 to use the 'prime' notation for derivatives. This includes writing $u'(\alpha)$ for the value of du/dx at $x = \alpha$. The dependent variable is denoted now by u rather than by y, to emphasise that different symbols for the variables are met in practice.

Suppose that D is an open interval of real numbers and that

$$p(x)\, u''(x) + q(x)\, u'(x) + r(x)\, u(x) = f(x) \qquad \text{(for all } x \text{ in } D)$$

is a linear differential equation for which $p(x)$ is not equal to zero for any x in D. Then the general solution of the differential equation contains two arbitrary constants.

A particular solution is obtained by allocating values to these arbitrary constants, and one way of doing this with which you should be familiar is to specify a pair of initial conditions,

$$u(\alpha) = a, \quad u'(\alpha) = b,$$

at some point α in D. Such initial conditions lead to unique values for the arbitrary constants in the general solution.

In this section we investigate a different way of assigning values to the arbitrary constants. Instead of specifying the values of u and u' at a single point, α, we shall consider conditions on u (and perhaps on u') at two distinct points, α and β. These are called *boundary conditions* for the function u. The differential equation is required to hold throughout the interval D between α and β, that is, for $\alpha < x < \beta$. The composite problem, consisting of the differential equation to be satisfied for $\alpha < x < \beta$ together with the boundary conditions at α and β, is called a **boundary-value problem**. A *solution* of a boundary-value problem is a function which satisfies both the differential equation and each of the boundary conditions.

Many models of physical situations lead to boundary-value problems. An example of such a model (for viscous flow in a pipe) was given in the Introduction to this unit.

For constant-coefficient equations, the uniqueness of the solution is stated in Theorem 3.1 of MST209 *Unit 3.*

We assume here that $\alpha < \beta$. The points α, β are the *endpoints* of the interval D.

Each solution holds for $\alpha \leq x \leq \beta$.

3.1 Boundary conditions

Solutions to a boundary-value problem are found by adopting the same approach that is applied to initial-value problems. The first step is to derive the general solution of the differential equation, containing two arbitrary constants, A and B say. Once this has been done, the general solution is substituted into each of the boundary conditions, which produces a pair of algebraic equations for A and B. We then attempt to solve these equations.

We start by looking at examples in which the boundary conditions are of the form

$$u(\alpha) = a, \qquad u(\beta) = b,$$

with α, β, a and b given real numbers. These examples all relate to the differential equation

$$u''(x) + u(x) = 0,$$

whose general solution is

$$u(x) = A\cos x + B\sin x.$$

The auxiliary equation is $\lambda^2 + 1 = 0$, with roots $\lambda = \pm i$.

72

Example 3.1

Solve the boundary-value problem

$$u''(x) + u(x) = 0, \qquad u(0) = 0, \quad u(\pi) = 1.$$

Here, 'solve' means 'find any solutions of'. The differential equation must hold throughout the interval $0 < x < \pi$ between the two endpoints.

Solution

Substituting the general solution of the differential equation into each of the boundary conditions gives

$$u(0) = A \cos 0 + B \sin 0 = 0,$$
$$u(\pi) = A \cos \pi + B \sin \pi = 1,$$

or

$$A = 0, \quad -A = 1.$$

These equations clearly have no solution! Hence the original problem has no solution. ■

If this boundary-value problem arose in modelling a physical situation, we should now have to check the details of the model. If no errors were discovered, a new model would be required.

Example 3.1 demonstrates that there may be no solution to a given boundary-value problem. However, if solutions do exist, then the strategy outlined above will find them.

Exercise 3.1

Solve each of the following boundary-value problems.

(a) $u''(x) + u(x) = 0, \qquad u(0) = 0, \quad u\left(\frac{1}{2}\pi\right) = 1.$

(b) $u''(x) + u(x) = 0, \qquad u(0) = 0, \quad u\left(\frac{1}{2}\pi\right) = 0.$

(c) $u''(x) + u(x) = 0, \qquad u(0) = 0, \quad u(\pi) = 0.$

(d) $u''(x) + u(x) = 0, \qquad u(0) = 1, \quad u(\pi) = -1.$

Do not be discouraged by the result of Example 3.1. All the boundary-value problems in this exercise *do* have solutions.

You have already seen that a boundary-value problem need not have a solution. The results of Exercise 3.1 show that, if solutions exist, then they may be unique (as in parts (a) and (b)) or non-unique (as in parts (c) and (d), where one arbitrary constant remains unspecified after applying the boundary conditions).

These properties of boundary-value problems are mentioned in MST209 *Unit 3*, Subsection 3.2.

Comparison of Example 3.1 and Exercise 3.1(a) illustrates the fact that the nature of the solution may be affected by altering the interval $\alpha \le x \le \beta$ of the problem while leaving unchanged the values specified for u at the endpoints. On comparing Example 3.1 with parts (c) and (d) of Exercise 3.1, we see that the outcome may also be affected by retaining the same interval but changing one or both of the values of u at the endpoints.

These properties have been exhibited in the context of a specific differential equation and of a particular type of boundary condition. They are, however, characteristic of the behaviour to be found generally in boundary-value problems.

In some sense, the case of non-unique solutions is 'special', in that it occurs only occasionally as the parameters of a problem are varied. However, this special case is of considerable interest, as you will see in Subsection 3.2 and later in the course.

Example 3.2

Solve the boundary-value problem
$$u''(x) + 4u'(x) + 13u(x) = 0, \qquad u\left(-\tfrac{1}{2}\pi\right) = 0, \quad u\left(\tfrac{1}{2}\pi\right) = 0.$$

Solution

The general solution of the differential equation is
$$u(x) = e^{-2x}\left(A\cos(3x) + B\sin(3x)\right).$$

Substituting this into each of the boundary conditions gives

The auxiliary equation is $\lambda^2 + 4\lambda + 13 = 0$, with roots $\lambda = -2 \pm 3i$.

$$u\left(-\tfrac{1}{2}\pi\right) = e^{\pi}(B) = 0,$$
$$u\left(\tfrac{1}{2}\pi\right) = e^{-\pi}(-B) = 0.$$

Hence $B = 0$ and A is arbitrary. The solution of the original problem is
$$u(x) = Ae^{-2x}\cos(3x). \quad \blacksquare$$

Exercise 3.2

Solve each of the following boundary-value problems.

(a) $u''(x) + 4u'(x) + 13u(x) = 0, \qquad u(0) = 1, \quad u\left(\tfrac{1}{2}\pi\right) = 2.$

(b) $u''(x) + 4u'(x) + 13u(x) = 26, \qquad u\left(-\tfrac{1}{2}\pi\right) = 0, \quad u\left(\tfrac{1}{2}\pi\right) = 0.$

(c) $4x^2 u''(x) + 4xu'(x) + u(x) = 0, \qquad u(1) = 0, \quad u(e^{2\pi}) = 0.$

The differential equation in part (b) is inhomogeneous, but once its general solution has been found, the method proceeds just as before.

You have now seen several examples involving boundary conditions of the form
$$u(\alpha) = a, \quad u(\beta) = b.$$

Here is an example which features a boundary condition of another type.

Example 3.3

Solve the boundary-value problem
$$u''(x) - 10u'(x) + 25u(x) = 0, \qquad u'(0) - u(0) = 1, \quad u(1) = 0.$$

Solution

The general solution of the differential equation is
$$u(x) = (A + Bx)e^{5x},$$

which has the derivative
$$u'(x) = (5A + B + 5Bx)e^{5x}.$$

The auxiliary equation is $\lambda^2 - 10\lambda + 25 = 0$, with the repeated root $\lambda = 5$.

Substitution of these into the boundary conditions gives
$$u'(0) - u(0) = (5A + B) - A = 1,$$
$$u(1) = (A + B)e^5 = 0,$$

or
$$4A + B = 1, \quad A + B = 0.$$

Hence $A = \tfrac{1}{3}$ and $B = -\tfrac{1}{3}$. The solution of the boundary-value problem is
$$u(x) = \tfrac{1}{3}(1 - x)e^{5x}. \quad \blacksquare$$

Types of boundary conditions

Various types of boundary conditions occur in practical applications, and we shall next look briefly at some of these. Imagine in each case that the given pair of conditions accompanies a linear differential equation,

$$p(x)\,u''(x) + q(x)\,u'(x) + r(x)\,u(x) = f(x).$$

Case 1 $u(\alpha) = a$, $u(\beta) = b$. This is the case that we considered prior to Example 3.3. It is possible that one (or both) of α, β is chosen to be 'at infinity'. If this is so for β, for example, we would replace $u(\beta)$ in the boundary condition by $\lim\limits_{x\to\infty} u(x)$.

Case 2   One or both of the boundary conditions may specify the value of u' at an endpoint. This leads to the following possibilities:

(i) $u'(\alpha) = a$, $u(\beta) = b$;

(ii) $u(\alpha) = a$, $u'(\beta) = b$;

(iii) $u'(\alpha) = a$, $u'(\beta) = b$.

If β is 'at infinity' in (ii) or (iii), then $u'(\beta)$ would be replaced by $\lim\limits_{x\to\infty} u'(x)$.

Case 3   The boundary conditions may occur in the form

$$\alpha_1 u'(\alpha) + \alpha_2 u(\alpha) = a, \quad \beta_1 u'(\beta) + \beta_2 u(\beta) = b,$$

where α_1, α_2, β_1, β_2 are constants such that at least one of α_1, α_2 and at least one of β_1, β_2 are non-zero. This case includes those described above.

Incidentally, a pair of boundary conditions of any of these types is described as *homogeneous* if $a = b = 0$, and as *inhomogeneous* if one or both of a, b is non-zero.

Case 4   It is sometimes appropriate to specify conditions which link the values of u or of u' at the two endpoints. One such example is provided by the *periodic boundary conditions*

$$u(\alpha) = u(\beta), \quad u'(\alpha) = u'(\beta).$$

Case 5   There are occasions when a boundary condition requires merely that u or u' should be a bounded function in the vicinity of an endpoint. If this is the case for the function u near an endpoint β, then we would write the condition as

$$\lim\limits_{x\to\beta} u(x) \text{ bounded.}$$

Such a condition might occur if β is

(i)   a singular point of the differential equation (that is, if $p(\beta) = 0$);

(ii) 'at infinity', in which case the condition would be written as

$$\lim\limits_{x\to\infty} u(x) \text{ bounded.}$$

The following example has a boundary condition from Case 5 above.

The boundary condition at $x = 0$ in Example 3.3 is of this type, with $\alpha = 0$, $\alpha_1 = 1$, $\alpha_2 = -1$ and $a = 1$.

We obtain Case 1, for example, by choosing $\alpha_1 = \beta_1 = 0$ and $\alpha_2 = \beta_2 = 1$.

In Exercise 3.1, for instance, the boundary conditions are homogeneous in parts (b) and (c) only.

For example, in the Introduction, we considered the flow speed $u(r)$ at a distance r from the centre of a pipe. In this case, the boundary condition at $r = 0$ is $\lim\limits_{r\to 0} u(r)$ bounded.

As mentioned in Subsection 1.1, a differential equation need not have a solution in an interval containing a singular point. Even if such solutions exist, there may be others which fail to be bounded as x approaches the point.

Example 3.4

Solve the boundary-value problem

$$2x^2 u''(x) + 7x u'(x) - 3u(x) = 0, \quad u'(1) = 3, \quad \lim\limits_{x\to\infty} u(x) \text{ bounded.}$$

Solution

The general solution of the differential equation is

$$u(x) = Ax^{1/2} + Bx^{-3},$$

which has the derivative

$$u'(x) = \tfrac{1}{2}Ax^{-1/2} - 3Bx^{-4}.$$

The boundary conditions give

$$u'(1) = \tfrac{1}{2}A - 3B = 3,$$

$$\lim_{x\to\infty} u(x) = \lim_{x\to\infty}(Ax^{1/2} + Bx^{-3}) \text{ bounded.}$$

Now, as x becomes large, x^{-3} tends towards zero, but $x^{1/2}$ is unbounded. To satisfy the second boundary condition, we must therefore choose $A = 0$. From the first condition, we then have $B = -1$. The solution of the original problem is

$$u(x) = -x^{-3}. \quad \blacksquare$$

This is a Cauchy–Euler equation. The corresponding indicial equation is $2\lambda^2 + 5\lambda - 3 = 0$, with roots $\lambda = \tfrac{1}{2}$ and $\lambda = -3$.

Note that
$$\lim_{x\to\infty} x^n = 0 \text{ for } n < 0,$$
but this limit does not exist for $n > 0$.

Exercise 3.3

Solve each of the following boundary-value problems.

(a) $u''(x) + \pi^2 u(x) = 0, \quad u'(0) = 0, \quad u'(1) = 0.$

(b) $u''(x) + \pi^2 u(x) = 0, \quad u(0) = u(1), \quad u'(0) = u'(1).$

(c) $x^2 u''(x) + xu'(x) - 4u(x) = 0, \quad \lim_{x\to 0} u(x) \text{ bounded}, \quad u(1) = 2.$

(d) $u''(x) - 4u'(x) + 5u(x) = 0, \quad u(0) = 0, \quad u'(\tfrac{1}{2}\pi) - 2u(\tfrac{1}{2}\pi) = 1.$

Exercise 3.4

From Exercise 1.3(b), the differential equation

$$(1 - x^2)u''(x) - xu'(x) + 4u(x) = 0 \quad (-1 < x < 1)$$

has general solution

$$u(x) = A\cos(2\arccos x) + B\sin(2\arccos x).$$

(a) Show that this general solution can be re-expressed as

$$u(x) = A(2x^2 - 1) + 2Bx\sqrt{1 - x^2}.$$

Hint: Put $\theta = \arccos x.$

(b) Solve the boundary-value problem

$$(1 - x^2)u''(x) - xu'(x) + 4u(x) = 0 \quad (-1 < x < 1),$$

$$\lim_{x\to -1} u'(x) \text{ and } \lim_{x\to 1} u'(x) \text{ both bounded.}$$

You have seen that the solution of a boundary-value problem may exist uniquely, exist non-uniquely or not exist at all. Any *homogeneous* boundary-value problem (that is, any problem in which *both* the differential equation and boundary conditions are homogeneous) has at least one solution, because the zero function is a solution to such a problem. In the next subsection, we concentrate on particular classes of homogeneous problems for which those problems having non-zero solutions can be readily identified.

For example, the homogeneous problem in Exercise 3.1(b) has the zero function as its unique solution, whereas that in Exercise 3.1(c) also has non-zero solutions.

3.2 *Eigenvalue problems (audio)*

In the Introduction to this unit, it was stated that a model for the motion of standing shallow water waves leads to the boundary-value problem

$$u''(x) + \lambda u(x) = 0, \qquad u'(0) = u'(L) = 0, \tag{3.1}$$

See Equations (0.2) in the Introduction.

where L is the channel length, and the constant λ depends on the frequency of oscillation. There are non-zero solutions only for certain values of λ.

In this subsection, we investigate problems of the same general type as that described by Equations (3.1). The differential equation is in each case linear, of second-order and homogeneous, taking the form

$$p(x)\,u''(x) + q(x)\,u'(x) + (r(x) + \lambda)\,u(x) = 0 \qquad (\alpha < x < \beta), \tag{3.2}$$

where λ is an undetermined constant, and $p(x)$ is non-zero for all x in the interval $\alpha < x < \beta$. For convenience, we shall use the notation

$$K[u(x)] = p(x)\,u''(x) + q(x)\,u'(x) + r(x)\,u(x), \tag{3.3}$$

which amounts to letting the symbol K stand for the differential operator

$$p(x)\frac{d^2}{dx^2} + q(x)\frac{d}{dx} + r(x).$$

(For example, if $q(x) = 0$ and $p(x) = r(x) = 1$, we have

$$K[u(x)] = u''(x) + u(x), \qquad \text{or} \qquad K = \frac{d^2}{dx^2} + 1.)$$

Using Equation (3.3), Equation (3.2) may be abbreviated to

$$(K + \lambda)[u(x)] = 0 \qquad (\alpha < x < \beta). \tag{3.4}$$

As with the operator ∇ introduced in MST209 *Unit 23*, K needs something (a twice differentiable function $u(x)$) to 'operate on and differentiate' in the manner indicated. We use square brackets to indicate the function operated on by K, to avoid any possible confusion.

To Equation (3.2) or (3.4) are attached homogeneous or periodic boundary conditions at the endpoints α and β. The resulting problem is called an **eigenvalue problem**. For example, Equations (3.1) form an eigenvalue problem, with $\alpha = 0$, $\beta = L$ and $K = d^2/dx^2$.

Homogeneous and periodic boundary conditions were introduced on page 75.

An eigenvalue problem is a whole set of homogeneous boundary-value problems, one for each value of λ.

As you saw in Subsection 3.1, such a boundary-value problem may or may not have a non-zero solution, and it turns out that we can encounter both these cases by assigning different values to λ. A value of λ for which there exists a non-zero solution is called an **eigenvalue** of the problem, and the corresponding non-zero solution is called an **eigenfunction**. In order to solve an eigenvalue problem completely, we must identify all the eigenvalues and find an eigenfunction corresponding to each of them.

The audio session discusses how to solve some examples of eigenvalue problems. The result of Exercise 3.5 below will be used in considering the first of these examples.

Exercise 3.5

Show that if $\lambda \leq 0$, then the boundary-value problem

$$u''(x) + \lambda u(x) = 0, \qquad u(0) = u(L) = 0$$

has no solution other than the zero function.

Since the symbol λ occurs in the problem statement, use another symbol, α say, in place of λ in the auxiliary equation.

When you are ready, start the audio at Track 4 of CD1.

1 **An eigenvalue problem**

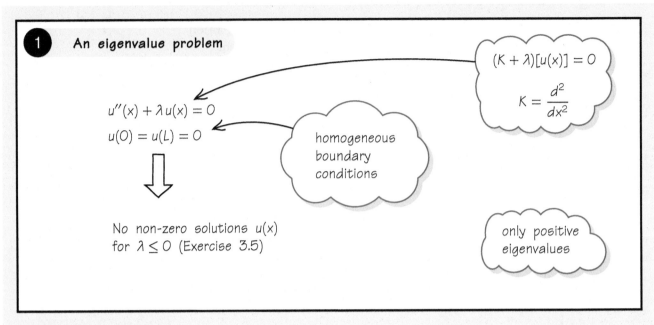

$(K + \lambda)[u(x)] = 0$

$K = \dfrac{d^2}{dx^2}$

$u''(x) + \lambda u(x) = 0$

$u(0) = u(L) = 0$

homogeneous boundary conditions

No non-zero solutions $u(x)$ for $\lambda \leq 0$ (Exercise 3.5)

only positive eigenvalues

2 **The case** $\lambda > 0$

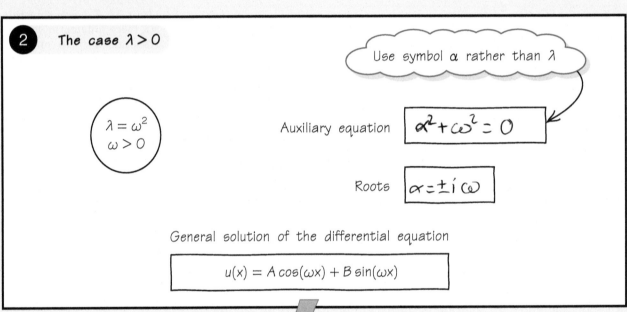

Use symbol α rather than λ

$\begin{cases} \lambda = \omega^2 \\ \omega > 0 \end{cases}$

Auxiliary equation $\boxed{\alpha^2 + \omega^2 = 0}$

Roots $\boxed{\alpha = \pm i\omega}$

General solution of the differential equation

$$\boxed{u(x) = A\cos(\omega x) + B\sin(\omega x)}$$

3 **Boundary conditions**

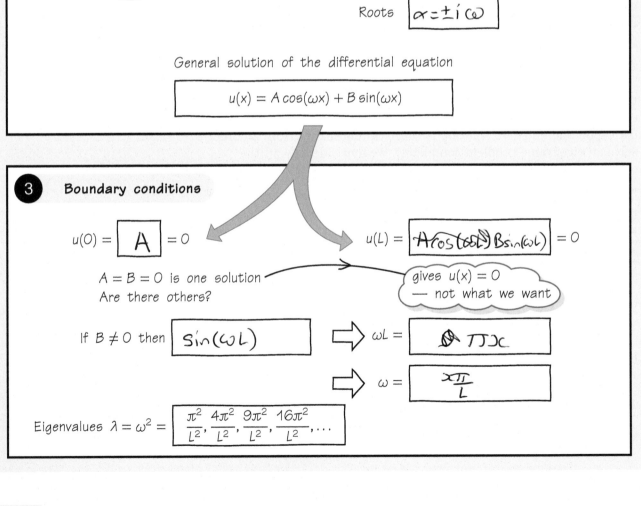

$u(0) = \boxed{A} = 0$

$u(L) = \boxed{A\cos(\omega L) + B\sin(\omega L)} = 0$

$A = B = 0$ is one solution
Are there others?

gives $u(x) = 0$ — not what we want

If $B \neq 0$ then $\boxed{\sin(\omega L)}$ $\Rightarrow$ $\omega L = \boxed{n\pi}$

$\Rightarrow$ $\omega = \boxed{\dfrac{n\pi}{L}}$

Eigenvalues $\lambda = \omega^2 = \boxed{\dfrac{\pi^2}{L^2}, \dfrac{4\pi^2}{L^2}, \dfrac{9\pi^2}{L^2}, \dfrac{16\pi^2}{L^2}, \ldots}$

4   **The eigenfunctions**

Eigenvalue λ	ω	An eigenfunction	Sketch
$\lambda_1 = \dfrac{\pi^2}{L^2}$	$\dfrac{\pi}{L}$	$u_1(x) = \sin\left(\dfrac{\pi}{L}x\right)$	
$\lambda_2 = \dfrac{4\pi^2}{L^2}$	$\dfrac{2\pi}{L}$	$u_2(x) = $	
$\lambda_3 = \dfrac{9\pi^2}{L^2}$	$\dfrac{3\pi}{L}$	$u_3(x) = $	
$\vdots$	$\vdots$		$\vdots$

Any non-zero multiple is another eigenfunction

$\lambda_n = \boxed{\left(\dfrac{n\pi}{L}\right)^2}$	$\dfrac{n\pi}{L}$	$u_n(x) = \boxed{\sin\left(\dfrac{n\pi}{L}x\right)}$	$(n = 1, 2, \ldots)$

5   **Another problem**

$$2\,u''(x) + 6\,u'(x) + (1 + \lambda)\,u(x) = 0$$
$$u(0) = u(L) = 0$$

$(K + \lambda)[u(x)] = 0$

$K = 2\dfrac{d^2}{dx^2} + 6\dfrac{d}{dx} + 1$

Solution

Step (a): find the general solution

Auxiliary equation $\boxed{2\alpha^2 + 6\alpha + 1 + \lambda = 0}$ Use α

Roots $\alpha = \boxed{\dfrac{1}{4}}$

$= \boxed{-\dfrac{3}{2} \pm \dfrac{1}{2}\sqrt{7 - 2\lambda}}$

Three cases $\begin{cases} \text{(i) two real roots if } \lambda < \tfrac{7}{2} \\ \text{(ii) one root if } \lambda = \tfrac{7}{2} \\ \text{(iii) complex roots if } \lambda > \tfrac{7}{2} \end{cases}$

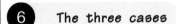

---

6   **The three cases**

(i) $\lambda < \frac{7}{2}$

Put $7 - 2\lambda = \nu^2$ $(\nu > 0)$

$\alpha = \boxed{-\frac{3}{2} \pm \frac{\nu}{2}}$

$u(x) = \boxed{A e^{\left(-\frac{3}{2} + \frac{\nu}{2}\right)x} + B e^{\left(-\frac{3}{2} - \frac{\nu}{2}\right)x}}$

(ii) $\lambda = \frac{7}{2}$

$\alpha = \boxed{-\frac{3}{2}}$

$u(x) = \boxed{A e^{-\frac{3x}{2}} + B x e^{-\frac{3x}{2}}}$

(iii) $\lambda > \frac{7}{2}$

Put $2\lambda - 7 = \omega^2$ $(\omega > 0)$

$\alpha = \boxed{-\frac{3}{2} \pm \frac{i\omega}{2}}$

$u(x) = \boxed{A e^{-\frac{3x}{2}} \cos\left(\frac{\omega x}{2}\right) + B e^{-\frac{3x}{2}} \sin\left(\frac{\omega x}{2}\right)}$

Step (b): boundary conditions $u(0) = u(L) = 0$

$u(0) = \boxed{A + B} = 0$

$u(L) = \boxed{A e^{\left(-\frac{3}{2} + \frac{\nu}{2}\right)L} + B e^{*}} = 0$
$\quad * \left(-\frac{3}{2} - \frac{\nu}{2}\right)L$

$u(0) = \boxed{A} = 0$

$u(L) = \boxed{A e^{\left(-\frac{3L}{2}\right)} + B L e^{\left(-\frac{3L}{2}\right)}} = 0$
$\quad B L e^{-\frac{3L}{2}}$

$u(0) = \boxed{A} = 0$

$u(L) = \boxed{B e^{\left(-\frac{3L}{2}\right)} \sin\left(\frac{\omega L}{2}\right)} = 0$

Step (c): find solutions other than $A = B = 0$

$B = -A$, where

$A e^{-\frac{3L}{2}} \left(e^{\frac{\nu L}{2}} - e^{-\frac{\nu L}{2}} \right) = 0,$

so $A = B = 0$ only.

> not zero whatever
> the value of $\nu > 0$

$A = B = 0$ only

$A = 0$ and

either $B = 0$

or $\omega = \boxed{\dfrac{2n\pi}{L}}$ $(n = 1, 2, \ldots)$

---

7   **The eigenvalues and eigenfunctions**

$2\lambda - 7 = \omega^2 \Rightarrow \lambda = \boxed{\frac{1}{2}\omega^2 + \frac{7}{2}}$

$\Rightarrow \lambda_n = \boxed{\dfrac{2n^2\pi^2}{L^2} + \frac{7}{2}}$

> eigenvalues $(n = 1, 2, \ldots)$

Step (d): find the eigenfunctions

$u(x) = B e^{-\frac{3x}{2}} \sin\left(\frac{\omega x}{2}\right)$

If $\lambda = \lambda_n$ then $\omega = \dfrac{2n\pi}{L}$.

Choose $B = 1$.

$u_n(x) = \boxed{e^{-\frac{3x}{2}} \sin\left(\frac{n\pi x}{L}\right)}$

> eigenfunction corresponding
> to nth eigenvalue λ_n

---

8   **Different boundary conditions**

Problem :
$u''(x) + \lambda u(x) = 0$
$u(0) = u'(L) = 0$

Find all the eigenvalues
and eigenfunctions.

Solution

Three cases to consider

(i) $\lambda < 0$

Put $\lambda = -\nu^2$ $(\nu > 0)$

$u(x) = Ae^{\nu x} + Be^{-\nu x}$

$u'(x) = A\nu e^{\nu x} - B\nu e^{-\nu x}$

Step (a): general solution

derivative

$u(0) = A + B = 0$

$u'(L) = A\nu e^{\nu L} - B\nu e^{-\nu L} = 0$

Step (b): boundary conditions

$B = -A$, where

$$A\nu \left(e^{\nu L} + e^{-\nu L} \right) = 0$$

so $A = B = 0$

Step (c): look for non-zero solutions

| No eigenvalues for $\lambda < 0$ |

Conclusions

(ii) $\lambda = 0$

$u(x) = Ax + B$

$u'(x) = A$

$u(0) = B = 0$

$u'(L) = A = 0$

$A = B = 0$

| $\lambda = 0$ is not an eigenvalue |

(iii) $\lambda > 0$

Step (a)

Put $\lambda = \omega^2$ $(\omega > 0)$

General solution: $u(x) = A\cos(\omega x) + B\sin(\omega x)$

Derivative: $u'(x) = -A\omega \sin(\omega x) + B\omega \cos(\omega x)$

Step (b)

Boundary conditions: $u(0) = A = 0$

$$u'(L) = B\omega \cos(\omega L) = 0$$

Step (c)

Solutions: $A = 0$ and **either** $B = 0$

or $\omega = \left(n - \frac{1}{2} \right) \frac{\pi}{L}$ $(n = 1, 2, \ldots)$

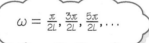 $\omega = \frac{\pi}{2L}, \frac{3\pi}{2L}, \frac{5\pi}{2L}, \ldots$

Eigenvalues: $\lambda = \omega^2$, so $\lambda_n = \boxed{\left(n - \frac{1}{2} \right)^2 \frac{\pi^2}{L^2}}$

$\left. \right\}$ $n = (1, 2, \ldots)$

Step (d)

Eigenfunctions: $u_n(x) = \boxed{\sin \left(\left(n - \frac{1}{2} \right) \frac{\pi}{L} x \right)}$

$u_1(x) = \sin\left(\frac{\pi}{2L} x \right)$

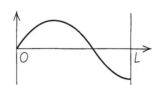

$u_2(x) = \sin\left(\frac{3\pi}{2L} x \right)$

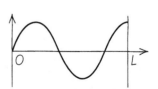

$u_3(x) = \sin\left(\frac{5\pi}{2L} x \right)$

⑨   Procedure 3.1

To solve the eigenvalue problem

$$(K + \lambda)[u(x)] = 0$$

plus

homogeneous or periodic boundary conditions at $x = \alpha$ and $x = \beta$

$$K = p(x)\frac{d^2}{dx^2} + q(x)\frac{d}{dx} + r(x),$$
where $p(x) \neq 0$ for $\alpha < x < \beta$

e.g. (i) $u(\alpha) = u(\beta) = 0$
(ii) $u'(\alpha) = u'(\beta) - 2u(\beta) = 0$
(iii) $u(\alpha) = u(\beta),\ u'(\alpha) = u'(\beta)$
(periodic)

Step (a): Find the general solution $u(x)$ of the differential equation, which contains two arbitrary constants, A and B, as well as λ.

> There will be 3 different cases here, depending on the range of values of λ being considered. The following steps should be undertaken for each of these cases in turn.

Step (b): Substitute the expression for $u(x)$ into each of the boundary conditions. This gives two algebraic equations for A and B in which λ also appears.

> You will need to differentiate the expression for $u(x)$ if the boundary conditions refer to $u'(\alpha)$ or $u'(\beta)$.

Step (c): Find all those values of λ (eigenvalues) for which these algebraic equations have solutions **other** than $A = B = 0$.

Step (d): For each eigenvalue λ_n, put $\lambda = \lambda_n$ and choose values for A and B (not both zero) which satisfy the algebraic equations from Step (b). The expression obtained for $u(x)$ is an eigenfunction $u_n(x)$ corresponding to the eigenvalue λ_n.

The next exercise gives further practice with eigenvalue problems.

Exercise 3.6

Solve each of the following eigenvalue problems.

(a) $u''(x) + 4u'(x) + (4 + \lambda)u(x) = 0, \qquad u(0) = u(1) = 0.$

(b) $x^2 u''(x) + xu'(x) + (2 + \lambda)u(x) = 0, \qquad u(1) = u(2) = 0.$

(c) $u''(x) + \lambda u(x) = 0, \qquad u(0) = u(2\pi), \qquad u'(0) = u'(2\pi).$

End-of-section exercises

Exercise 3.7

In the Introduction to this unit, we considered the steady flow of an incompressible viscous fluid along a straight pipe of uniform circular cross-section. The speed $u(r)$ at a distance r from the pipe's axis satisfies the boundary-value problem

$$r^2 u''(r) + r u'(r) = -kr^2,$$

$$\lim_{r \to 0} u(r) \text{ bounded}, \quad u(a) = 0,$$

This is Equation (0.1).

where a is the internal radius of the pipe, and k is a positive constant. Solve this boundary-value problem.

Hint: Use the substitution $r = e^t$.

Exercise 3.8

In the Introduction to this unit, we considered a model of standing shallow water wave motion in a channel of length L. This model leads to the eigenvalue problem

$$u''(x) + \lambda u(x) = 0, \qquad u'(0) = u'(L) = 0.$$

These are Equations (0.2).

Solve this eigenvalue problem.

4   Power series solutions

In Sections 1–3, you studied analytical methods for solving linear differential equations of the form

We now revert to use of y for the dependent variable.

$$p(x)\frac{d^2 y}{dx^2} + q(x)\frac{dy}{dx} + r(x)y = f(x).$$

When $p(x)$, $q(x)$ and $r(x)$ are all constants, and $f(x)$ has an appropriate form, there is a procedure which can be used to determine the solution. Certain other equations in which $p(x)$, $q(x)$ and $r(x)$ are not constants can be transformed into constant-coefficient equations by changing the independent variable, x. There are further possibilities involving a change of variable for simplifying the equations to be solved. However, for many

See MST209 *Unit 3*.

For example, the Cauchy–Euler equations in Subsection 1.1 are of this type.

second-order differential equations, there are no known procedures for finding a solution in terms of elementary functions such as $\sin x$, $\ln x$, e^x and so on. Despite this, there are important equations for which analytical (rather than numerical) solutions are required.

The method of solution to be explored in the remainder of this unit is based on the idea that sometimes the solution can be represented as a **power series**, of the form

$$y = a_0 + a_1 x + a_2 x^2 + a_3 x^3 + \cdots = \sum_{j=0}^{\infty} a_j x^j.$$

For the moment, we assume that such a power series solution is valid for values of x 'near' $x = 0$. In Subsection 5.2, we shall examine in more detail the conditions under which the power series solution, evaluated at a particular value of x, converges to the required solution of the differential equation at that point.

A power series in x is a sum of terms, each of which is a constant times a non-negative integer power of x. Any polynomial is a finite power series.

You should be familiar with the idea of approximating a function by a Taylor polynomial of suitable degree about some point $x = a$. Here, we employ a similar idea, and use the differential equation to determine the values of the coefficients in the power series. To simplify the examples, the discussion starts with linear first-order differential equations.

Taylor polynomials and Taylor series are discussed in MS221 *Chapter C3*. See also Appendix 2 of this unit.

4.1   Linear first-order equations

The method is best introduced within the context of a specific example.

Example 4.1

Determine the power series solution, of the form

$$y = a_0 + a_1 x + a_2 x^2 + a_3 x^3 + \cdots + a_j x^j + \cdots, \tag{4.1}$$

which satisfies the differential equation

$$\frac{dy}{dx} - y = 0 \qquad (0 < x < 1). \tag{4.2}$$

This problem could also be solved using separation of variables or the integrating factor method, to give the general solution

$$y = Ae^x.$$

Solution

Since we are going to replace the left-hand side of Equation (4.2) by a power series, we need a power series for dy/dx. Differentiating Equation (4.1) term by term (assuming that this is valid), we have

$$\frac{dy}{dx} = a_1 + 2a_2 x + 3a_3 x^2 + \cdots + j a_j x^{j-1} + (j+1)a_{j+1} x^j + \cdots. \tag{4.3}$$

Subtracting Equation (4.1) from Equation (4.3) gives

$$\frac{dy}{dx} - y = (a_1 - a_0) + (2a_2 - a_1)x + (3a_3 - a_2)x^2 + \cdots$$
$$+ ((j+1)a_{j+1} - a_j)x^j + \cdots$$
$$= 0. \tag{4.4}$$

Since this equation is to hold for all values of x in the interval $0 < x < 1$, we require that the coefficient of each power of x must be zero; that is,

$$a_1 - a_0 = 0, \qquad 2a_2 - a_1 = 0, \qquad 3a_3 - a_2 = 0,$$

and, in general,

$$(j+1)a_{j+1} - a_j = 0.$$

Thus we have

$$a_{j+1} = \frac{a_j}{j+1} \qquad (j = 0, 1, 2, \ldots). \tag{4.5}$$

This is a first-order recurrence relation which can be used to generate the coefficients $a_1, a_2, \ldots$, given a value for a_0. For this example we have, using Equation (4.5),

First-order recurrence relations were investigated in MST121 *Chapter A1*.

$$a_1 = a_0, \qquad a_2 = \frac{a_1}{2} = \frac{a_0}{2!}, \qquad a_3 = \frac{a_2}{3} = \frac{a_0}{3!},$$

and, in general,

$$a_j = \frac{a_{j-1}}{j} = \frac{a_0}{j!}.$$

The power series solution (4.1) of the differential equation (4.2) is

$$y = a_0 \left(1 + x + \frac{x^2}{2!} + \frac{x^3}{3!} + \frac{x^4}{4!} + \cdots + \frac{x^j}{j!} + \cdots \right),$$

and this is the general solution.

If an initial condition is given at $x = 0$, then the particular solution can be determined by choosing the appropriate value of a_0 (for example, if $y(0) = 2$, then we have $a_0 = 2$).

The power series

$$1 + x + \frac{x^2}{2!} + \frac{x^3}{3!} + \cdots + \frac{x^j}{j!} + \cdots$$

is the Taylor series about 0 for e^x. Hence the solution may be written as

See Appendix 2.

$$y = a_0 e^x.$$

This agrees with the solution obtained using other methods. ■

The expression of the solution as a power series in x is clearly not as convenient as writing it in terms of elementary functions, but in many cases this will be the only method of representing the solution analytically. The power series does give sufficient information to analyse the behaviour of the solution near $x = 0$. However, we do not yet know the range of values of x for which this power series solution is valid. We postpone this discussion until Subsection 5.2.

In fact, the Taylor series for e^x is valid for any value of x.

Note that in some cases, as above, it is possible to recognise the power series solution as the Taylor series for some combination of elementary functions. In such cases, either form of the solution would be deemed acceptable for the purposes of this course. However, for many differential equations, the only available expression for the coefficients in the series will be a recurrence relation like Equation (4.5). Where no simple pattern for the coefficients emerges, it may be feasible to use the recurrence relation to generate only the first few coefficients.

Exercise 4.1

Find the general solution of the differential equation

$$\frac{dy}{dx} - xy = 0,$$

using a power series of the form

$$y = a_0 + a_1 x + a_2 x^2 + \cdots + a_j x^j + \cdots.$$

Solving a differential equation by writing out the power series each time is rather cumbersome; we can save work by using sigma (Σ) notation. However, the use of sigma notation requires a little extra care to ensure that terms are not omitted.

The sigma notation for summations was introduced in MST121 *Chapter B1*.

If in doubt, you can always resort to writing the power series out as in Example 4.1. To illustrate the use of sigma notation, Example 4.1 is now reworked as Example 4.2.

Example 4.2

Determine the power series solution, of the form

$$y = \sum_{j=0}^{\infty} a_j x^j, \tag{4.1a}$$

which satisfies the differential equation

Each of the equations numbered with an 'a' or 'b' in Example 4.2 has its counterpart in Example 4.1.

$$\frac{dy}{dx} - y = 0 \qquad (0 < x < 1). \tag{4.2}$$

Solution

To obtain the derivative, we differentiate Equation (4.1a) term by term, to give

$$\frac{dy}{dx} = \sum_{j=1}^{\infty} j a_j x^{j-1}. \tag{4.3a}$$

Subtracting Equation (4.1a) from Equation (4.3a) gives

Compare this with Equation (4.3), and also observe that this summation starts at $j = 1$, not at $j = 0$.

$$\frac{dy}{dx} - y = \sum_{j=1}^{\infty} j a_j x^{j-1} - \sum_{j=0}^{\infty} a_j x^j = 0. \tag{4.4a}$$

An important part of the procedure is the manipulation of these summations so as to express the differential equation as a power series in x equal to zero. To do this, we need to express the representative term within each summation as a constant times x^j. Replacing j by $j+1$ throughout Equation (4.3a), we have

$$\frac{dy}{dx} = \sum_{j=0}^{\infty} (j+1) a_{j+1} x^j. \tag{4.3b}$$

This new expression enables us to rewrite Equation (4.4a) as

Note that the first term in this power series (which is a_1) is now given by $j = 0$ rather than by $j = 1$.

$$\begin{aligned}\frac{dy}{dx} - y &= \sum_{j=0}^{\infty} (j+1) a_{j+1} x^j - \sum_{j=0}^{\infty} a_j x^j \\ &= \sum_{j=0}^{\infty} [(j+1) a_{j+1} - a_j] x^j \\ &= 0. \end{aligned} \tag{4.4b}$$

Since this equation is to hold at all values of x in the interval $0 < x < 1$, we must have, as before,

$$(j+1) a_{j+1} - a_j = 0.$$

The solution of this recurrence relation is found as in Example 4.1, yielding the general solution

$$y = a_0 \sum_{j=0}^{\infty} \frac{x^j}{j!}. \quad \blacksquare$$

Exercise 4.2

Verify that the summations

(a) $\displaystyle\sum_{j=2}^{\infty} j(j-1)x^{j-2}$,   (b) $\displaystyle\sum_{j=1}^{\infty}(j+1)jx^{j-1}$ and

(c) $\displaystyle\sum_{j=k}^{\infty}(j+2-k)(j+1-k)x^{j-k}$

are all equivalent expressions for the power series $\displaystyle\sum_{j=0}^{\infty}(j+2)(j+1)x^{j}$.

Exercise 4.3

(a) Find the general solution of the differential equation

$$\frac{dy}{dx} - xy = 0,$$

This differential equation was the subject of Exercise 4.1, but here you are asked to use sigma notation.

using a power series of the form

$$y = \sum_{j=0}^{\infty} a_j x^j.$$

(b) Show that the solution is the Taylor series about 0 for the function $Ae^{x^2/2}$, for some arbitrary constant A.

Either separation of variables or the integrating factor method could be used to solve this problem.

The procedure used to solve the problems in Example 4.2 and Exercise 4.3 is summarised below.

Procedure 4.1

To solve linear differential equations by the **method of power series**, proceed as follows.

This method can be applied to linear differential equations of any order.

(a) Let the solution be of the form $y = \displaystyle\sum_{j=0}^{\infty} a_j x^j$.

(b) Substitute for y and its derivatives into the differential equation.

(c) Express the statement of the differential equation as a power series in x equal to zero, by collecting up all the terms in x^j for each j.

(d) Use the power series in Step (c) to obtain a recurrence relation which can be used to determine the coefficients a_j.

This approach to series solutions works in many cases. In Subsection 5.2 you will meet an equation for which it does not work, but for the present, we want to extend the scope of the method to some further problems.

Example 4.3

Determine the power series solution for the differential equation

$$\frac{dy}{dx} + (1-x)y = e^x,$$

This differential equation cannot be solved using elementary functions.

for which $y = 0$ when $x = 0$.

Solution

A new complication here is the appearance of e^x on the right-hand side of the differential equation. However, this may be replaced by its Taylor series about 0, that is,

See Appendix 2.

$$e^x = 1 + x + \frac{x^2}{2!} + \frac{x^3}{3!} + \cdots = \sum_{j=0}^{\infty} \frac{x^j}{j!}.$$

Putting $y = \sum_{j=0}^{\infty} a_j x^j$, the differential equation becomes

$$\sum_{j=1}^{\infty} j a_j x^{j-1} + (1-x) \sum_{j=0}^{\infty} a_j x^j = \sum_{j=0}^{\infty} \frac{x^j}{j!},$$

or

$$\sum_{j=1}^{\infty} j a_j x^{j-1} + \sum_{j=0}^{\infty} a_j x^j - \sum_{j=0}^{\infty} a_j x^{j+1} = \sum_{j=0}^{\infty} \frac{x^j}{j!}.$$

On the left-hand side, the first summation will have terms in x^j if we replace j by $j+1$, making the lower limit $j = 0$. For the third summation, we obtain terms in x^j on replacing j by $j-1$, making the lower limit $j = 1$. Implementation of these adjustments, as in Step (c) of Procedure 4.1, gives

$$\sum_{j=0}^{\infty} (j+1)a_{j+1} x^j + \sum_{j=0}^{\infty} a_j x^j - \sum_{j=1}^{\infty} a_{j-1} x^j = \sum_{j=0}^{\infty} \frac{x^j}{j!}.$$

Now all but one of the summations start with $j = 0$. Since the third summation begins at $j = 1$, we must consider the coefficient of x^0 separately, giving the power series for the differential equation as

This 'separate consideration' means picking out the terms for $j = 0$ from the other three summations.

$$a_1 + a_0 - 1 + \sum_{j=1}^{\infty} \left[(j+1)a_{j+1} + a_j - a_{j-1} - \frac{1}{j!} \right] x^j = 0.$$

Putting each coefficient in this power series equal to zero, we have

$$a_1 = 1 - a_0, \tag{4.6}$$

$$a_{j+1} = \frac{-a_j + a_{j-1} + 1/j!}{(j+1)} \qquad (j = 1, 2, \ldots). \tag{4.7}$$

Given a value for a_0, Equation (4.6) yields a_1. The second-order recurrence relation (4.7) can then be used to generate subsequent coefficients.

Linear second-order constant-coefficient homogeneous recurrence relations were studied in MS221 *Chapter A1*. This recurrence relation is linear, but is neither homogeneous nor constant-coefficient.

For this problem, the initial condition $y(0) = 0$ gives $a_0 = 0$, and hence Equation (4.6) yields $a_1 = 1$. Using the recurrence relation (4.7) to generate the next three coefficients, we have

$$a_2 = \frac{-a_1 + a_0 + 1/1!}{1+1} = \frac{-1 + 0 + 1}{2} = 0,$$

$$a_3 = \frac{-a_2 + a_1 + 1/2!}{2+1} = \frac{0 + 1 + \frac{1}{2}}{3} = \frac{1}{2},$$

$$a_4 = \frac{-a_3 + a_2 + 1/3!}{3+1} = \frac{-\frac{1}{2} + 0 + \frac{1}{6}}{4} = -\frac{1}{12}.$$

Hence the power series solution is

$$y = x + \tfrac{1}{2}x^3 - \tfrac{1}{12}x^4 + \cdots.$$

For small values of x, the first few terms would be sufficient to give an accurate approximation to this solution. ■

Exercise 4.4

Determine the power series solution for the differential equation

$$\frac{dy}{dx} + y = \cos x,$$

for which $y = 1$ when $x = 0$. Use the Taylor series expansion

$$\cos x = 1 - \frac{x^2}{2!} + \frac{x^4}{4!} - \frac{x^6}{6!} + \cdots = \sum_{k=0}^{\infty} \frac{(-1)^k x^{2k}}{(2k)!}.$$

Give numerical values for the coefficients only up to the term in x^4.

The solution using the integrating factor method is
$$y = \tfrac{1}{2}e^{-x} + \tfrac{1}{2}(\cos x + \sin x).$$

The initial condition may be specified at a point other than $x = 0$. For an initial condition given at $x = \alpha$, the behaviour of the solution near this point can be determined by looking for a power series solution of the form

$$y = \sum_{j=0}^{\infty} a_j (x - \alpha)^j.$$

This is the same modification that is used for Taylor series expansions about α.

While it is possible to use this form of the power series directly for solving differential equations, changing the variable to $t = x - \alpha$ allows y to be sought as a power series in t, in the form

$$y = \sum_{j=0}^{\infty} a_j t^j.$$

Exercise 4.5

Determine the power series solution about $x = 1$ for the differential equation

$$\frac{dy}{dx} + (1 - x)y = \frac{1}{2 - x},$$

for which $y = 1$ when $x = 1$. Use the Taylor series expansion (about $t = 0$)

$$\frac{1}{1 - t} = 1 + t + t^2 + t^3 + \cdots = \sum_{j=0}^{\infty} t^j.$$

Give numerical values for the coefficients only up to the term in $(x - 1)^5$.

4.2 Linear second-order equations

Power series solutions for higher-order linear differential equations are not significantly more difficult to obtain than power series solutions for first-order differential equations. However, there is one important difference. An nth-order differential equation has n linearly independent solutions. Thus, for example, when we look for the general solution of a second-order differential equation, the power series solution will contain *two* arbitrary constants. Initial conditions may be used to pick out a particular solution.

Example 4.4

(a) Determine the general solution, using power series, of the homogeneous differential equation

$$\frac{d^2y}{dx^2} + y = 0.$$

The general solution is
$$y = A\cos x + B\sin x.$$

(b) Determine the particular solution for which $y = 1$ and $dy/dx = 2$ when $x = 0$.

Solution

(a) We look for a solution of the form $y = \sum_{j=0}^{\infty} a_j x^j$.

Differentiating twice gives

$$\frac{dy}{dx} = \sum_{j=1}^{\infty} j a_j x^{j-1} \quad \text{and} \quad \frac{d^2y}{dx^2} = \sum_{j=2}^{\infty} j(j-1)a_j x^{j-2}.$$

Thus we replace the differential equation by

$$\sum_{j=2}^{\infty} j(j-1)a_j x^{j-2} + \sum_{j=0}^{\infty} a_j x^j = 0.$$

The first summation will have terms in x^j if we replace j by $j + 2$, making the lower limit $j = 0$. This gives

$$\sum_{j=0}^{\infty} (j+2)(j+1)a_{j+2} x^j + \sum_{j=0}^{\infty} a_j x^j = 0.$$

Equating the coefficient of x^j to zero for each value of j gives

$$(j+2)(j+1)a_{j+2} + a_j = 0 \quad (j = 0, 1, 2, \ldots),$$

so that

$$a_{j+2} = -\frac{a_j}{(j+1)(j+2)} \quad (j = 0, 1, 2, \ldots). \tag{4.8}$$

This is a linear second-order recurrence relation requiring two initial values, a_0 and a_1, to generate the values of subsequent coefficients. In this case, it is easy to represent each coefficient in terms of either a_0 or a_1, since

$$a_2 = -\frac{a_0}{2!}, \qquad\qquad a_3 = -\frac{a_1}{3!},$$

$$a_4 = -\frac{a_2}{3 \times 4} = \frac{a_0}{4!}, \qquad a_5 = -\frac{a_3}{4 \times 5} = \frac{a_1}{5!},$$

$$\vdots$$

$$a_{2k} = -\frac{a_{2k-2}}{(2k-1) \times 2k} = \frac{(-1)^k a_0}{(2k)!},$$

There are two general cases to consider: for j even ($j = 2k$), and for j odd ($j = 2k + 1$).

$$a_{2k+1} = -\frac{a_{2k-1}}{2k \times (2k+1)} = \frac{(-1)^k a_1}{(2k+1)!}.$$

Hence the power series solution can be written as

$$y = a_0 \left(1 - \frac{x^2}{2!} + \frac{x^4}{4!} - \frac{x^6}{6!} + \cdots + \frac{(-1)^k x^{2k}}{(2k)!} + \cdots\right)$$

$$+ a_1 \left(x - \frac{x^3}{3!} + \frac{x^5}{5!} - \cdots + \frac{(-1)^k x^{2k+1}}{(2k+1)!} + \cdots\right)$$

$$= a_0 \sum_{k=0}^{\infty} \frac{(-1)^k}{(2k)!} x^{2k} + a_1 \sum_{k=0}^{\infty} \frac{(-1)^k}{(2k+1)!} x^{2k+1}. \tag{4.9}$$

The two summations are, respectively, the Taylor series about 0 for $\cos x$ and for $\sin x$, so it can be seen that we have the general solution of the differential equation. For a more difficult problem it would be sufficient to leave the solution in the form

$$y = \sum_{j=0}^{\infty} a_j x^j,$$

where

$$a_{j+2} = -\frac{a_j}{(j+1)(j+2)} \qquad (j = 0, 1, 2, \ldots). \tag{4.8}$$

(b) From Equation (4.9), $y = a_0$ when $x = 0$. Hence $a_0 = 1$.

Differentiating the power series gives

$$\frac{dy}{dx} = \sum_{j=1}^{\infty} j a_j x^{j-1},$$

so that $dy/dx = a_1$ when $x = 0$. Hence $a_1 = 2$.

We could now use the recurrence relation (4.8) to generate subsequent coefficients but, since in this case we have been able to express the solution in terms of a_0 and a_1 in Equation (4.9), we have the particular solution with $a_0 = 1$ and $a_1 = 2$ as

$$y = \sum_{k=0}^{\infty} \frac{(-1)^k}{(2k)!} x^{2k} + 2 \sum_{k=0}^{\infty} \frac{(-1)^k}{(2k+1)!} x^{2k+1}$$

This is the power series for $\cos x + 2 \sin x$.

$$= 1 + 2x - \tfrac{1}{2}x^2 - \tfrac{1}{3}x^3 + \tfrac{1}{24}x^4 + \tfrac{1}{60}x^5 - \cdots. \quad \blacksquare$$

Exercise 4.6

Determine the power series solution about $x = 0$ of the differential equation

$$\frac{d^2 y}{dx^2} + x \frac{dy}{dx} - y = 0,$$

for which $y = 0$ and $dy/dx = 1$ when $x = 0$.

Exercise 4.7

Determine the general solution of the differential equation

$$\frac{d^2 y}{dx^2} + xy = x,$$

using a power series about $x = 0$. Do not explicitly find the terms beyond that for x^4.

End-of-section exercise

Exercise 4.8

Determine the first three non-zero terms in the power series solution of the differential equation

$$\frac{d^2y}{dx^2} + xy = \ln(1+x),$$

for which $y = 1$ and $dy/dx = 0$ when $x = 0$. Use the Taylor series

$$\ln(1+x) = x - \tfrac{1}{2}x^2 + \tfrac{1}{3}x^3 - \tfrac{1}{4}x^4 + \cdots = \sum_{j=1}^{\infty} \frac{(-1)^{j+1}x^j}{j}.$$

5 Convergence of the power series

In the last section, you solved differential equations in y by determining the coefficients $a_0, a_1, \ldots$ of the power series about $x = \alpha$, given by

$$y = \sum_{j=0}^{\infty} a_j(x-\alpha)^j.$$

In this section, we look at the problem of using these power series to obtain an approximate value of y at a particular point, $x = x_1$. If x_1 is close to α, then the first few terms in the power series may give a good approximation to the value of $y(x_1)$. If x_1 is further away from α, we may require more terms of the power series to obtain a good approximation. However, if x_1 is too far from α, we may not obtain a good approximation for $y(x_1)$, no matter how many terms we use. The following example illustrates these points.

Example 5.1

Evaluate the power series

$$y = \sum_{j=0}^{\infty} x^j$$

In this example, $\alpha = 0$.

at (a) $x = 0.1$, (b) $x = 0.9$, (c) $x = 1.0$.

Give your answers correct to three decimal places.

Solution

(a) For $x = 0.1$, we have

$$y(0.1) = 1 + 0.1 + 0.1^2 + 0.1^3 + \cdots$$
$$= 1 + 0.1 + 0.01 + 0.001 + 0.0001 + \cdots.$$

It is clear that the first four terms are sufficient to give the solution correct to three decimal places, as $y(0.1) = 1.111$.

(b) For $x = 0.9$, we have

$$y(0.9) = 1 + 0.9 + 0.9^2 + 0.9^3 + 0.9^4 + \cdots$$
$$= 1 + 0.9 + 0.81 + 0.729 + 0.6561 + \cdots .$$

Approximately 100 terms are required to give the value $y(0.9) = 10.000$, correct to three decimal places.

(c) For $x = 1$, we have

$$y(1) = 1 + 1 + 1^2 + 1^3 + \cdots .$$

Clearly, the series has no finite value for this value of x; that is, the series *does not converge* for $x = 1$.   ■

As is shown in Example 5.2, below, the series

$$\sum_{j=0}^{\infty} x^j$$

converges to $1/(1-x)$ if and only if $-1 < x < 1$. Hence, $y(0.9) = 1/(0.1) = 10$.

5.1   What convergence means

Consider the general power series

$$\sum_{j=0}^{\infty} a_j (x - \alpha)^j .$$

We say that this series is **convergent** (or **converges**) at a point $x = x_1$ if

$$\lim_{n \to \infty} \sum_{j=0}^{n} a_j (x_1 - \alpha)^j$$

exists. By this definition, we mean that the sequence of *partial sums*, $s_0, s_1, s_2, \ldots$, where

$$s_n = \sum_{j=0}^{n} a_j (x_1 - \alpha)^j ,$$

is such that s_n tends to some limiting value as n tends to infinity. This limiting value is the value of the power series at $x = x_1$.

Example 5.2

Write down the partial sums for the power series

$$y = \sum_{j=0}^{\infty} x^j ,$$

This is a *geometric series*.

and show that they tend to a finite limit if and only if $-1 < x < 1$. Hence deduce that the series converges to $1/(1-x)$ if and only if $-1 < x < 1$.

Solution

For this series, the partial sum s_n is given by

$$s_n = 1 + x + x^2 + x^3 + \cdots + x^n ,$$

so that we also have

$$x s_n = x + x^2 + x^3 + x^4 + \cdots + x^{n+1} .$$

On subtracting the expression for $x s_n$ from that for s_n, there is cancellation of most of the terms, leaving

$$(1 - x) s_n = 1 - x^{n+1} .$$

Provided that $x \neq 1$, we therefore have

$$s_n = \frac{1 - x^{n+1}}{1 - x} = \frac{1}{1 - x} - \frac{x^{n+1}}{1 - x} .$$

Now, if $-1 < x < 1$, then $x^{n+1} \to 0$ as $n \to \infty$, and s_n tends to $1/(1-x)$. If $x > 1$ or $x < -1$, then the limit of x^{n+1} as $n \to \infty$ does not exist, and hence no limit for s_n exists.

If $x = 1$, then $s_n = 1 + 1 + \cdots + 1 = n + 1$, and as $n \to \infty$, no limit for s_n exists. If $x = -1$, then

$$s_n = 1 - 1 + 1 - 1 + 1 + \cdots + (-1)^n = \begin{cases} 0 & \text{for } n \text{ odd,} \\ 1 & \text{for } n \text{ even.} \end{cases}$$

Again, as $n \to \infty$, no limit for s_n exists.

Hence, the series $\sum_{j=0}^{\infty} x^j$ converges to $\dfrac{1}{1-x}$ if and only if $-1 < x < 1$. ■

This example showed that for a range of values of x the series converges, whereas outside this interval the series is *divergent* (or *diverges*; that is, it does not converge). For any power series about $x = \alpha$, there is a **radius of convergence**, R, such that the power series converges if

$$-R < x - \alpha < R,$$

and diverges if

$$x - \alpha > R \qquad \text{or} \qquad x - \alpha < -R.$$

The interval $\alpha - R < x < \alpha + R$ is called the **interval of convergence**. In Example 5.2, $\alpha = 0$ and $R = 1$, so the interval of convergence is $-1 < x < 1$.

This can be written as
$$|x - \alpha| < R.$$

This can be written as
$$|x - \alpha| > R.$$

When $|x - \alpha| = R$, the series may or may not converge, in general.

Exercise 5.1

What are

(a) the radius of convergence, and

(b) the interval of convergence,

for the following power series?

$$y = \sum_{j=0}^{\infty} (x - \tfrac{1}{2})^j$$

Hint: Compare this series with that in Example 5.2.

5.2 A convergence theorem

In this subsection, we state a theorem about power series solutions of differential equations which allows us to derive convergence results without having to compute the power series solution.

Consider the linear homogeneous second-order differential equation

$$p(x)\frac{d^2 y}{dx^2} + q(x)\frac{dy}{dx} + r(x)y = 0,$$

where, for simplicity, we assume that p, q and r are all polynomial functions. As defined in Subsection 1.1, the differential equation has a singular point at $x = x_0$ if $p(x_0) = 0$. Differential equations possessing a singular point in the interval of interest cause difficulties, in that the solution may 'misbehave' at the singular point, as in the following example.

Example 5.3

Consider the Cauchy–Euler problems, on the interval $-1 \leq x \leq 1$, given by

(a) $x^2 \dfrac{d^2y}{dx^2} + 4x \dfrac{dy}{dx} + 2y = 0$,

   with $y = 1$ and $dy/dx = -2$ when $x = -1$, where the general solution is

   $$y = Ax^{-1} + Bx^{-2};$$

(b) $x^2 \dfrac{d^2y}{dx^2} - 4x \dfrac{dy}{dx} + 6y = 0$,

   with $y = 0$ and $dy/dx = 1$ when $x = -1$, where the general solution is

   $$y = Ax^2 + Bx^3.$$

In each case, discuss the behaviour of the solution at $x = 0$.

Solution

In both cases, there is a singular point at $x = 0$.

(a) The initial conditions give the particular solution

   $$y = -4x^{-1} - 3x^{-2}.$$

   This solution is valid for $-1 \leq x < 0$. However, the solution is not continuous at $x = 0$, and hence its form on the interval $-1 \leq x < 0$ tells us nothing about the solution on the interval $0 \leq x \leq 1$. (We know only that $y = Ax^{-1} + Bx^{-2}$ for $0 < x < 1$; the conditions at $x = -1$ can have no effect on the solution for $0 < x < 1$.)

   In fact, the solution is not defined at $x = 0$.

(b) The initial conditions give the particular solution

   $$y = x^2 + x^3,$$

   which is certainly valid for $-1 \leq x < 0$, and is continuous at $x = 0$. However, we still cannot give a unique particular solution for $x > 0$, since for any arbitrary constant B, the function

   $$y = \begin{cases} x^2 + x^3 & (-1 \leq x < 0), \\ x^2 + Bx^3 & (0 \leq x \leq 1) \end{cases}$$

   is also a solution for which y, dy/dx and d^2y/dx^2 are continuous on the interval $-1 \leq x \leq 1$, and in particular at $x = 0$. ∎

This example illustrates that a unique solution may not be obtainable for an initial-value problem over an interval which contains a singular point of the differential equation. Thus we would expect the corresponding power series solution to behave badly at a singular point. Note, however, that singular points may be real or complex. For example, $p(x) = 1 + x^2$ has zeros at $x = \pm i$. For simplicity, we shall restrict attention in this course to the case in which the singular points are real.

Suppose that we wish to obtain a power series solution for the differential equation about $x = \alpha$, where the minimum distance from α to a singular point of the equation is μ. The following theorem can be used to give a lower bound for the radius of convergence.

Theorem 5.1   Convergence Theorem

Consider the linear homogeneous second-order differential equation

$$p(x)\frac{d^2y}{dx^2} + q(x)\frac{dy}{dx} + r(x)y = 0,$$

where $p(x)$, $q(x)$ and $r(x)$ are polynomial functions, and all the zeros of $p(x)$ are real. Any power series solution of this equation about α is convergent in an interval $-\mu < x - \alpha < \mu$, where μ is the minimum distance from α to a zero of $p(x)$.

If $p(x)$ is a constant function then $\mu = \infty$, and the power series solution converges for any value of x.

If $p(\alpha) = 0$, then $\mu = 0$, and the power series solution may not converge for any value of x.

We make the following observations.

(i) The value μ will be a lower bound for the radius of convergence R; that is, $R \geq \mu$. In practice, $\mu = R$ except in special circumstances (see Exercise 5.2).

(ii) If $|x_1 - \alpha| > \mu$, we do not know whether or not a series solution converges at $x = x_1$.

Example 5.4

Determine an interval of convergence for the power series solution to each of the following differential equations.

(a) $\dfrac{d^2y}{dx^2} + 3x\dfrac{dy}{dx} + y = 0$ about $x = 0$

(b) $(x^2 - 4)\dfrac{d^2y}{dx^2} + y = 0$ about (i) $x = 0$ and (ii) $x = 1$

(c) $(1 - x^2)\dfrac{d^2y}{dx^2} - 2x\dfrac{dy}{dx} + 6y = 0$ about $x = 0$

This is *Legendre's equation* of order 2. The order 1 case was the subject of Exercise 2.5. There is more on Legendre's equation in *Unit 10*.

Solution

Without computing the power series solution, we can determine a lower bound μ for the radius of convergence R, using the Convergence Theorem.

(a) Since $p(x) = 1$ is non-zero for all values of x, we have $\mu = \infty$, and the power series solution will converge for all values of x.

(b) In this case, $p(x) = x^2 - 4$ has zeros at $x = \pm 2$.

   (i) Power series about $x = 0$: The point $x = 0$ is equidistant from the two zeros, and the minimum distance to a zero of $p(x)$ is $\mu = 2$. Hence, an interval of convergence is $-2 < x < 2$.

   (ii) Power series about $x = 1$: The distance from $x = 1$ to the positive zero $(+2)$ is 1, and the distance to the negative zero (-2) is 3. Thus the minimum distance to a zero of $p(x)$ is $\mu = 1$, and the power series converges if $-1 < x - 1 < 1$. Thus an interval of convergence is $0 < x < 2$.

(c) We have $p(x) = 1 - x^2$, and $p(x) = 0$ when $x = \pm 1$. The minimum distance from $x = 0$ to a zero of $p(x)$ is 1. Hence, an interval of convergence is $-1 < x < 1$. ∎

Exercise 5.2

Verify by direct substitution that $y = 3x^2 - 1$ is a solution of the differential equation

$$(1 - x^2)\frac{d^2y}{dx^2} - 2x\frac{dy}{dx} + 6y = 0$$

for all values of x, and hence comment on the interval of convergence found in Example 5.4(c).

Exercise 5.3

Determine an interval of convergence for the power series solution about $x = 0$ of each of the following differential equations.

(a) $\dfrac{d^2y}{dx^2} - 2x\dfrac{dy}{dx} + 2y = 0$

(b) $(1 - x^2)\dfrac{d^2y}{dx^2} - x\dfrac{dy}{dx} + y = 0$

(c) $x^2\dfrac{d^2y}{dx^2} + x\dfrac{dy}{dx} + (x^2 - 1)y = 0$

When the power series method breaks down

In all of the examples so far where a power series solution to a differential equation was sought, it was a fairly straightforward process to derive the recurrence relation required to generate terms in the series. We now ask: When does the method fail? From the Convergence Theorem, trouble might be expected if we choose to determine the power series solution about α, where α is one of the singular points, since then $\mu = 0$ and there is no guaranteed interval of convergence.

To illustrate how the method breaks down, consider the first-order linear differential equation

$$x\frac{dy}{dx} + y = 0,$$

which has a singular point at $x = 0$. If we attempt to determine the power series solution about $x = 0$ given by

$$y = \sum_{j=0}^{\infty} a_j x^j,$$

then on substituting into the differential equation we have

$$\sum_{j=1}^{\infty} j a_j x^j + \sum_{j=0}^{\infty} a_j x^j = 0, \qquad \text{that is,} \qquad a_0 + \sum_{j=1}^{\infty}(j+1)a_j x^j = 0.$$

Thus $a_0 = 0$ and

$$(j + 1)a_j = 0 \qquad (j = 1, 2, \ldots).$$

Hence the only solution we can obtain with this method is $y = 0$, which is not the general solution of the differential equation. The separation of variables method gives the general solution as $y = A/x$, where A is an arbitrary constant. The power series method has failed to detect this solution.

There is an extensive theory for power series solutions of differential equations about singular points, following the work of Frobenius. We do not have space to outline the Frobenius method in this course.

A first-order differential equation of the form

$$p(x)\frac{dy}{dx} + q(x)y = 0,$$

where $p(x)$ and $q(x)$ are polynomials, has a singular point at $x = x_0$ if $p(x_0) = 0$.

Ferdinand Georg Frobenius (1848–1917) was a German mathematician.

Finding polynomial solutions

By way of a conclusion, it is worth pointing out that while the method presented in Section 4 assumes a form of solution that is an infinite series, this includes the possibility that the solution may be a polynomial, of degree n say, for which all coefficients beyond the nth in the assumed infinite series are zero.

For example, if we assume a power series solution

$$y = \sum_{j=0}^{\infty} a_j x^j$$

for the differential equation

$$(1 - x^2)\frac{d^2y}{dx^2} - 2x\frac{dy}{dx} + 6y = 0 \qquad (-1 < x < 1),$$

then we arrive at conditions on the coefficients given by the recurrence relation

$$a_{j+2} = \frac{(j-2)(j+3)}{(j+1)(j+2)}a_j \qquad (j = 0, 1, 2, \ldots).$$

You could check this, if you have time.

Since the right-hand side contains the factor $j - 2$, we must have (by putting $j = 2$) $a_4 = 0$, whatever the value of a_2. By repeated application of the recurrence relation, all coefficients a_{2k} with $k > 2$ will also be zero. Choosing $a_1 = 0$ ensures in a similar way that $a_{2k+1} = 0$ for all $k > 0$. We are left with the solution $a_0 + a_2 x^2$, where (putting $j = 0$) $a_2 = -3a_0$. Hence $y = 3x^2 - 1$ is a polynomial solution of the differential equation.

You were asked to verify this in Exercise 5.2.

Only one independent elementary solution has been found here, but the method of reduction of order then offers the possibility of finding the general solution, which in this case turns out to be

You also found a simple polynomial solution, using power series, in Exercise 4.6.

$$y = A(3x^2 - 1) + B\left(-6x + (3x^2 - 1)\ln\left(\frac{1+x}{1-x}\right)\right).$$

(Do not attempt to check this unless you have plenty of time in hand.)

End-of-section exercise

Exercise 5.4

(a) Determine the first five non-zero terms in the power series solution about $x = 0$ of the differential equation

$$(4 - x^2)\frac{d^2y}{dx^2} + (1 + x)\frac{dy}{dx} + y = 0,$$

for which $y = 1$ and $dy/dx = 0$ at $x = 0$.

(b) Determine an interval of convergence for this power series.

(c) Determine the value of y at $x = 1$, correct to three decimal places.

Outcomes

After studying this unit you should be able to:

- solve second-order Cauchy–Euler differential equations;
- by changing the independent variable, solve certain other linear differential equations;
- apply the method of reduction of order, where appropriate;
- apply the method of variation of parameters, where appropriate;
- solve boundary-value problems, appreciating that such problems may not have solutions and that, where a solution exists, it may not be unique;
- solve eigenvalue problems that arise as families of boundary-value problems;
- apply the method of power series, where appropriate;
- state the conditions under which a power series solution for a given differential equation can be expected to give valid results.

Appendix 1: Hyperbolic functions

The **hyperbolic functions** sinh and cosh are defined in terms of the exponential function by the equations

$$\sinh x = \tfrac{1}{2}(e^x - e^{-x}) \qquad \text{and} \qquad \cosh x = \tfrac{1}{2}(e^x + e^{-x}).$$

The graphs of sinh and cosh are shown in Figure A1.1.

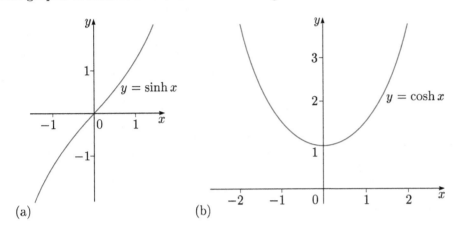

(a)   (b)

Figure A1.1 Graphs of the functions sinh and cosh

These functions have many properties analogous to those of the trigonometric functions sin and cos. For example, cosh, like cos, is an even function, and sinh, like sin, is an odd function. Also the derivative of $\sinh x$ is $\cosh x$ and, for any real values x and y,

$$\sinh(x + y) = \sinh x \cosh y + \cosh x \sinh y.$$

These two properties are directly analogous to properties of sin and cos. Some other properties of sinh and cosh are similar, but not directly analogous, to those of sin and cos. For example, the derivative of $\cosh x$ is $\sinh x$, and not the negative of this, as suggested by considering $\cos' = -\sin$. Also, the counterpart of the identity $\cos^2 x + \sin^2 x = 1$ for the hyperbolic functions is $\cosh^2 x - \sinh^2 x = 1$.

Starting from the standard Taylor series for e^x about 0, it is straightforward to show that, for all x,

$$\cosh x = 1 + \frac{1}{2!}x^2 + \frac{1}{4!}x^4 + \cdots, \qquad \sinh x = x + \frac{1}{3!}x^3 + \frac{1}{5!}x^5 + \cdots.$$

These Taylor series are similar to those for cos and sin, respectively. However, the coefficients in the series for $\cosh x$ and $\sinh x$ are positive, whereas the coefficients of the series for $\cos x$ and $\sin x$ alternate in sign. Since

$$\cosh' x = \sinh x \qquad \text{and} \qquad \sinh' x = \cosh x,$$

it follows that the general solution of the differential equation $y''(x) - \omega^2 y(x) = 0$, which is $y(x) = Ae^{\omega x} + Be^{-\omega x}$, may also be written as

$$y(x) = C\cosh(\omega x) + D\sinh(\omega x),$$

where C, D are arbitrary constants. In fact, $y(x) = \sinh(\omega x)$ is a solution for which $y(0) = 0$, while $y(x) = \cosh(\omega x)$ is a solution for which $y'(0) = 0$.

Hyperbolic functions were introduced in MS221 *Chapter C3*, from which much of this appendix is taken.

There are various pronunciations in use for the functions sinh and cosh; the most common are 'shine' or 'sine-sh' for sinh and simply 'cosh' for cosh.

There are other hyperbolic functions, such as tanh, which is defined by

$$\tanh x = \frac{\sinh x}{\cosh x},$$

and usually pronounced 'than' (as in 'thank') or 'tansh'.

These properties of sinh and cosh can be verified by using the given expressions for sinh and cosh in terms of exp.

The identity

$$\cosh^2 x - \sinh^2 x = 1$$

allows cosh and sinh to be used to define parametric equations for a hyperbola in standard form. This is why such functions are called hyperbolic.

This form for the general solution will be of use later in the course.

Appendix 2: Taylor polynomials and series

Let f be a function that is n-times differentiable at 0. The **Taylor polynomial** of degree n about 0 for f is

$$p_n(x) = f(0) + f'(0)x + \frac{f''(0)}{2!}\,x^2 + \frac{f^{(3)}(0)}{3!}\,x^3 + \cdots + \frac{f^{(n)}(0)}{n!}\,x^n$$

$$= \sum_{j=0}^{n} \frac{f^{(j)}(0)}{j!}\,x^j.$$

Taylor polynomials and series were introduced in MS221 *Chapter C3*, from which this summary is taken.

The Taylor polynomial of degree n about a for f is

$$p_n(x) = f(a) + f'(a)(x-a) + \frac{f''(a)}{2!}\,(x-a)^2 + \frac{f^{(3)}(a)}{3!}\,(x-a)^3$$

$$+ \cdots + \frac{f^{(n)}(a)}{n!}\,(x-a)^n = \sum_{j=0}^{n} \frac{f^{(j)}(a)}{j!}\,(x-a)^j.$$

Note that, by definition,
$$0! = 1.$$

The key property of such Taylor polynomials is that
$$p_n^{(j)}(a) = f^{(j)}(a)$$
for $j = 0, 1, \ldots, n$, so that $p_n(x)$ approximates $f(x)$ closely when x is close to a.

Let f be a function that is differentiable infinitely many times at a. The **Taylor series** about a for f is

$$f(a) + f'(a)(x-a) + \frac{f''(a)}{2!}\,(x-a)^2 + \frac{f^{(3)}(a)}{3!}(x-a)^3$$

$$+ \cdots + \frac{f^{(j)}(a)}{j!}\,(x-a)^j + \cdots = \sum_{j=0}^{\infty} \frac{f^{(j)}(a)}{j!}\,(x-a)^j.$$

The point a is called the **centre** of the Taylor series. If $a = 0$, then the Taylor series reduces to

$$f(0) + f'(0)x + \frac{f''(0)}{2!}\,x^2 + \frac{f^{(3)}(0)}{3!}x^3 + \cdots = \sum_{j=0}^{\infty} \frac{f^{(j)}(0)}{j!}\,x^j.$$

Any range of values of x for which a Taylor series for a function f sums to (converges to) $f(x)$ is called a **range of validity** for the series.

Some standard Taylor series about 0 are as follows.

A range of validity may also be called an interval of convergence, as in Section 5.

$$\sin x = x - \frac{1}{3!}\,x^3 + \frac{1}{5!}\,x^5 - \frac{1}{7!}\,x^7 + \frac{1}{9!}\,x^9 - \cdots \qquad (x \in \mathbb{R})$$

$$\cos x = 1 - \frac{1}{2!}x^2 + \frac{1}{4!}\,x^4 - \frac{1}{6!}\,x^6 + \frac{1}{8!}\,x^8 - \cdots \qquad (x \in \mathbb{R})$$

Here $x \in \mathbb{R}$ means 'for all real values of x'. This can also be written as $-\infty < x < \infty$.

$$e^x = 1 + x + \frac{1}{2!}\,x^2 + \frac{1}{3!}\,x^3 + \frac{1}{4!}\,x^4 + \cdots \qquad (x \in \mathbb{R})$$

$$\ln(1+x) = x - \tfrac{1}{2}x^2 + \tfrac{1}{3}x^3 - \tfrac{1}{4}x^4 + \tfrac{1}{5}x^5 - \cdots \qquad (-1 < x < 1)$$

$$\frac{1}{1-x} = 1 + x + x^2 + x^3 + x^4 + \cdots \qquad (-1 < x < 1)$$

$$(1+x)^\alpha = 1 + \alpha x + \frac{\alpha(\alpha-1)}{2!}\,x^2 + \frac{\alpha(\alpha-1)(\alpha-2)}{3!}\,x^3 + \cdots$$

$$(-1 < x < 1), \text{ where } \alpha \in \mathbb{R}$$

Further Taylor series can be obtained from standard Taylor series by:
- substituting for the variable;
- adding, subtracting and multiplying Taylor series;
- differentiating and integrating Taylor series term by term.

In each case, a range of validity of the new Taylor series can be found from the known range(s) of validity of the standard Taylor series involved.

Solutions to the exercises

Section 1

Solution 1.1

(a) Step (a): Putting $y = x^\lambda$ gives the indicial equation

$$2\lambda(\lambda - 1) + 11\lambda - 5 = 0,$$

or (on simplifying)

$$2\lambda^2 + 9\lambda - 5 = 0,$$

that is,

$$(2\lambda - 1)(\lambda + 5) = 0.$$

Step (b): The roots are $\lambda = \frac{1}{2}$ and $\lambda = -5$.

Step (c): The general solution is

$$y = Ax^{1/2} + Bx^{-5}.$$

Derivative: $\dfrac{dy}{dx} = \frac{1}{2}Ax^{-1/2} - 5Bx^{-6}.$

Initial conditions: $1 = A + B$, $-2 = \frac{1}{2}A - 5B$.

Solution of these: $A = \frac{6}{11}$, $B = \frac{5}{11}$.

Particular solution: $y = \frac{6}{11}x^{1/2} + \frac{5}{11}x^{-5}.$

(b) Step (a): Putting $y = x^\lambda$ gives the indicial equation

$$\lambda(\lambda - 1) + 3\lambda + 10 = 0,$$

or

$$\lambda^2 + 2\lambda + 10 = 0.$$

Step (b): The roots are $\lambda = -1 \pm 3i$.

Step (c): The general solution is

$$y = x^{-1}[A\cos(3\ln x) + B\sin(3\ln x)].$$

Derivative:

$$\frac{dy}{dx} = (-x^{-2})[A\cos(3\ln x) + B\sin(3\ln x)]$$
$$+ (x^{-1})(3x^{-1})[-A\sin(3\ln x) + B\cos(3\ln x)]$$
$$= x^{-2}[(3B - A)\cos(3\ln x) - (3A + B)\sin(3\ln x)].$$

Initial conditions: $1 = A$, $-2 = 3B - A$.

Solution of these: $A = 1$, $B = -\frac{1}{3}$.

Particular solution:

$$y = x^{-1}[\cos(3\ln x) - \frac{1}{3}\sin(3\ln x)].$$

(c) Step (a): Putting $y = x^\lambda$ gives the indicial equation

$$9\lambda(\lambda - 1) - 3\lambda + 4 = 0,$$

or

$$9\lambda^2 - 12\lambda + 4 = 0,$$

that is,

$$(3\lambda - 2)^2 = 0.$$

Step (b): The only root is $\lambda = \frac{2}{3}$.

Step (c): The general solution is

$$y = (A + B\ln x)x^{2/3}.$$

Derivative: $\dfrac{dy}{dx} = (\frac{2}{3}A + B + \frac{2}{3}B\ln x)x^{-1/3}.$

Initial conditions: $1 = A$, $-2 = \frac{2}{3}A + B$.

Solution of these: $A = 1$, $B = -\frac{8}{3}$.

Particular solution: $y = (1 - \frac{8}{3}\ln x)x^{2/3}.$

(d) Step (a): Putting $y = x^\lambda$ gives the indicial equation

$$\lambda(\lambda - 1) + \lambda + 7 = 0,$$

or

$$\lambda^2 + 7 = 0.$$

Step (b): The roots are $\lambda = \pm\sqrt{7}\,i$.

Step (c): The general solution is

$$y = A\cos(\sqrt{7}\ln x) + B\sin(\sqrt{7}\ln x).$$

Derivative:

$$\frac{dy}{dx} = \sqrt{7}x^{-1}[-A\sin(\sqrt{7}\ln x) + B\cos(\sqrt{7}\ln x)].$$

Initial conditions: $1 = A$, $-2 = \sqrt{7}B$.

Solution of these: $A = 1$, $B = -\frac{2}{7}\sqrt{7}$.

Particular solution:

$$y = \cos(\sqrt{7}\ln x) - \frac{2}{7}\sqrt{7}\sin(\sqrt{7}\ln x).$$

(e) Step (a): Putting $y = x^\lambda$ gives the indicial equation

$$5\lambda(\lambda - 1) + 3\lambda = 0,$$

or

$$5\lambda^2 - 2\lambda = 0,$$

that is,

$$\lambda(5\lambda - 2) = 0.$$

Step (b): The roots are $\lambda = 0$ and $\lambda = \frac{2}{5}$.

Step (c): The general solution is

$$y = A + Bx^{2/5}.$$

Derivative: $\dfrac{dy}{dx} = \frac{2}{5}Bx^{-3/5}.$

Initial conditions: $1 = A + B$, $-2 = \frac{2}{5}B$.

Solution of these: $A = 6$, $B = -5$.

Particular solution: $y = 6 - 5x^{2/5}.$

Solution 1.2

(a) Here $x^{-1/3}$ is unbounded as $x \to 0$, whereas x^2 tends to 0. Thus only solutions of the form $y = Bx^2$ are bounded as $x \to 0$, and each of them has the limiting value 0.

(b) Putting $B = 0$ will eliminate multiples of the unbounded function x^{-5}, leaving solutions of the form

$$y = Ax^{1/2},$$

which tend to 0 as $x \to 0$. (Note, however, that the derivative of $x^{1/2}$ is $\frac{1}{2}x^{-1/2}$, which is *not* bounded as $x \to 0$. We conclude that the only solution for which *both* y and dy/dx have limits as $x \to 0$ is $y = 0$.)

Solution 1.3

(a) Put $x = t + \mu$. Then $dx/dt = 1$, so that
$$\frac{du}{dt} = \frac{du}{dx}.$$
Consequently,
$$\frac{dy}{dt} = \frac{dy}{dx} \quad \text{and}$$
$$\frac{d^2y}{dt^2} = \frac{d}{dt}\left(\frac{dy}{dt}\right) = \frac{d}{dx}\left(\frac{dy}{dx}\right) = \frac{d^2y}{dx^2}.$$
The differential equation becomes
$$2t^2\frac{d^2y}{dt^2} + 11t\frac{dy}{dt} - 5y = 0 \qquad (t > 0),$$
and from Exercise 1.1(a), the general solution of this is
$$y = At^{1/2} + Bt^{-5}.$$
The general solution of the original equation is therefore
$$y = A(x - \mu)^{1/2} + B(x - \mu)^{-5}.$$

(b) If $x = \cos t$ then
$$\frac{dx}{dt} = -\sin t = -\sqrt{1 - \cos^2 t} = -(1 - x^2)^{1/2}.$$
(The sign for the square root here is chosen as shown because $0 < t < \pi$, so $\sin t > 0$.)
Hence
$$\frac{du}{dt} = -(1 - x^2)^{1/2}\frac{du}{dx},$$
so that
$$\frac{dy}{dt} = -(1 - x^2)^{1/2}\frac{dy}{dx}$$
and
$$\frac{d^2y}{dt^2} = \frac{d}{dt}\left(\frac{dy}{dt}\right)$$
$$= -(1 - x^2)^{1/2}\frac{d}{dx}\left(-(1 - x^2)^{1/2}\frac{dy}{dx}\right)$$
$$= -(1 - x^2)^{1/2}\left(x(1 - x^2)^{-1/2}\frac{dy}{dx} - (1 - x^2)^{1/2}\frac{d^2y}{dx^2}\right)$$
$$= -x\frac{dy}{dx} + (1 - x^2)\frac{d^2y}{dx^2}.$$
Chebyshev's equation becomes
$$\frac{d^2y}{dt^2} + \lambda y = 0,$$
and since λ is positive, this has general solution
$$y = A\cos(\sqrt{\lambda}\, t) + B\sin(\sqrt{\lambda}\, t).$$
Thus the general solution of Chebyshev's equation is
$$y = A\cos(\sqrt{\lambda}\arccos x) + B\sin(\sqrt{\lambda}\arccos x).$$

Alternative approach:
Since $x = \cos t$ and $dx/dt = -\sin t$, we have
$$\frac{du}{dt} = -\sin t\frac{du}{dx},$$
which is used below with $u = y$ and with $u = dy/dx$.
Hence
$$\frac{dy}{dt} = -\sin t\frac{dy}{dx} \qquad \text{and (using the Product Rule)}$$

$$\frac{d^2y}{dt^2} = \frac{d}{dt}\left(\frac{dy}{dt}\right) = \frac{d}{dt}\left(-\sin t\frac{dy}{dx}\right)$$
$$= -\cos t\frac{dy}{dx} - \sin t\frac{d}{dt}\left(\frac{dy}{dx}\right)$$
$$= -\cos t\frac{dy}{dx} - \sin t\left(-\sin t\frac{d^2y}{dx^2}\right)$$
$$= -x\frac{dy}{dx} + (1 - x^2)\frac{d^2y}{dx^2},$$
since $\cos t = x$ and $\sin^2 t = 1 - \cos^2 t = 1 - x^2$.
The solution then proceeds as before.

Solution 1.4

(a) Putting $u = t^\lambda$ gives the indicial equation
$$\lambda^2 - 4\lambda + 4 = 0,$$
whose only root is $\lambda = 2$. The general solution is
$$u = (A + B\ln t)t^2.$$

(b) The change of variable $x = t + 3$ gives
$$t^2\frac{d^2y}{dt^2} + 5t\frac{dy}{dt} + 5y = 0 \quad (t > 0),$$
which has indicial equation
$$\lambda^2 + 4\lambda + 5 = 0,$$
with roots $\lambda = -2 \pm i$. Hence the general solution is
$$y = t^{-2}[A\cos(\ln t) + B\sin(\ln t)]$$
$$= (x - 3)^{-2}[A\cos(\ln(x - 3)) + B\sin(\ln(x - 3))].$$

Solution 1.5

If $x = \cosh t$, then
$$\frac{dx}{dt} = \sinh t = \sqrt{\cosh^2 t - 1} = (x^2 - 1)^{1/2}.$$
(We take the plus sign for the square root here because $t > 0$, so $\sinh t > 0$.) The Chain Rule becomes
$$\frac{du}{dt} = (x^2 - 1)^{1/2}\frac{du}{dx}.$$
Hence
$$\frac{dy}{dt} = (x^2 - 1)^{1/2}\frac{dy}{dx}$$
and
$$\frac{d^2y}{dt^2} = \frac{d}{dt}\left(\frac{dy}{dt}\right) = (x^2 - 1)^{1/2}\frac{d}{dx}\left((x^2 - 1)^{1/2}\frac{dy}{dx}\right)$$
$$= x\frac{dy}{dx} + (x^2 - 1)\frac{d^2y}{dx^2}.$$
Thus Chebyshev's equation for $x > 1$ becomes
$$-\frac{d^2y}{dt^2} + \lambda y = 0,$$
and since λ is positive, this has general solution
$$y = Ae^{\sqrt{\lambda}t} + Be^{-\sqrt{\lambda}t}.$$
The general solution of the original equation is therefore
$$y = Ae^{\sqrt{\lambda}\operatorname{arccosh} x} + Be^{-\sqrt{\lambda}\operatorname{arccosh} x}.$$

Section 2

Solution 2.1

(a) If $y_1 = x^2$, then $y_1' = 2x$ and $y_1'' = 2$. Hence we have

$$x^2 y_1'' - x(3x + 4)y_1' + 6(x + 1)y_1$$
$$= x^2(2) - x(3x + 4)(2x) + 6(x + 1)(x^2)$$
$$= (2 - 8 + 6)x^2 + (-6 + 6)x^3 = 0,$$

so $y_1 = x^2$ is a solution of the differential equation.

(b) With $y_1 = x^2$, put $y = uy_1 = ux^2$. Substitution of this into the differential equation leads to Equation (2.5) for $v(x) = u'(x)$, where

$$y_1 = x^2, \quad y_1' = 2x, \quad p = x^2, \quad q = -x(3x + 4),$$

that is,

$$v' + \left(\frac{2(2x)}{x^2} - \frac{x(3x + 4)}{x^2} \right) v = 0$$

or

$$v' - 3v = 0.$$

Hence $v = Ae^{3x}$ and so, on integrating, $u = \frac{1}{3}Ae^{3x} + B$ (but since A is arbitrary, the factor $\frac{1}{3}$ here can be dropped). Thus

$$y = ux^2 = x^2(Ae^{3x} + B)$$

is the general solution of the differential equation.

Solution 2.2

(a) If $y_1 = e^{-2x}$, then $y_1' = -2e^{-2x}$ and $y_1'' = 4e^{-2x}$. Hence we have

$$xy_1'' + 2(x - 1)y_1' - 4y_1$$
$$= x(4e^{-2x}) + 2(x - 1)(-2e^{-2x}) - 4(e^{-2x})$$
$$= (4x - 4x + 4 - 4)e^{-2x} = 0,$$

so $y_1 = e^{-2x}$ is a solution of the differential equation.

(b) With $y_1 = e^{-2x}$, put $y = uy_1 = ue^{-2x}$. Substitution of this into the differential equation leads to Equation (2.5) for $v(x) = u'(x)$, where

$$y_1 = e^{-2x}, \quad y_1' = -2e^{-2x}, \quad p = x, \quad q = 2(x - 1),$$

that is,

$$v' + \left(-4 + \frac{2(x - 1)}{x} \right) v = 0$$

or

$$v' - \left(\frac{2}{x} + 2 \right) v = 0.$$

The integrating factor is

$$\exp \left[- \int \left(\frac{2}{x} + 2 \right) dx \right] = x^{-2} e^{-2x},$$

so that

$$\frac{d}{dx} \left(x^{-2} e^{-2x} v \right) = 0,$$

giving

$$v = Ax^2 e^{2x}.$$

Since $u'(x) = v(x)$, we have (integrating by parts twice)

$$u = A \int x^2 e^{2x} \, dx = A \left(\tfrac{1}{2} x^2 - \tfrac{1}{2} x + \tfrac{1}{4} \right) e^{2x} + B.$$

Replacing the arbitrary constant A by $4A$, to remove fractions, this becomes

$$u = A \left(2x^2 - 2x + 1 \right) e^{2x} + B.$$

Hence the general solution of the given equation is

$$y = ue^{-2x} = A \left(2x^2 - 2x + 1 \right) + Be^{-2x}.$$

Solution 2.3

The homogeneous equation, $y'' + 4y = 0$, has general solution $A\cos(2x) + B\sin(2x)$. Hence we take $y_1(x) = \cos(2x)$, $y_2(x) = \sin(2x)$, and assume a solution to the given equation of the form

$$y = u_1 y_1 + u_2 y_2,$$

subject to Equation (2.9). From Equation (2.14),

$$W(y_1, y_2) = y_1 y_2' - y_2 y_1'$$
$$= \cos(2x)(2\cos(2x)) - \sin(2x)(-2\sin(2x)) = 2.$$

Hence from Equations (2.15), with $p(x) = 1$ and $f(x) = \sec(2x)$, we have

$$u_1 = - \int \frac{y_2 f}{Wp} \, dx = -\tfrac{1}{2} \int \sin(2x) \sec(2x) \, dx$$
$$= -\tfrac{1}{2} \int \tan(2x) \, dx = \tfrac{1}{4} \ln(\cos(2x)) + A,$$
$$u_2 = \int \frac{y_1 f}{Wp} \, dx = \tfrac{1}{2} \int \cos(2x) \sec(2x) \, dx$$
$$= \tfrac{1}{2} \int 1 \, dx = \tfrac{1}{2} x + B.$$

Hence the general solution of the given equation is

$$y = u_1 y_1 + u_2 y_2$$
$$= \left(\tfrac{1}{4} \ln(\cos(2x)) + A \right) \cos(2x) + \left(\tfrac{1}{2} x + B \right) \sin(2x).$$

Solution 2.4

Take $y_1(x) = x/(1 - x)$, $y_2(x) = x$, and assume a solution to the given equation of the form

$$y = u_1 y_1 + u_2 y_2,$$

subject to Equation (2.9). Equation (2.14) gives

$$W(y_1, y_2) = y_1 y_2' - y_2 y_1'$$
$$= \left(\frac{x}{1 - x} \right)(1) - (x) \left(\frac{1}{(1 - x)^2} \right) = - \left(\frac{x}{1 - x} \right)^2.$$

Applying Equations (2.15), with $p(x) = x^2(1 - x)$ and $f(x) = x^3$, we have

$$u_1 = - \int \frac{y_2 f}{Wp} \, dx = \int \left(\frac{1 - x}{x} \right)^2 \frac{(x)(x^3)}{x^2(1 - x)} \, dx$$
$$= \int (1 - x) \, dx = x - \tfrac{1}{2} x^2 + A,$$
$$u_2 = \int \frac{y_1 f}{Wp} \, dx = - \int \left(\frac{1 - x}{x} \right)^2 \frac{(x/(1 - x))(x^3)}{x^2(1 - x)} \, dx$$
$$= - \int 1 \, dx = -x + B.$$

Hence the general solution of the given differential equation is

$$y = u_1 y_1 + u_2 y_2$$
$$= (x - \tfrac{1}{2} x^2 + A) \frac{x}{1 - x} + (-x + B)x$$
$$= \frac{Ax}{1 - x} + Bx + \frac{x^3}{2(1 - x)}.$$

Solution 2.5

With $y_1 = x$, put $y = uy_1 = ux$. Substitution of this into the differential equation leads to Equation (2.5) for $v(x) = u'(x)$, where

$$y_1 = x, \quad y_1' = 1, \quad p = 1 - x^2, \quad q = -2x,$$

that is,

$$v' + \left(\frac{2}{x} + \frac{-2x}{1 - x^2} \right) v = 0.$$

The integrating factor is (for $x > 0$)

$$\exp\left[\int \left(\frac{2}{x} + \frac{-2x}{1 - x^2} \right) dx \right]$$
$$= \exp\left[2 \ln x + \ln(1 - x^2) \right] = x^2(1 - x^2),$$

so that

$$\frac{d}{dx} \left(x^2(1 - x^2)v \right) = 0,$$

giving

$$v = \frac{A}{x^2(1 - x^2)}.$$

Since $u'(x) = v(x)$, we have (using the hint)

$$u = \tfrac{1}{2} A \int \left(\frac{2}{x^2} + \frac{1}{1 + x} + \frac{1}{1 - x} \right) dx$$

$$= \tfrac{1}{2} A \left(-\frac{2}{x} + \ln(1 + x) - \ln(1 - x) \right) + B$$

$$= \tfrac{1}{2} A \left(-\frac{2}{x} + \ln\left(\frac{1 + x}{1 - x} \right) \right) + B.$$

Hence the general solution of the given equation is

$$y = ux = A \left(-1 + \frac{x}{2} \ln\left(\frac{1 + x}{1 - x} \right) \right) + Bx.$$

(While $x > 0$ was assumed in the argument above, the final result holds for $-1 < x < 1$.)

Solution 2.6

(a) The auxiliary equation is

$$\lambda^2 - 2\lambda + 1 = (\lambda - 1)^2 = 0.$$

Hence the general solution is

$$y = Ae^x + Bxe^x.$$

(b) Take $y_1(x) = e^x$ and $y_2(x) = xe^x$, and assume a solution to the given equation of the form

$$y = u_1 y_1 + u_2 y_2,$$

subject to Equation (2.9). Equation (2.14) gives

$$W(y_1, y_2) = y_1 y_2' - y_2 y_1'$$
$$= (e^x)(e^x + xe^x) - (xe^x)(e^x) = e^{2x}.$$

Applying Equations (2.15), with $p(x) = 1$ and $f(x) = e^x/(1 + x^2)$, we have

$$u_1 = -\int \frac{y_2 f}{Wp} dx = -\int \frac{(xe^x)\left(e^x/(1 + x^2)\right)}{(e^{2x})(1)} dx$$

$$= -\int \frac{x}{1 + x^2} dx = -\tfrac{1}{2} \ln(1 + x^2) + A,$$

$$u_2 = \int \frac{y_1 f}{Wp} dx = \int \frac{(e^x)\left(e^x/(1 + x^2)\right)}{(e^{2x})(1)} dx$$

$$= \int \frac{1}{1 + x^2} dx = \arctan x + B.$$

Hence the general solution of the given differential equation is

$$y = u_1 y_1 + u_2 y_2$$
$$= \left(-\tfrac{1}{2} \ln(1 + x^2) + A \right) e^x + (\arctan x + B)xe^x$$
$$= e^x \left(A + Bx - \tfrac{1}{2} \ln(1 + x^2) + x \arctan x \right).$$

Section 3

Solution 3.1

In each case, the general solution of the differential equation is

$$u(x) = A \cos x + B \sin x.$$

(a) Boundary conditions:

$$u(0) = A = 0, \qquad u\left(\tfrac{1}{2}\pi \right) = B = 1.$$

Solution of boundary-value problem: $u(x) = \sin x$.

(b) Boundary conditions:

$$u(0) = A = 0, \qquad u\left(\tfrac{1}{2}\pi \right) = B = 0.$$

Solution of boundary-value problem: $u(x) = 0$.

(c) Boundary conditions:

$$u(0) = A = 0, \qquad u(\pi) = -A = 0.$$

Solution of these: $A = 0$, B arbitrary.

Solution of boundary-value problem: $u(x) = B \sin x$.

(d) Boundary conditions:

$$u(0) = A = 1, \qquad u(\pi) = -A = -1.$$

Solution of these: $A = 1$, B arbitrary.

Solution of boundary-value problem:

$$u(x) = \cos x + B \sin x.$$

Solution 3.2

(a) The differential equation is that of Example 3.2, with general solution

$$u(x) = e^{-2x} \left(A \cos(3x) + B \sin(3x) \right).$$

The boundary conditions give

$$u(0) = A = 1, \qquad u\left(\tfrac{1}{2}\pi \right) = e^{-\pi}(-B) = 2.$$

Hence $A = 1$ and $B = -2e^\pi$. The solution of the boundary-value problem is

$$u(x) = e^{-2x} \left(\cos(3x) - 2e^\pi \sin(3x) \right).$$

(b) The differential equation has a particular integral $u(x) = 2$, and the solution of the associated homogeneous equation is given in Example 3.2. The general solution here is therefore

$$u(x) = e^{-2x} \left(A \cos(3x) + B \sin(3x) \right) + 2.$$

The boundary conditions give

$$u\left(-\tfrac{1}{2}\pi \right) = e^\pi(B) + 2 = 0,$$

$$u\left(\tfrac{1}{2}\pi \right) = e^{-\pi}(-B) + 2 = 0.$$

From the first of these equations, $B = -2e^{-\pi}$, and from the second, $B = 2e^\pi$. This provides a contradiction, so the original problem has no solution.

(c) This is a Cauchy–Euler equation. Putting $u = x^\lambda$ gives the indicial equation

$$4\lambda^2 + 1 = 0,$$

with roots $\lambda = \pm\frac{1}{2}i$, so the general solution is

$$u(x) = A\cos(\tfrac{1}{2}\ln x) + B\sin(\tfrac{1}{2}\ln x).$$

The boundary conditions give

$$u(1) = A = 0, \qquad u(e^{2\pi}) = -A = 0,$$

so that $A = 0$ and B is arbitrary.

The solution of the boundary-value problem is

$$u(x) = B\sin(\tfrac{1}{2}\ln x).$$

Solution 3.3

(a) Auxiliary equation: $\lambda^2 + \pi^2 = 0$.

Roots: $\lambda = \pm\pi i$.

General solution: $u(x) = A\cos(\pi x) + B\sin(\pi x)$.

Derivative: $u'(x) = -\pi A\sin(\pi x) + \pi B\cos(\pi x)$.

Boundary conditions:

$$u'(0) = \pi B = 0, \qquad u'(1) = -\pi B = 0.$$

Solution of these: A is arbitrary, $B = 0$.

Solution of boundary-value problem:

$$u(x) = A\cos(\pi x).$$

(b) General solution:

$$u(x) = A\cos(\pi x) + B\sin(\pi x) \qquad \text{(as in part (a))}.$$

Derivative: $u'(x) = -\pi A\sin(\pi x) + \pi B\cos(\pi x)$.

Boundary conditions:

$$u(0) - u(1) = A - (-A) = 0,$$
$$u'(0) - u'(1) = \pi B - (-\pi B) = 0.$$

Solution of these: $A = B = 0$.

Solution of boundary-value problem: $u(x) = 0$.

(Note that if, in this problem, the boundary conditions had been $u(0) = u(2)$, $u'(0) = u'(2)$, then *any* solution of the differential equation would also satisfy the boundary conditions.)

(c) Indicial equation: $\lambda^2 - 4 = 0$.

Roots: $\lambda = \pm 2$.

General solution: $u(x) = Ax^2 + Bx^{-2}$.

Boundary conditions:

$$\lim_{x\to 0} u(x) = \lim_{x\to 0}(Ax^2 + Bx^{-2}) \text{ bounded,}$$
$$u(1) = A + B = 2.$$

As x approaches zero, x^2 tends towards zero but x^{-2} is unbounded. To satisfy the first boundary condition, we must therefore choose $B = 0$. Then from the second condition, $A = 2$. The solution of the boundary-value problem is $u(x) = 2x^2$.

(d) Auxiliary equation: $\lambda^2 - 4\lambda + 5 = 0$.

Roots: $\lambda = 2 \pm i$.

General solution: $u(x) = e^{2x}(A\cos x + B\sin x)$.

Derivative: $u'(x) = e^{2x}[(2A + B)\cos x + (2B - A)\sin x]$.

Boundary conditions: $u(0) = A = 0$,

$$u'(\tfrac{1}{2}\pi) - 2u(\tfrac{1}{2}\pi) = e^{\pi}(2B - A - 2B) = 1.$$

These equations have no solution, so the boundary-value problem has no solution.

Solution 3.4

(a) Put $\theta = \arccos x$. Then $\cos\theta = x$, so that $\sin\theta = \sqrt{1 - x^2}$ (taking the positive square root for $\sin\theta$ because if $\theta = \arccos x$ then $0 \le x \le \pi$). Also, we have

$$\cos(2\theta) = 2\cos^2\theta - 1, \qquad \sin(2\theta) = 2\sin\theta\cos\theta.$$

Applying each of these results gives

$$\begin{aligned}
u(x) &= A\cos(2\arccos x) + B\sin(2\arccos x) \\
&= A\cos(2\theta) + B\sin(2\theta) \\
&= A(2\cos^2\theta - 1) + 2B\sin\theta\cos\theta \\
&= A(2x^2 - 1) + 2Bx\sqrt{1 - x^2}.
\end{aligned}$$

(b) The derivative of the general solution is

$$\begin{aligned}
u'(x) &= 4Ax + 2B[(1 - x^2)^{1/2} - x^2(1 - x^2)^{-1/2}] \\
&= 4Ax + 2B(1 - 2x^2)(1 - x^2)^{-1/2}.
\end{aligned}$$

In the limit as x approaches -1 or 1, the first term is bounded but the second is not, unless $B = 0$. Hence the solution of the boundary-value problem is

$$u(x) = A(2x^2 - 1).$$

Solution 3.5

Consider the cases $\lambda = 0$ and $\lambda < 0$ separately.

If $\lambda = 0$ then $u''(x) = 0$, so that $u(x) = Ax + B$. (The auxiliary equation is $\alpha^2 = 0$.) The boundary conditions give

$$u(0) = B = 0, \qquad u(L) = AL + B = 0.$$

Hence $A = B = 0$, and the solution of the original problem is $u(x) = 0$.

Suppose that $\lambda < 0$. Then we may put $\lambda = -\nu^2$, where $\nu > 0$. The equation

$$u''(x) - \nu^2 u(x) = 0$$

has the general solution

$$u(x) = Ae^{\nu x} + Be^{-\nu x}.$$

(The auxiliary equation is $\alpha^2 - \nu^2 = 0$, so $\alpha = \pm\nu$.) Substituting this into the boundary conditions, we have

$$u(0) = A + B = 0, \qquad u(L) = Ae^{\nu L} + Be^{-\nu L} = 0.$$

Hence $B = -A$, where

$$A(e^{\nu L} - e^{-\nu L}) = 0.$$

The expression in brackets (which is in fact $2\sinh(\nu L)$) is not zero for any non-zero value of νL, so that $B = A = 0$. The solution of the original problem is again $u(x) = 0$.

Solution 3.6

(a) Step (a): Auxiliary equation is $\alpha^2 + 4\alpha + 4 + \lambda = 0$. Roots are $\alpha = -2 \pm \sqrt{-\lambda}$.

Case (i) $\lambda < 0$; put $\lambda = -\nu^2$ for $\nu > 0$.

Roots are $\alpha = -2 \pm \nu$.

General solution is $u(x) = Ae^{(-2+\nu)x} + Be^{(-2-\nu)x}$.

Step (b): Boundary conditions are $u(0) = u(1) = 0$:
$$A + B = 0, \qquad Ae^{-2+\nu} + Be^{-2-\nu} = 0.$$
Step (c): Only solution for $\nu > 0$ is $A = B = 0$.

Case (ii) $\lambda = 0$. Root is $\alpha = -2$.
General solution is $u(x) = Ae^{-2x} + Bxe^{-2x}$.
Step (b): Boundary conditions are $u(0) = u(1) = 0$:
$$A = 0, \qquad e^{-2}(A + B) = 0.$$
Step (c): Only solution is $A = B = 0$.

Case (iii) $\lambda > 0$; put $\lambda = \omega^2$ for $\omega > 0$.
Roots are $\alpha = -2 \pm i\omega$.
General solution is
$$u(x) = e^{-2x}\left(A\cos(\omega x) + B\sin(\omega x)\right).$$
Step (b): Boundary conditions are $u(0) = u(1) = 0$:
$$A = 0, \qquad e^{-2}(A\cos\omega + B\sin\omega) = 0.$$
Step (c): Solutions other than $A = B = 0$ occur if
$$\omega = n\pi \qquad (n = 1, 2, \ldots).$$
Eigenvalues are $\lambda_n = n^2\pi^2 \qquad (n = 1, 2, \ldots)$.
Step (d): Eigenfunctions are
$$u_n(x) = e^{-2x}\sin(n\pi x) \qquad (n = 1, 2, \ldots).$$

(b) Step (a): This Cauchy–Euler equation has indicial equation $\alpha^2 + 2 + \lambda = 0$ (obtained from $u = x^\alpha$).
Roots are $\alpha = \pm\sqrt{-(2 + \lambda)}$.

Case (i) $2 + \lambda < 0$; put $2 + \lambda = -\nu^2$ for $\nu > 0$.
Roots are $\alpha = \pm\nu$.
General solution is $u(x) = Ax^\nu + Bx^{-\nu}$.
Step (b): Boundary conditions are $u(1) = u(2) = 0$:
$$A + B = 0, \qquad A2^\nu + B2^{-\nu} = 0.$$
Step (c): Only solution for $\nu > 0$ is $A = B = 0$.

Case (ii) $2 + \lambda = 0$. Root is $\alpha = 0$.
General solution is $u(x) = A + B\ln x$.
Step (b): Boundary conditions are $u(1) = u(2) = 0$:
$$A = 0, \qquad A + B\ln 2 = 0.$$
Step (c): Only solution is $A = B = 0$.

Case (iii) $2 + \lambda > 0$; put $2 + \lambda = \omega^2$ for $\omega > 0$.
Roots are $\alpha = \pm i\omega$.
General solution is $u(x) = A\cos(\omega \ln x) + B\sin(\omega \ln x)$.
Step (b): Boundary conditions are $u(1) = u(2) = 0$:
$$A = 0, \qquad A\cos(\omega \ln 2) + B\sin(\omega \ln 2) = 0.$$
Step (c): Solutions other than $A = B = 0$ occur if
$$\omega \ln 2 = n\pi \qquad (n = 1, 2, \ldots).$$
Eigenvalues are $\lambda_n = \left(\dfrac{n\pi}{\ln 2}\right)^2 - 2 \qquad (n = 1, 2, \ldots)$.
Step (d): Eigenfunctions are
$$u_n(x) = \sin\left(\frac{n\pi}{\ln 2}\ln x\right) \qquad (n = 1, 2, \ldots).$$

(c) Step (a): Auxiliary equation is $\alpha^2 + \lambda = 0$.
Roots are $\alpha = \pm\sqrt{-\lambda}$.

Case (i) $\lambda < 0$; put $\lambda = -\nu^2$ for $\nu > 0$.
Roots are $\alpha = \pm\nu$.
General solution is $u(x) = Ae^{\nu x} + Be^{-\nu x}$.
Derivative is $u'(x) = A\nu e^{\nu x} - B\nu e^{-\nu x}$.
Step (b): Boundary conditions are
$$u(0) = u(2\pi), \qquad u'(0) = u'(2\pi), \qquad \text{or}$$
$$u(0) - u(2\pi) = 0, \qquad u'(0) - u'(2\pi) = 0,$$
giving
$$A(1 - e^{2\nu\pi}) + B(1 - e^{-2\nu\pi}) = 0,$$
$$A\nu(1 - e^{2\nu\pi}) - B\nu(1 - e^{-2\nu\pi}) = 0.$$
Step (c): Only solution is $A = B = 0$.

Case (ii) $\lambda = 0$. Root is $\alpha = 0$.
General solution is $u(x) = A + Bx$.
Derivative is $u'(x) = B$.
Step (b): Boundary conditions are
$$u(0) - u(2\pi) = 0, \qquad u'(0) - u'(2\pi) = 0,$$
giving $\qquad -2B\pi = 0, \qquad 0 = 0.$
Step (c): $B = 0$ but A is arbitrary.
$\lambda_0 = 0$ is an eigenvalue.
Step (d): $u_0(x) = 1$ is a corresponding eigenfunction.

Case (iii) $\lambda > 0$; put $\lambda = \omega^2$ for $\omega > 0$.
Roots are $\alpha = \pm i\omega$.
General solution is $u(x) = A\cos(\omega x) + B\sin(\omega x)$.
Derivative is $u'(x) = -A\omega\sin(\omega x) + B\omega\cos(\omega x)$.
Step (b): Boundary conditions are
$$u(0) - u(2\pi) = 0, \qquad u'(0) - u'(2\pi) = 0,$$
giving
$$A\left(1 - \cos(2\omega\pi)\right) - B\sin(2\omega\pi) = 0,$$
$$A\omega\sin(2\omega\pi) + B\omega\left(1 - \cos(2\omega\pi)\right) = 0.$$
Putting
$$\cos(2\omega\pi) = 1 - 2\sin^2(\omega\pi),$$
$$\sin(2\omega\pi) = 2\sin(\omega\pi)\cos(\omega\pi),$$
the boundary conditions become
$$2\sin(\omega\pi)\left(A\sin(\omega\pi) - B\cos(\omega\pi)\right) = 0,$$
$$2\omega\sin(\omega\pi)\left(A\cos(\omega\pi) + B\sin(\omega\pi)\right) = 0.$$
Step (c): Either $\sin(\omega\pi) = 0$, in which case *both* A and B are arbitrary, or
$$A\sin(\omega\pi) - B\cos(\omega\pi) = 0,$$
$$A\cos(\omega\pi) + B\sin(\omega\pi) = 0,$$
for which $A = B = 0$ is the only solution.
If $\sin(\omega\pi) = 0$, then $\omega = n \quad (n = 1, 2, \ldots)$.
Eigenvalues are $\lambda_n = n^2 \quad (n = 1, 2, \ldots)$.
Step (d): Eigenfunctions are $\cos(nx)$ and $\sin(nx)$, or any linear combination of these $(n = 1, 2, \ldots)$.
(Note that, in this case, with periodic boundary conditions, there are *two* linearly independent eigenfunctions corresponding to each positive eigenvalue.)

Solution 3.7

The given Cauchy–Euler equation is

$$r^2 \frac{d^2 u}{dr^2} + r \frac{du}{dr} = -kr^2.$$

Putting $r = e^t$ gives the constant-coefficient equation

$$\frac{d^2 u}{dt^2} = -ke^{2t},$$

which has general solution

$$u(t) = -\tfrac{1}{4}ke^{2t} + At + B.$$

Therefore the original Cauchy–Euler equation has general solution

$$u(r) = -\tfrac{1}{4}kr^2 + A\ln r + B.$$

We must choose $A = 0$ to satisfy the boundary condition in the limit as $r \to 0$. Then

$$u(a) = -\tfrac{1}{4}ka^2 + B = 0,$$

so that $B = \tfrac{1}{4}ka^2$. The solution of the boundary-value problem is

$$u(r) = \tfrac{1}{4}k(a^2 - r^2).$$

(This answer predicts that the speed increases steadily as r decreases, and attains its maximum value, $\tfrac{1}{4}ka^2$, at $r = 0$, that is, on the axis of the pipe.)

Solution 3.8

Auxiliary equation is $\alpha^2 + \lambda = 0$.

Roots are $\alpha = \pm\sqrt{-\lambda}$.

Case (i) $\lambda < 0$; put $\lambda = -\nu^2$ for $\nu > 0$.

Roots are $\alpha = \pm\nu$.

General solution is $u(x) = Ae^{\nu x} + Be^{-\nu x}$.

Derivative is $u'(x) = A\nu e^{\nu x} - B\nu e^{-\nu x}$.

Boundary conditions are $u'(0) = u'(L) = 0$:

$$A\nu - B\nu = 0, \qquad A\nu e^{\nu L} - B\nu e^{-\nu L} = 0.$$

Only solution is $A = B = 0$.

Case (ii) $\lambda = 0$.   Root is $\alpha = 0$.

General solution is $u(x) = A + Bx$.

Derivative is $u'(x) = B$.

Boundary conditions are $u'(0) = u'(L) = 0$, so

$B = 0$, but A is arbitrary.

$\lambda_0 = 0$ is an eigenvalue.

$u_0(x) = 1$ is a corresponding eigenfunction.

Case (iii) $\lambda > 0$; put $\lambda = \omega^2$ for $\omega > 0$.

Roots are $\alpha = \pm i\omega$.

General solution is $u(x) = A\cos(\omega x) + B\sin(\omega x)$.

Derivative is $u'(x) = -A\omega\sin(\omega x) + B\omega\cos(\omega x)$.

Boundary conditions are $u'(0) = u'(L) = 0$:

$$B\omega = 0, \quad -A\omega\sin(\omega L) + B\omega\cos(\omega L) = 0.$$

So $B = 0$ and either $A = 0$ or $\omega = n\pi/L$ $(n = 1, 2, \ldots)$.

Eigenvalues are $\lambda_n = \dfrac{n^2\pi^2}{L^2}$ $(n = 1, 2, \ldots)$.

Eigenfunctions are

$$u_n(x) = \cos\left(\frac{n\pi}{L}x\right) \quad (n = 1, 2, \ldots).$$

Section 4

Solution 4.1

The power series is

$$y = a_0 + a_1 x + a_2 x^2 + \cdots + a_j x^j + \cdots,$$

and its derivative is

$$\frac{dy}{dx} = a_1 + 2a_2 x + \cdots + ja_j x^{j-1} + (j+1)a_{j+1}x^j + \cdots.$$

Hence the differential equation can be written as

$$\frac{dy}{dx} - xy = (a_1 + 2a_2 x + \cdots + (j+1)a_{j+1}x^j + \cdots)$$
$$- x(a_0 + a_1 x + a_2 x^2 + \cdots + a_j x^j + \cdots)$$
$$= a_1 + (2a_2 - a_0)x + (3a_3 - a_1)x^2 + \cdots$$
$$+ ((j+1)a_{j+1} - a_{j-1})x^j + \cdots$$
$$= 0.$$

Thus we have

$$a_1 = 0, \qquad 2a_2 = a_0, \qquad 3a_3 = a_1,$$

and, in general,

$$(j+1)a_{j+1} = a_{j-1}.$$

The recurrence relation for the coefficients is given by

$$a_{j+1} = \frac{a_{j-1}}{j+1} \qquad (j = 1, 2, \ldots).$$

This is a second-order recurrence relation for generating the coefficients. However, since $a_1 = 0$, we have

$$a_3 = \frac{a_1}{3} = 0, \qquad a_5 = \frac{a_3}{5} = 0,$$

and so on. Thus all the odd coefficients are zero. Starting with a_0, we have

$$a_2 = \frac{a_0}{2}, \qquad a_4 = \frac{a_2}{4} = \frac{a_0}{8},$$
$$a_6 = \frac{a_4}{6} = \frac{a_0}{48}, \qquad a_8 = \frac{a_6}{8} = \frac{a_0}{384}.$$

Hence the first few terms in the power series are

$$y = a_0\left(1 + \frac{x^2}{2} + \frac{x^4}{8} + \frac{x^6}{48} + \frac{x^8}{384} + \cdots\right).$$

Solution 4.2

(a) Let $i = j - 2$. Then $j = i + 2$ and $i = 0$ when $j = 2$. Hence

$$\sum_{j=2}^{\infty} j(j-1)x^{j-2} = \sum_{i=0}^{\infty} (i+2)(i+1)x^i,$$

and so the summations are equivalent.

(b) Let $i = j - 1$. Then $j = i + 1$, and $i = 0$ when $j = 1$. Hence

$$\sum_{j=1}^{\infty} (j+1)jx^{j-1} = \sum_{i=0}^{\infty} (i+2)(i+1)x^i,$$

and again the two summations are equivalent.

(c) Let $i = j - k$. Then $j = i + k$, and $i = 0$ when $j = k$. Hence

$$\sum_{j=k}^{\infty} (j+2-k)(j+1-k)x^{j-k} = \sum_{i=0}^{\infty} (i+2)(i+1)x^i.$$

Thus all the expressions are equivalent. Each is a representation for the series

$$(2 \times 1) + (3 \times 2)x + (4 \times 3)x^2 + \cdots.$$

Solution 4.3

(a) Let the solution be of the form
$$y = \sum_{j=0}^{\infty} a_j x^j, \quad \text{so that} \quad \frac{dy}{dx} = \sum_{j=1}^{\infty} j a_j x^{j-1}.$$
Hence we have
$$\frac{dy}{dx} - xy = \sum_{j=1}^{\infty} j a_j x^{j-1} - x \sum_{j=0}^{\infty} a_j x^j$$
$$= \sum_{j=1}^{\infty} j a_j x^{j-1} - \sum_{j=0}^{\infty} a_j x^{j+1}$$
$$= \sum_{j=0}^{\infty} (j+1) a_{j+1} x^j - \sum_{j=1}^{\infty} a_{j-1} x^j$$
$$= a_1 + \sum_{j=1}^{\infty} [(j+1)a_{j+1} - a_{j-1}] x^j = 0.$$
This gives $a_1 = 0$ and
$$a_{j+1} = \frac{a_{j-1}}{j+1} \quad (j = 1, 2, \ldots),$$
as in Exercise 4.1, and all the odd coefficients are zero.
As before, but taking more account this time of the pattern of terms, we have
$$a_2 = \frac{a_0}{2}, \quad a_4 = \frac{a_2}{4} = \frac{a_0}{2 \times 4},$$
$$a_6 = \frac{a_4}{6} = \frac{a_0}{2 \times 4 \times 6}, \quad \ldots,$$
$$a_{2k} = \frac{a_{2k-2}}{2k} = \frac{a_0}{2 \times 4 \times 6 \times 8 \times \cdots \times 2k} = \frac{a_0}{2^k k!}.$$
Hence the solution is
$$y = a_0 \sum_{k=0}^{\infty} \frac{x^{2k}}{2^k k!}$$
(Note that the summation is now over k, where $j = 2k$.)

(b) Writing this summation as
$$y = a_0 \sum_{k=0}^{\infty} \frac{(\frac{1}{2}x^2)^k}{k!},$$
and comparing with the standard Taylor series for exp, we have $y = a_0 e^{x^2/2}$, as required.

Solution 4.4

With $y = \sum_{j=0}^{\infty} a_j x^j$, the differential equation becomes
$$\sum_{j=1}^{\infty} j a_j x^{j-1} + \sum_{j=0}^{\infty} a_j x^j = \cos x.$$
Adjusting the first summation, and using the given Taylor series for $\cos x$, this is
$$\sum_{j=0}^{\infty} (j+1) a_{j+1} x^j + \sum_{j=0}^{\infty} a_j x^j = \sum_{k=0}^{\infty} \frac{(-1)^k x^{2k}}{(2k)!}.$$
Equating the coefficients for x^j, we have:
- for $j = 2k$,
$$(2k+1)a_{2k+1} + a_{2k} = \frac{(-1)^k}{(2k)!}; \quad \text{(S.1)}$$

- for $j = 2k+1$,
$$(2k+2)a_{2k+2} + a_{2k+1} = 0. \quad \text{(S.2)}$$

With $a_0 = 1$, to satisfy the initial condition, we have:
from Equation (S.1) with $k = 0$,
$$a_1 = -a_0 + 1 = 0;$$
from Equation (S.2) with $k = 0$,
$$2a_2 = -a_1 = 0, \quad \text{and so} \quad a_2 = 0;$$
from Equation (S.1) with $k = 1$,
$$3a_3 = -a_2 - \tfrac{1}{2}, \quad \text{and so} \quad a_3 = -\tfrac{1}{6};$$
from Equation (S.2) with $k = 1$,
$$4a_4 = -a_3, \quad \text{and so} \quad a_4 = \tfrac{1}{24}.$$
Hence the power series solution is
$$y = 1 - \tfrac{1}{6}x^3 + \tfrac{1}{24}x^4 + \cdots.$$

Solution 4.5

Writing $t = x - 1$, the differential equation becomes
$$\frac{dy}{dt} - ty = \frac{1}{1-t} = \sum_{j=0}^{\infty} t^j.$$
With $y = \sum_{j=0}^{\infty} a_j t^j$, we obtain
$$\sum_{j=1}^{\infty} j a_j t^{j-1} - t \sum_{j=0}^{\infty} a_j t^j = \sum_{j=0}^{\infty} t^j,$$
that is,
$$\sum_{j=0}^{\infty} (j+1) a_{j+1} t^j - \sum_{j=1}^{\infty} a_{j-1} t^j = \sum_{j=0}^{\infty} t^j.$$
Expressing this as a power series in t, we have
$$a_1 - 1 + \sum_{j=1}^{\infty} [(j+1)a_{j+1} - a_{j-1} - 1] t^j = 0.$$
Equating the coefficient of t^j to zero for each j gives
$$a_1 = 1 \quad \text{and} \quad (j+1)a_{j+1} = a_{j-1} + 1,$$
that is,
$$a_{j+1} = \frac{a_{j-1} + 1}{j+1} \quad (j = 1, 2, \ldots).$$
The initial condition, $y = 1$ when $x = 1$ (when $t = 0$), gives $a_0 = 1$. Hence further coefficients can be deduced from the recurrence relation; we have
$$a_2 = \frac{a_0+1}{2} = 1, \quad a_3 = \frac{a_1+1}{3} = \tfrac{2}{3},$$
$$a_4 = \frac{a_2+1}{4} = \tfrac{1}{2}, \quad a_5 = \frac{a_3+1}{5} = \tfrac{1}{3}.$$
Hence the solution is given by
$$y = 1 + t + t^2 + \tfrac{2}{3}t^3 + \tfrac{1}{2}t^4 + \tfrac{1}{3}t^5 + \cdots$$
$$= 1 + (x-1) + (x-1)^2 + \tfrac{2}{3}(x-1)^3 + \tfrac{1}{2}(x-1)^4 + \tfrac{1}{3}(x-1)^5 + \cdots.$$

Solution 4.6

With $y = \sum_{j=0}^{\infty} a_j x^j$, the differential equation becomes

$$\sum_{j=2}^{\infty} j(j-1)a_j x^{j-2} + x\sum_{j=1}^{\infty} ja_j x^{j-1} - \sum_{j=0}^{\infty} a_j x^j = 0,$$

that is,

$$\sum_{j=0}^{\infty} (j+2)(j+1)a_{j+2}x^j + \sum_{j=1}^{\infty} ja_j x^j - \sum_{j=0}^{\infty} a_j x^j = 0.$$

Collecting up the terms in x^j gives

$$2a_2 - a_0 + \sum_{j=1}^{\infty}[(j+2)(j+1)a_{j+2} + (j-1)a_j]x^j = 0.$$

Thus, $a_2 = \frac{1}{2}a_0$ and

$$a_{j+2} = \frac{(1-j)a_j}{(j+1)(j+2)} \qquad (j=1,2,\ldots).$$

The initial conditions give $a_0 = 0$ and $a_1 = 1$. With these two values, we can use the recurrence relation to generate further coefficients. Now, $a_2 = \frac{1}{2}a_0 = 0$ and

$$a_3 = \frac{(1-1)a_1}{2 \times 3} = 0.$$

Hence all subsequent coefficients are zero, and the solution is given by $y = x$.

(You can verify directly that this is, indeed, the solution of the differential equation which satisfies the given initial conditions.)

Solution 4.7

With $y = \sum_{j=0}^{\infty} a_j x^j$, we replace the differential equation by

$$\sum_{j=2}^{\infty} j(j-1)a_j x^{j-2} + x\sum_{j=0}^{\infty} a_j x^j = x,$$

that is,

$$\sum_{j=0}^{\infty} (j+2)(j+1)a_{j+2}x^j + \sum_{j=1}^{\infty} a_{j-1}x^j = x,$$

giving

$$2a_2 + (6a_3 + a_0 - 1)x$$
$$+ \sum_{j=2}^{\infty}[(j+2)(j+1)a_{j+2} + a_{j-1}]x^j = 0.$$

Hence

$$a_2 = 0, \qquad a_3 = \tfrac{1}{6}(1-a_0) \qquad \text{and}$$
$$a_{j+2} = -\frac{a_{j-1}}{(j+2)(j+1)} \qquad (j=2,3,\ldots).$$

Thus the solution is of the form

$$y = \sum_{j=0}^{\infty} a_j x^j = a_0 + a_1 x + \tfrac{1}{6}(1-a_0)x^3 - \tfrac{1}{12}a_1 x^4 + \cdots,$$

where the coefficients can be determined in terms of a_0 and a_1 using the recurrence relation.

(Note that the recurrence relation is of third order, so that with a_0 and a_1 specified by the initial conditions, and $a_2 = 0$, we can generate all subsequent coefficients.)

Solution 4.8

Expressing the solution as

$$y = \sum_{j=0}^{\infty} a_j x^j,$$

the differential equation becomes

$$\sum_{j=2}^{\infty} j(j-1)a_j x^{j-2} + x\sum_{j=0}^{\infty} a_j x^j = \sum_{j=1}^{\infty} \frac{(-1)^{j+1}x^j}{j},$$

that is,

$$\sum_{j=0}^{\infty} (j+2)(j+1)a_{j+2}x^j + \sum_{j=1}^{\infty} a_{j-1}x^j = \sum_{j=1}^{\infty} \frac{(-1)^{j+1}x^j}{j}.$$

Expressing this as a power series in x^j, and treating the term in x^0 separately, gives

$$2a_2 + \sum_{j=1}^{\infty}\left[(j+2)(j+1)a_{j+2} + a_{j-1} - \frac{(-1)^{j+1}}{j}\right]x^j = 0.$$

The initial conditions give $a_0 = 1$ and $a_1 = 0$, while the above form of the differential equation gives $a_2 = 0$ and

$$a_{j+2} = \frac{-a_{j-1} + (-1)^{j+1}/j}{(j+1)(j+2)} \qquad (j=1,2,\ldots).$$

With $j=1$, $\quad a_3 = \dfrac{-a_0+1}{2\times 3} = 0;$

with $j=2$, $\quad a_4 = \dfrac{-a_1 - \frac{1}{2}}{3 \times 4} = -\frac{1}{24};$

with $j=3$, $\quad a_5 = \dfrac{-a_2 + \frac{1}{3}}{4 \times 5} = \frac{1}{60}.$

Hence the power series solution is

$$y = 1 - \tfrac{1}{24}x^4 + \tfrac{1}{60}x^5 + \cdots.$$

Section 5

Solution 5.1

This is another geometric series. Comparing it with that in Example 5.2 (by putting $t = x - \frac{1}{2}$), we see that the series converges if and only if

$$-1 < x - \tfrac{1}{2} < 1,$$

that is,

$$-\tfrac{1}{2} < x < \tfrac{3}{2}.$$

(a) The radius of convergence is $R = 1$.

(b) The interval of convergence is $-\frac{1}{2} < x < \frac{3}{2}$.

Solution 5.2

With $y = 3x^2 - 1$, we have

$$\frac{dy}{dx} = 6x \qquad \text{and} \qquad \frac{d^2y}{dx^2} = 6.$$

Substituting these into the differential equation gives

$$(1-x^2)6 - 2x(6x) + 6(3x^2 - 1)$$
$$= 6 - 6x^2 - 12x^2 + 18x^2 - 6 = 0.$$

Hence $y = 3x^2 - 1$ is a solution, for all values of x.

Clearly, a polynomial will give a finite value for all finite values of x, so that for this solution the radius of convergence is $R = \infty$. The solution to Example 5.4(c) gives a lower bound for the radius of convergence as $\mu = 1$. (However, note that the bound applies to *any* power series solution of this differential equation. For a series solution independent of $y = 3x^2 - 1$, the radius of convergence is indeed $R = 1$.)

Solution 5.3

(a) This differential equation has no singular points, and hence the interval of convergence is $-\infty < x < \infty$. (This can also be written as $x \in \mathbb{R}$.)

(b) This equation has singular points at $x = \pm 1$. Thus $\mu = 1$, and an interval of convergence is $-1 < x < 1$.

(c) This equation has a singular point at $x = 0$, and hence $\mu = 0$. There is no interval of convergence guaranteed by the theorem.

Solution 5.4

(a) We look for a solution of the form

$$y = \sum_{j=0}^{\infty} a_j x^j.$$

The differential equation becomes

$$(4 - x^2) \sum_{j=2}^{\infty} j(j-1)a_j x^{j-2} + (1+x) \sum_{j=1}^{\infty} ja_j x^{j-1}$$

$$+ \sum_{j=0}^{\infty} a_j x^j = 0.$$

Collecting up the terms in x^j gives

$$4 \sum_{j=0}^{\infty} (j+2)(j+1)a_{j+2} x^j - \sum_{j=2}^{\infty} j(j-1)a_j x^j$$

$$+ \sum_{j=0}^{\infty} (j+1)a_{j+1} x^j + \sum_{j=1}^{\infty} ja_j x^j + \sum_{j=0}^{\infty} a_j x^j = 0,$$

that is,

$$(8a_2 + a_1 + a_0) + (24a_3 + 2a_2 + 2a_1)x$$

$$+ \sum_{j=2}^{\infty} [4(j+2)(j+1)a_{j+2} + (j+1)a_{j+1}$$
$$- (j^2 - 2j - 1)a_j]x^j = 0.$$

The initial conditions give $a_0 = 1$ and $a_1 = 0$.
Hence $\quad 8a_2 + a_1 + a_0 = 0 \quad$ yields $a_2 = -\frac{1}{8}$,
and $\quad 24a_3 + 2a_2 + 2a_1 = 0 \quad$ yields $a_3 = \frac{1}{96}$.
With $j \geq 2$, we have

$$a_{j+2} = \frac{(j^2 - 2j - 1)a_j - (j+1)a_{j+1}}{4(j+2)(j+1)};$$

with $j = 2$,

$$a_4 = \frac{-a_2 - 3a_3}{48} = \frac{1}{512};$$

with $j = 3$,

$$a_5 = \frac{2a_3 - 4a_4}{80} = \frac{1}{6144}.$$

Hence the first five non-zero terms in the series are

$$1 - \frac{x^2}{8} + \frac{x^3}{96} + \frac{x^4}{512} + \frac{x^5}{6144}.$$

(b) The differential equation has singular points at $x = \pm 2$, and hence an interval of convergence is

$$-2 < x < 2.$$

(c) Since the coefficients in the series are diminishing very rapidly, and $x = 1$ is in the interval $-2 < x < 2$, we can be reasonably confident that the first five non-zero terms will yield a value for y at $x = 1$ which is correct to three decimal places. At $x = 1$, we have

$$y \simeq 1 - \frac{1}{8} + \frac{1}{96} + \frac{1}{512} + \frac{1}{6144}$$

$$\simeq 0.887\,53$$

$$= 0.888 \qquad \text{(to three decimal places)}.$$

UNIT 3   First-order partial differential equations

Study guide

This unit looks at first-order partial differential equations, and it is
assumed that you will not have studied these previously. However, you will
need to be familiar from the outset with partial derivatives and partial
differentiation, together with a corresponding version of the Chain Rule.
These were introduced in MST209 *Unit 12*; see also Subsections 2.1
and 2.3 of the *Revision Booklet*.

You will also need to recall some methods for solving ordinary first-order
differential equations, namely, direct integration, separation of variables
and the integrating factor method. These were included in MST209
Unit 2; see also Subsections 1.1–1.3 of the *Revision Booklet*.

Unit 3 is somewhat lighter than the other units in Block 1 of this course.
Since *Unit 4* is long, by contrast, you should aim to finish off your study of
Unit 3 as early as possible, so as to leave enough time for *Unit 4*.

There is an audio activity associated with Subsection 2.1.

Introduction

The models of fluid flow that occur later in the course pose a variety of
mathematical problems. This unit develops some of the techniques that
are needed to solve such problems.

In general, the parameters which describe the behaviour of a fluid (such as
velocity, pressure and density) are not constant. They may vary from one
point to another, or from one instant of time to the next, or they may vary
with both position and time. The rates of change of these properties are
described by the appropriate *partial derivatives*. For example, if the
density of a fluid is a function of position only, and is denoted by $\rho(x, y, z)$,
then the spatial rate of change of density in the x-direction is $\partial \rho / \partial x$. The
equations that relate the partial derivatives of the flow variables are
examples of *partial differential equations*. Most of this unit is about such
equations in which only first-order derivatives are present.

The simplest first-order equations are solved in Section 1, starting with
those that can be integrated directly, and leading on to an integrating
factor method like that for certain ordinary differential equations.

Section 2 extends the Chain Rule to cover situations where the variables,
being thought of as coordinates, may be transformed into a new set of
variables. This form of the Chain Rule can be used to simplify partial
differential equations.

113

Section 3 formalises the transformation approach by introducing the *method of characteristics* for first-order equations. In fluid flow problems, we are often concerned with second-order partial differential equations, such as

$$\frac{\partial^2 u}{\partial t^2} - c^2 \frac{\partial^2 u}{\partial x^2} = 0.$$

The method of characteristics is a very valuable tool when solving such equations, as you will see in *Unit 9*.

Section 4 takes a first step towards methods for solving second-order partial differential equations, by showing how to deal with cases that can be reduced rapidly to first-order equations of the type considered earlier.

You will see more of this equation later in the course. It is called the *wave equation*, and was introduced in MST209 *Unit 22*.

1   Solutions of partial differential equations

Previously, you have solved equations such as

$$(y - 1)\frac{dy}{dx} = xy,$$

which is an example of a first-order *ordinary* differential equation. It features y as an unknown function of a single independent variable, x.

If u, say, is a function of the two independent variables x and y, then we can form equations that contain the partial derivatives of u with respect to x and y. One such equation is

$$\frac{\partial u}{\partial x} + \frac{\partial u}{\partial y} + u = 1. \tag{1.1}$$

This is an example of a *partial differential equation*, and is called a *first-order* partial differential equation because the equation involves only first-order partial derivatives.

Equation (1.1) is a particular example of the general **first-order linear partial differential equation**

$$a(x, y)\frac{\partial u}{\partial x} + b(x, y)\frac{\partial u}{\partial y} + c(x, y)u = d(x, y), \tag{1.2}$$

where a, b, c and d are continuous functions of two variables. We say that Equation (1.2) is *linear* because, on the left-hand side, there is a linear combination of u and its partial derivatives.

Other examples of linear first-order partial differential equations are

$$\frac{\partial u}{\partial x} + \frac{\partial u}{\partial y} = 0$$

and

$$x(x + y)\frac{\partial u}{\partial x} + y(x + y)\frac{\partial u}{\partial y} = -(x - y)(2x + 2y + u).$$

In each case only first-order partial derivatives occur, and all the terms involving them and the function u itself are linear. This section and Section 3 investigate methods of finding solutions for such equations.

The adjective 'ordinary' is used when needed to distinguish such equations from *partial* differential equations.

Some texts (e.g. MS324 Block I) use an alternative notation for partial derivatives, writing u_x for $\partial u/\partial x$ and u_y for $\partial u/\partial y$. This extends to u_{xx} for $\partial^2 u/\partial x^2$, etc.

In Equation (1.1), each of a, b, c and d has the value 1.

The term 'linear' was defined for ordinary differential equations in MST209 *Units 2* and *3*.

By contrast, the equation

$$u\frac{\partial u}{\partial x} = 0$$

is *not* linear, but it is first-order. The equation

$$\frac{\partial^2 u}{\partial x^2} + \frac{\partial u}{\partial y} = 0$$

is linear, but not first-order (it is second-order).

1.1 The general solution

Before embarking on methods of solution for equations of type (1.2), consider what is meant by the solution of a partial differential equation. Going back to ordinary differential equations, you know that the equation

$$\frac{dy}{dx} - \lambda y = e^{\lambda x} \qquad \text{(where } \lambda \text{ is a constant)}$$

has the general solution

$$y(x) = (x + c)e^{\lambda x} \qquad \text{(where } c \text{ is an arbitrary constant).}$$

That is, if we substitute this function for y into the left-hand side of the differential equation, the result will be equal to the right-hand side, and also every solution has the form $(x + c)e^{\lambda x}$ for some value of c.

Consider the partial differential equation

$$\frac{\partial u}{\partial x} + \frac{\partial u}{\partial y} = 0 \qquad (1.3)$$

and the function

$$u(x, y) = e^{x-y}.$$

Now $\partial u/\partial x = e^{x-y}$ and $\partial u/\partial y = -e^{x-y}$, so substitution into the left-hand side of Equation (1.3) gives

$$\frac{\partial u}{\partial x} + \frac{\partial u}{\partial y} = e^{x-y} - e^{x-y} = 0.$$

This shows that the function $u(x, y) = e^{x-y}$ is a solution of the partial differential equation.

This is not the only function u for which $\partial u/\partial x + \partial u/\partial y = 0$, and the next exercise asks you to test some other functions, to see whether or not they satisfy this partial differential equation.

See MST209 *Unit 2*.

Unless stated otherwise, we assume that the unknown, u, is a function of the other variables in the equation (and no others).

Exercise 1.1

Test the following functions to see whether or not they are solutions of the partial differential equation

$$\frac{\partial u}{\partial x} + \frac{\partial u}{\partial y} = 0.$$

(a) $u(x, y) = \cos(x - y)$ (b) $u(x, y) = \ln(x - y) \qquad (x > y)$

(c) $u(x, y) = x^2 + 2xy + y^2$ (d) $u(x, y) = x^2 - 2xy + y^2 + 6$

You will have found that, of the four functions in Exercise 1.1, only $u(x, y) = x^2 + 2xy + y^2$ is not a solution. In each of the other cases, $u(x, y)$ may be written as

$$u(x, y) = f(\phi),$$

where $\phi = x - y$ and f is a differentiable function of one variable. We shall usually say that 'u is a function of $x - y$'. In Exercise 1.1(d), for example, the function f is

$$f(\phi) = \phi^2 + 6.$$

In Exercise 1.1(c), factorising $x^2 + 2xy + y^2$ gives $u(x, y) = (x + y)^2$. There is no way of writing this as a function of $x - y$ and, as you have seen, it is not a solution of Equation (1.3).

Note that

$$x^2 - 2xy + y^2 = (x - y)^2.$$

We have four functions of the form $u(x, y) = f(x - y)$ that satisfy the partial differential equation (1.3), and there are many more. In fact, every solution of this equation can be written in the form $u = f(x - y)$, and every function of this form is a solution.

This will be established in Subsection 2.2.

We say that $u = f(x - y)$, where f is an arbitrary differentiable function of the combination $x - y$, is the *general solution* of the equation. Note that this general solution features an arbitrary *function*, unlike the general solution of an ordinary differential equation, which contains an arbitrary *constant*.

The word differentiable means that f has a derivative at all points where the equation is to hold.

From here on we shall omit the word 'differentiable' when specifying general solutions.

1.2   The integration of partial derivatives

You have seen certain functions that satisfy a partial differential equation, but to solve such an equation we must be able to work *from* the partial differential equation *to* the general solution. In order to do this, one technique required is the ability to integrate partial derivatives of specific functions.

Consider the following functions $u(x, y)$:

(i) if $u(x, y) = y$, then $\dfrac{\partial u}{\partial x} = 0$;

(ii) if $u(x, y) = \sin y$, then $\dfrac{\partial u}{\partial x} = 0$.

In fact, for any arbitrary (differentiable) function f of one variable,

$$\text{if } u(x, y) = f(y), \text{ then } \frac{\partial u}{\partial x} = 0.$$

In practice, the situation faced is the reverse of this, in which the partial differential equation $\partial u / \partial x = 0$ is given, and the general solution for $u(x, y)$ is sought. From the above, you can see that the function $u(x, y) = f(y)$, where f is an arbitrary function, is a solution of

$$\frac{\partial u}{\partial x} = 0, \qquad \text{where } u = u(x, y). \tag{1.4}$$

The statement that $u = u(x, y)$ means that u is a function of at most x and y. This includes the possibilities that u may in fact be a function of x alone or of y alone (or, indeed, a constant).

But is this the general solution? The equivalent problem in one variable is to find the general solution of

$$\frac{dy}{dx} = 0, \qquad \text{where } y = y(x).$$

On integrating this, we have

$$y(x) = c, \qquad \text{where } c \text{ is an arbitrary constant.}$$

Now, with more than one variable, the constant is replaced by an arbitrary function of the variable being held constant during the process of integration. So from Equation (1.4), we may write

$$\int \frac{\partial u}{\partial x}(x, y)\, dx = \int 0\, dx,$$

and, on performing the integration, we have

$$u(x, y) = f(y), \qquad \text{where } f \text{ is an arbitrary function.}$$

In performing the integration of $\partial u / \partial x$ with respect to x, we assume that y is held constant.

This has 'undone' the partial differentiation with respect to x, and so gives the general solution of Equation (1.4).

Clearly $u(x, y)$ cannot involve any differentiable function containing x, because if it did, the result of differentiating u with respect to x would be non-zero, and so u would not qualify as a solution of Equation (1.4).

There is nothing special about having just two independent variables, or about using x and y as symbols for them. The arguments apply to other pairs, such as x and t, and to three or four independent variables. So, if u is a function of x and t, and

$$\frac{\partial u}{\partial x} = 0,$$

then the general solution is

$u(x, t) = f(t),$ where f is an arbitrary function.

Also, if u is a function of x, y and z, and

$$\frac{\partial u}{\partial x} = 0,$$

then the general solution is an arbitrary function of the *two* variables y and z, which are held constant during the integration. Thus the general solution is

$u(x, y, z) = f(y, z),$ where f is an arbitrary function of two variables.

Exercise 1.2

Find the general solution for each of the following equations.

(a) $\dfrac{\partial u}{\partial y} = 0,$ where $u = u(x, y)$.   (b) $\dfrac{\partial u}{\partial t} = 0,$ where $u = u(z, t)$.

Note that, whenever a general solution is found, it is possible (and advisable) to check the result by substitution back into the partial differential equation.

Now consider the equation

$$\frac{\partial u}{\partial x} = x, \qquad \text{where } u = u(x, y).$$

What kind of function must $u(x, y)$ be?

First, observe that $\frac{1}{2}x^2$ is an integral of x, so that $u(x, y) = \frac{1}{2}x^2$ satisfies the partial differential equation. But, further, we can add to $\frac{1}{2}x^2$ any function of y, say $f(y)$, and still satisfy the equation, because $(\partial/\partial x)f(y) = 0$. Thus the general solution is given by

$$u(x, y) = \tfrac{1}{2}x^2 + f(y),$$

where f is an arbitrary function. Note how $f(y)$ is added to $\frac{1}{2}x^2$, in a similar way to the addition of a constant for the one-variable case.

In the one-variable case, the arbitrary constant may be specified by applying a given condition. Similarly, the arbitrary function here is specified by applying given conditions to obtain a particular solution. This aspect is dealt with in Section 3; in the remainder of this section we focus on ways of finding the general solution of a partial differential equation.

Exercise 1.3

Find $u(x, y)$ when

(a) $\dfrac{\partial u}{\partial y} = 2;$ (b) $\dfrac{\partial u}{\partial x} = \sin x.$

This is a brief way of asking you to find the general solutions.

To take the integration of partial derivatives a stage further, consider

$$\frac{\partial u}{\partial x} = xy, \qquad \text{where } u = u(x, y).$$

Recall that, when differentiating with respect to x, the variable y is held constant. Hence, on integrating with respect to x, the general solution is

$$u(x, y) = \tfrac{1}{2}x^2 y + f(y), \qquad \text{where } f \text{ is an arbitrary function.}$$

Now do the next exercise, remembering that if we integrate a function of several variables with respect to one of its variables, then instead of an arbitrary constant of integration, we must include an arbitrary function of the variables that are treated as constant during the integration.

Exercise 1.4

Find

(a) $u(x, y)$ when $\dfrac{\partial u}{\partial x} = y$; (b) $u(x, y)$ when $\dfrac{\partial u}{\partial y} = xy$;

(c) $u(x, t)$ when $\dfrac{\partial u}{\partial t} = x^2 + t^2$; (d) $u(x, y, z, t)$ when $\dfrac{\partial u}{\partial z} = 2ze^{-4t}$.

Another case is when a function satisfies two partial differential equations simultaneously. The following example illustrates the method of solution.

Example 1.1

Find the general solution of the simultaneous partial differential equations

$$\frac{\partial u}{\partial x} = 2x \qquad \text{and} \qquad \frac{\partial u}{\partial y} = 2y, \qquad \text{where } u = u(x, y).$$

Solution

All we know about u is that it is a function of x and y, and satisfies these two partial differential equations. Integrating the first with respect to x gives

$$u(x, y) = x^2 + f(y), \qquad \text{where } f \text{ is an arbitrary function.} \qquad (1.5)$$

For this to be the general solution of the pair of equations, it must also satisfy $\partial u / \partial y = 2y$. On differentiating Equation (1.5) with respect to y, we have

$$\frac{\partial u}{\partial y} = 0 + \frac{df}{dy} = 2y.$$

This is an ordinary differential equation for f, which we can solve to give

$$f(y) = y^2 + c, \qquad \text{where } c \text{ is an arbitrary constant.}$$

The general solution is then

$$u(x, y) = x^2 + y^2 + c. \quad \blacksquare$$

This method works for all pairs of simultaneous first-order partial differential equations which have a solution.

If $\dfrac{\partial u}{\partial x} = F_1$ and $\dfrac{\partial u}{\partial y} = F_2$,

then

$$\mathbf{F} = F_1\,\mathbf{i} + F_2\,\mathbf{j} = \mathbf{grad}\,u.$$

Thus if $\mathbf{F}$ is a conservative field, a solution for u is guaranteed (see MST209 *Unit 24*).

Exercise 1.5

Find the general solution, for $u = u(x, y)$, of each of the following pairs of partial differential equations.

(a) $\dfrac{\partial u}{\partial x} = 3x^2, \qquad \dfrac{\partial u}{\partial y} = 8y.$

(b) $\dfrac{\partial u}{\partial x} = 3x^2 y - a\sin(ax), \qquad \dfrac{\partial u}{\partial y} = x^3 - e^{-y}.$

(c) $\dfrac{\partial u}{\partial x} = 3x^2 e^y, \qquad \dfrac{\partial u}{\partial y} = e^y(x^3 + y^3) + 3y^2 e^y.$

1.3 Equations with one partial derivative

We now consider linear partial differential equations of the type

$$\frac{\partial u}{\partial x} + a(x, y)u = b(x, y) \qquad \text{or} \qquad \frac{\partial u}{\partial y} + a(x, y)u = b(x, y), \qquad (1.6)$$

where a and b are known functions of x and y. As in the previous subsection, we shall call on experience of ordinary differential equations to integrate such partial differential equations.

Consider the ordinary differential equation

$$\frac{dy}{dx} - \frac{1}{x}y = x \qquad (x \neq 0), \qquad \text{where } y = y(x).$$

To solve this equation, we use the integrating factor method. The method works because, if we multiply the equation by the integrating factor (here it is the function $p(x) = \exp\left(\int(-1/x)\,dx\right) = 1/x$), then we can write the differential equation as

$$\frac{d}{dx}\left(\frac{1}{x}y\right) = \frac{1}{x}x = 1.$$

See MST209 *Unit 2* or Subsection 1.2 of the *Revision Booklet*.

This can be integrated to give

$$\frac{1}{x}y = x + c, \qquad \text{where } c \text{ is an arbitrary constant.}$$

The general solution is

$$y(x) = x^2 + cx.$$

Now, the same integrating factor can be used to find the general solution of the partial differential equation given in the next example.

Example 1.2

Find the general solution of the partial differential equation

$$\frac{\partial u}{\partial x} - \frac{1}{x}u = x, \qquad \text{where } u = u(x, y),$$

by comparing it with the ordinary differential equation above.

Solution

Multiplying both sides by the integrating factor $1/x$ gives

$$\frac{1}{x}\frac{\partial u}{\partial x} - \frac{1}{x^2}u = 1,$$

which we rewrite as

$$\frac{\partial}{\partial x}\left(\frac{1}{x}u\right) = 1.$$

On integrating with respect to x, instead of an arbitrary constant there is now an arbitrary function of y. We have

$$\frac{1}{x}u = x + f(y), \qquad \text{where } f \text{ is an arbitrary function.}$$

Hence the general solution is

$$u(x,y) = x^2 + xf(y). \quad \blacksquare$$

Exercise 1.6

(a) Find the integrating factor for the ordinary differential equation

$$\frac{dy}{dx} - \lambda y = e^{\lambda x}, \qquad \text{where } y = y(x) \text{ and } \lambda \text{ is a constant.}$$

(b) Find the general solution of the partial differential equation

$$\frac{\partial u}{\partial x} - \lambda u = e^{\lambda x}, \qquad \text{where } u = u(x,y).$$

The same method works for equations where the derivative of $u(x,y)$ is with respect to y.

Example 1.3

Find the general solution of the partial differential equation

$$\frac{\partial u}{\partial y} + \frac{1}{y}u = y \qquad (y \neq 0), \qquad \text{where } u = u(x,y).$$

Solution

The integrating factor for the ordinary differential equation

$$\frac{du}{dy} + \frac{1}{y}u = y \qquad \text{is} \qquad p(y) = \exp\left(\int \frac{1}{y}\,dy\right) = y.$$

Using this integrating factor for the partial differential equation gives

$$y\frac{\partial u}{\partial y} + u = y^2, \qquad \text{that is,} \qquad \frac{\partial}{\partial y}(yu) = y^2.$$

On integrating with respect to y, we obtain

$$yu = \tfrac{1}{3}y^3 + g(x),$$

where g is an arbitrary function. Hence the general solution is

$$u(x,y) = \tfrac{1}{3}y^2 + \frac{g(x)}{y}. \quad \blacksquare$$

Exercise 1.7

(a) Find the integrating factor for the ordinary differential equation

$$\frac{du}{dy} + \frac{3}{y}u = y^2 \qquad (y \neq 0), \qquad \text{where } u = u(y).$$

(b) Find the general solution of the partial differential equation

$$\frac{\partial u}{\partial y} + \frac{3}{y}u = y^2 \qquad (y \neq 0), \qquad \text{where } u = u(x,y).$$

The examples and exercises above have two things in common. Firstly, for each case there has been an ordinary differential equation, whose solution we know, with which to compare the partial differential equation. Secondly, the function $a(x,y)$ (see Equations (1.6)) has contained only one variable, and the partial derivative has been with respect to the same variable.

We conclude this section by considering another kind of partial differential equation which may be compared with an ordinary differential equation, but for which the function $a(x,y)$ is not restricted as before.

Example 1.4

Find the general solution of the partial differential equation

$$\frac{\partial u}{\partial x} - \frac{1}{y}u = 1 \qquad (y \neq 0), \qquad \text{where } u = u(x,y).$$

Here $a(x,y) = -1/y$, but the derivative is with respect to x.

Solution

The integrating factor is given by

$$p(x,y) = \exp\left(\int \left(-\frac{1}{y}\right) dx\right).$$

Remembering that we are integrating with respect to x while holding y constant, we obtain

$$p(x,y) = \exp\left(-\frac{1}{y}\int 1\, dx\right) = \exp\left(-\frac{x}{y}\right) = e^{-x/y}.$$

Now multiplying the partial differential equation by this integrating factor gives

$$e^{-x/y}\frac{\partial u}{\partial x} - \frac{e^{-x/y}}{y}u = e^{-x/y}.$$

Combining the two terms on the left-hand side, we obtain

$$\frac{\partial}{\partial x}\left(e^{-x/y}u\right) = e^{-x/y}.$$

Integrating with respect to x gives

$$e^{-x/y}u = \int e^{-x/y}\, dx$$

$$= -y\,e^{-x/y} + f(y), \qquad \text{where } f \text{ is an arbitrary function.}$$

In this integration we are holding y constant.

On multiplying through by $e^{x/y}$, we have

$$u(x,y) = -y + e^{x/y}f(y). \quad \blacksquare$$

Exercise 1.8

Use the integrating factor method to find the general solution, for $u = u(x, y)$, of each of the following partial differential equations.

(a) $\dfrac{\partial u}{\partial x} + \dfrac{1}{y} u = 1 \qquad (y \neq 0)$

(b) $\dfrac{\partial u}{\partial y} - xy\, u = y \qquad (x \neq 0)$

End-of-section exercises

Exercise 1.9

Find the general solution of the simultaneous partial differential equations

$$\frac{\partial u}{\partial x} = 2x + e^{x-y}, \qquad \frac{\partial u}{\partial y} = 2y - e^{x-y}, \qquad \text{where } u = u(x, y).$$

Exercise 1.10

Find the general solution for $u = u(x, y)$ of the partial differential equation

$$\frac{\partial u}{\partial x} + \frac{1}{x^2(1+y)} u = -2(1-y)\exp\left(\frac{1}{x(1+y)}\right) \qquad (x \neq 0,\ y \neq -1),$$

by using the integrating factor method.

2   The Chain Rule

In the last section, we solved simple first-order partial differential equations using straightforward methods. Not all equations lend themselves to such an approach.

In *Unit 2*, we extended our methods of solution of ordinary differential equations by using the Chain Rule for functions of one variable to change from one independent variable to another, thus reducing the equation to a familiar type.

A similar approach is extremely useful when solving partial differential equations. In this section, we extend the Chain Rule to a case which is applicable when dealing with partial derivatives.

For example, the change of variable $x = e^t$ reduces the Cauchy-Euler equation
$$x^2 y''(x) + 3xy'(x) + 2y(x) = 0$$
to the constant-coefficient equation
$$y''(t) + 2y'(t) + 2y(t) = 0.$$

2.1   Extending the Chain Rule (audio)

The audio session will introduce you to extensions of the Chain Rule. It is assumed that you are already familiar with the version that describes the rate of change of $u(x, y)$ with respect to s along a parametrised curve $(x(s), y(s))$, which is

$$\frac{du}{ds} = \frac{\partial u}{\partial x}\frac{dx}{ds} + \frac{\partial u}{\partial y}\frac{dy}{ds}.$$

See MST209 *Unit 12*.

Since some of the applications to be considered will use polar coordinates, r and θ, the following exercise asks you to find the partial derivatives of a function $u(r, \theta)$ with respect to these variables.

The audio session below leads up to an extended version of the Chain Rule that is given by Equations (2.1) on page 127. If you are prepared to accept that this is a natural extension of the Chain Rule as given above, then there is no need to study the audio session.

Exercise 2.1

Let $u(r, \theta) = r^2 \sin^2 \theta + a^2 \cos^2 \theta$, where a is a constant. Find the partial derivatives $\partial u/\partial r$ and $\partial u/\partial \theta$.

Once you have checked your solution to Exercise 2.1, you are ready to start the audio session, where the solution will be discussed.

When you are ready, start the audio at Track 19 of CD1.

1   Partial derivatives in polar coordinates

(a) $\dfrac{\partial u}{\partial r}$

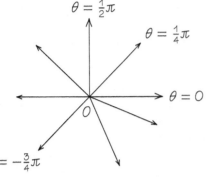

$\theta = \frac{1}{2}\pi$

$\theta = \frac{1}{4}\pi$

$\theta = 0$

$\theta = -\frac{3}{4}\pi$

$\theta =$ constant along rays from the origin

(b) $\dfrac{\partial u}{\partial \theta}$

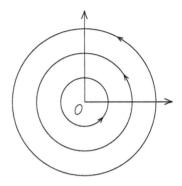

$r =$ constant around concentric circles

2   Problem

Given $u(x, y) = x^2 - y^3$

and $x(s) = \sin s, \quad y(s) = \cos s,$

find $\dfrac{du}{ds}$ by (a) using the Chain Rule;

(b) substituting for x and y and differentiating.

2a   Solution

(a) $\dfrac{du}{ds} = \dfrac{\partial u}{\partial x}\dfrac{dx}{ds} + \dfrac{\partial u}{\partial y}\dfrac{dy}{ds} = 2x(\cos s) + (-3y^2)(-\sin s)$

$\qquad\qquad = 2\sin s \cos s + 3\cos^2 s \sin s$

(b) $u(s) = \sin^2 s - \cos^3 s, \quad \dfrac{du}{ds} = 2\sin s(\cos s) - 3\cos^2 s(-\sin s)$

$\qquad\qquad\qquad\qquad\qquad = 2\sin s \cos s + 3\cos^2 s \sin s$

3   The Chain Rule diagram

u thought of as a function of s

$\dfrac{du}{ds} = \dfrac{\partial u\, dx}{\partial x\, ds} + \dfrac{\partial u\, dy}{\partial y\, ds}$

u thought of as a function of x and y

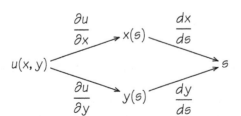

$u(x, y)$

$\dfrac{\partial u}{\partial x} \rightarrow x(s) \quad \dfrac{dx}{ds}$

$\dfrac{\partial u}{\partial y} \rightarrow y(s) \quad \dfrac{dy}{ds}$

s

Multiply along the routes

Add up the contributions from each route

4   **The Chain Rule for coordinate transformations**

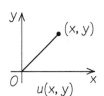

$$x = r\cos\theta$$
$$y = r\sin\theta$$

$\dfrac{\partial u}{\partial r}$? $\dfrac{\partial u}{\partial r}$ is calculated with θ held constant.

$\dfrac{\partial u}{\partial \theta}$? $\dfrac{\partial u}{\partial \theta}$ is calculated with r held constant.

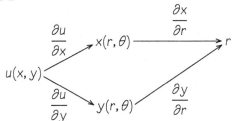

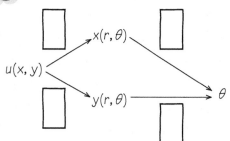

$$\frac{\partial u}{\partial r} = \boxed{\frac{du}{dx}\frac{dx}{dr} + \frac{du}{dy}\frac{dy}{dr}}$$

$$= \cos\theta\,\frac{\partial u}{\partial x} + \sin\theta\,\frac{\partial u}{\partial y}$$

$$\frac{\partial u}{\partial \theta} = \boxed{}$$

$$= \boxed{}$$

---

5   **Problem** $c(x, y) = a(1 - x^2 - y^2), \quad x = r\cos\theta, \quad y = r\sin\theta$

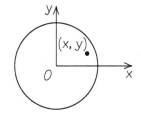

$$\frac{\partial c}{\partial r} = \cos\theta\,\frac{\partial c}{\partial x} + \sin\theta\,\frac{\partial c}{\partial y}$$

$$= \cos\theta\,\boxed{} + \sin\theta\,\boxed{}$$

$$= \boxed{}$$

Substitute for x and y

$$\frac{\partial c}{\partial \theta} = -r\sin\theta\,\frac{\partial c}{\partial x} + r\cos\theta\,\frac{\partial c}{\partial y}$$

$$= \boxed{}$$

$$= \boxed{}$$

Substitute for x and y

125

4a Solution

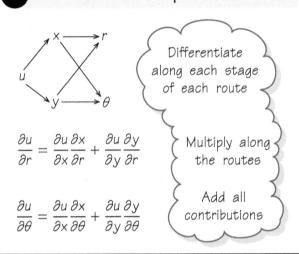

$$\frac{\partial u}{\partial \theta} = \frac{\partial u}{\partial x}\frac{\partial x}{\partial \theta} + \frac{\partial u}{\partial y}\frac{\partial y}{\partial \theta}$$

$$= -r\sin\theta \frac{\partial u}{\partial x} + r\cos\theta \frac{\partial u}{\partial y}$$

$$\frac{\partial u}{\partial r} = \frac{\partial u}{\partial x}\frac{\partial x}{\partial r} + \frac{\partial u}{\partial y}\frac{\partial y}{\partial r}$$

$$= \cos\theta \frac{\partial u}{\partial x} + \sin\theta \frac{\partial u}{\partial y}$$

5a Solution

$$\frac{\partial c}{\partial r} = \cos\theta(-2ax) + \sin\theta(-2ay)$$

$$= \cos\theta(-2ar\cos\theta) + \sin\theta(-2ar\sin\theta)$$

$$= -2ar(\cos^2\theta + \sin^2\theta) = -2ar$$

$$\frac{\partial c}{\partial \theta} = -r\sin\theta(-2ax) + r\cos\theta(-2ay)$$

$$= -r\sin\theta(-2ar\cos\theta)$$

$$+ r\cos\theta(-2ar\sin\theta) = 0$$

6 The Chain Rule for partial derivatives

$$\frac{\partial u}{\partial r} = \frac{\partial u}{\partial x}\frac{\partial x}{\partial r} + \frac{\partial u}{\partial y}\frac{\partial y}{\partial r}$$

$$\frac{\partial u}{\partial \theta} = \frac{\partial u}{\partial x}\frac{\partial x}{\partial \theta} + \frac{\partial u}{\partial y}\frac{\partial y}{\partial \theta}$$

Differentiate along each stage of each route

Multiply along the routes

Add all contributions

7 Problem

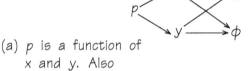

(a) p is a function of x and y. Also $x = x(\zeta, \phi)$, $y = y(\zeta, \phi)$.

Write down the Chain Rules for $\frac{\partial p}{\partial \zeta}, \frac{\partial p}{\partial \phi}$.

(b) Given that

$$x = \zeta^2 - \phi^2, \quad y = 2\zeta\phi,$$

evaluate $\frac{\partial p}{\partial \zeta}$ and $\frac{\partial p}{\partial \phi}$.

7a Solution

(a) The Chain Rules are

$$\frac{\partial p}{\partial \zeta} = \frac{\partial p}{\partial x}\frac{\partial x}{\partial \zeta} + \frac{\partial p}{\partial y}\frac{\partial y}{\partial \zeta}$$

$$\frac{\partial p}{\partial \phi} = \frac{\partial p}{\partial x}\frac{\partial x}{\partial \phi} + \frac{\partial p}{\partial y}\frac{\partial y}{\partial \phi}$$

These equations have the same form: replace ζ by ϕ

(b) Now $\frac{\partial x}{\partial \zeta} = 2\zeta$, $\frac{\partial y}{\partial \zeta} = 2\phi$, $\frac{\partial x}{\partial \phi} = -2\phi$, $\frac{\partial y}{\partial \phi} = 2\zeta$;

so $\frac{\partial p}{\partial \zeta} = 2\zeta\frac{\partial p}{\partial x} + 2\phi\frac{\partial p}{\partial y}$ and $\frac{\partial p}{\partial \phi} = -2\phi\frac{\partial p}{\partial x} + 2\zeta\frac{\partial p}{\partial y}$.

8 Summary

(i)   Draw the Chain Rule diagram
(ii) Write down the Chain Rules
(iii) Substitute

The Chain Rule developed in the audio session is similar to the one you have met before, but remember that all the derivatives here are partial derivatives, not ordinary derivatives.

Chain Rule (extended)

If $u = u(x, y)$, where $x = x(\zeta, \phi)$ and $y = y(\zeta, \phi)$, then

$$\frac{\partial u}{\partial \zeta} = \frac{\partial u}{\partial x}\frac{\partial x}{\partial \zeta} + \frac{\partial u}{\partial y}\frac{\partial y}{\partial \zeta} \quad \text{and} \quad \frac{\partial u}{\partial \phi} = \frac{\partial u}{\partial x}\frac{\partial x}{\partial \phi} + \frac{\partial u}{\partial y}\frac{\partial y}{\partial \phi}. \qquad (2.1)$$

Also, the Chain Rule always has the same pattern, no matter how many variables are involved. For a function u of three variables, if coordinates x, y and z are transformed to coordinates ζ, ϕ and ω, then the Chain Rule for $\partial u/\partial \zeta$ is

The Greek letters here are zeta (ζ), phi (ϕ) and omega (ω).

$$\frac{\partial u}{\partial \zeta} = \frac{\partial u}{\partial x}\frac{\partial x}{\partial \zeta} + \frac{\partial u}{\partial y}\frac{\partial y}{\partial \zeta} + \frac{\partial u}{\partial z}\frac{\partial z}{\partial \zeta};$$

the formulas for $\partial u/\partial \phi$ and $\partial u/\partial \omega$ are obtained from this by replacing ζ throughout with ϕ and with ω, respectively.

The exercises which follow give practice in using the Chain Rule (2.1).

Exercise 2.2

Consider a cylindrical dish containing salt solution (see Figure 2.1). The concentration c of the solution is given by

$$c(x, y, z) = c_0(\tfrac{1}{4} + z^2 - zx^2 - zy^2),$$

where c_0 is a constant. It is required to change to cylindrical polar coordinates r, θ, z, where

$$x = r\cos\theta, \qquad y = r\sin\theta, \qquad z = z.$$

Use the Chain Rule to find $\partial c/\partial r$, $\partial c/\partial \theta$ and $\partial c/\partial z$.

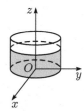

Figure 2.1

Exercise 2.3

A density ρ is given by

$$\rho(x, y, z) = \rho_0(x^2 + y^2 + z^2)^{1/2},$$

where ρ_0 is a constant.

It is required to change to spherical polar coordinates r, θ, ϕ, where

$$x = r\sin\theta\cos\phi, \qquad y = r\sin\theta\sin\phi, \qquad z = r\cos\theta.$$

Use the Chain Rule to find $\partial\rho/\partial r$, $\partial\rho/\partial \theta$ and $\partial\rho/\partial \phi$.

2.2 Transforming partial differential equations

In Section 1, we solved some first-order partial differential equations, either directly or by using an integrating factor. In this subsection, you will see how the Chain Rule can be used in the solution process. The following example illustrates the technique.

Example 2.1

Consider the first-order partial differential equation

$$\frac{\partial u}{\partial x} + \frac{\partial u}{\partial y} = 0.$$

This was Equation (1.3).

(a) Defining new variables ζ, ϕ such that

$$x = \zeta, \qquad y = \zeta - \phi,$$

use the Chain Rule to find $\partial u/\partial \zeta$ in terms of $\partial u/\partial x$ and $\partial u/\partial y$.

(b) Hence transform the partial differential equation to $\partial u/\partial \zeta = 0$.

(c) Solve this equation for $u(\zeta, \phi)$, and hence show that the general solution to the original equation is

$$u = f(x - y), \qquad \text{where } f \text{ is an arbitrary function.}$$

Although $x = \zeta$, we distinguish throughout between the pairs x, y and ζ, ϕ. In Exercise 2.2, we wrote $z = z$ since z is the established label in both coordinate systems. Also $\partial/\partial z$ with x, y constant has the same effect as $\partial/\partial z$ with r, θ constant, whereas here, $\partial u/\partial x \neq \partial u/\partial \zeta$ (since the left-hand side holds y constant while the right-hand side holds ϕ constant).

Solution

(a) With $x = \zeta$ and $y = \zeta - \phi$, the Chain Rule diagram in Figure 2.2 (or the first of Equations (2.1)) gives

$$\frac{\partial u}{\partial \zeta} = \frac{\partial u}{\partial x}\frac{\partial x}{\partial \zeta} + \frac{\partial u}{\partial y}\frac{\partial y}{\partial \zeta}$$

$$= \frac{\partial u}{\partial x} + \frac{\partial u}{\partial y}, \qquad \text{since } \frac{\partial x}{\partial \zeta} = 1 \text{ and } \frac{\partial y}{\partial \zeta} = 1.$$

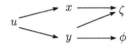

Figure 2.2

(b) This is the left-hand side of the partial differential equation, so on substituting, we have $\partial u/\partial \zeta = 0$.

(c) This equation is one that can be integrated directly (holding ϕ constant), to give

$$u(\zeta, \phi) = f(\phi), \qquad \text{where } f \text{ is an arbitrary function.}$$

Now, from the transformation, we have

$$\phi = \zeta - y = x - y.$$

Hence, in terms of x and y,

$$u(x, y) = f(x - y). \quad \blacksquare$$

The same technique will work for the next exercise.

Exercise 2.4

Consider the first-order partial differential equation

$$\frac{\partial u}{\partial x} - \frac{\partial u}{\partial y} + u = 2.$$

(a) Defining new variables ζ, ϕ such that $x = \zeta$ and $y = \phi - \zeta$, use the Chain Rule to find $\partial u/\partial \zeta$ in terms of $\partial u/\partial x$ and $\partial u/\partial y$.

(b) Hence transform the partial differential equation to

$$\frac{\partial u}{\partial \zeta} + u = 2.$$

(c) Solve this equation for $u(\zeta, \phi)$, and hence show that the general solution to the original equation is

$$u(x, y) = 2 + e^{-x} f(x + y), \qquad \text{where } f \text{ is an arbitrary function.}$$

In Example 2.1 and Exercise 2.4, the old variables, x and y, are expressed in terms of the new variables, ζ and ϕ. In practice, we usually have to define new variables in terms of the old and then use the Chain Rule for $\partial u/\partial x$ and $\partial u/\partial y$. This approach requires application of the equations from the Chain Rule (2.1) with the roles of x, y and ζ, ϕ reversed, that is,

$$\frac{\partial u}{\partial x} = \frac{\partial u}{\partial \zeta}\frac{\partial \zeta}{\partial x} + \frac{\partial u}{\partial \phi}\frac{\partial \phi}{\partial x} \quad \text{and} \quad \frac{\partial u}{\partial y} = \frac{\partial u}{\partial \zeta}\frac{\partial \zeta}{\partial y} + \frac{\partial u}{\partial \phi}\frac{\partial \phi}{\partial y}. \quad (2.2)$$

For Exercise 2.4, this would mean choosing $\zeta = x$, $\phi = x + y$; then application of Equations (2.2) gives

$$\frac{\partial u}{\partial x} = \frac{\partial u}{\partial \zeta} + \frac{\partial u}{\partial \phi} \quad \text{and} \quad \frac{\partial u}{\partial y} = \frac{\partial u}{\partial \phi}.$$

Next substitute for $\partial u/\partial x$ and $\partial u/\partial y$ in the partial differential equation, to obtain the same simplified equation as before.

Note that, for clarity, Equations (2.2) are referred to as the Chain Rule (2.2) in the text to follow.

Exercise 2.5

Consider the partial differential equation

$$x^2\frac{\partial u}{\partial x} + y^2\frac{\partial u}{\partial y} - x^2 u = 1 \qquad (x \neq 0, \ y \neq 0)$$

and the transformation

$$\zeta = x, \qquad \phi = \frac{1}{y} - \frac{1}{x}.$$

Use the Chain Rule (2.2) to find expressions for $\partial u/\partial x$ and $\partial u/\partial y$ in terms of $\partial u/\partial \zeta$ and $\partial u/\partial \phi$. Hence simplify the partial differential equation to the form

$$\frac{\partial u}{\partial \zeta} - u = \frac{1}{\zeta^2} \qquad (\zeta \neq 0).$$

During the solution to an exercise such as this, it is permissible at any intermediate stage to use a mixture of both pairs of variables, x, y and ζ, ϕ. However, a final answer must be expressed in terms of one pair only.

This approach is of particular value when we transform second-order partial derivatives, as the following example and exercise illustrate.

There is no need to transform second-order partial derivatives when solving first-order equations! The development here looks ahead to the solution of second-order partial differential equations in *Unit 9*.

Example 2.2

A change in coordinates from (x, y) to (ζ, ϕ) is defined by $\zeta = x^2 + y$, $\phi = x^2 - y$. Given that u is a function of the two variables x and y, find $\partial^2 u/\partial x^2$ in terms of partial derivatives of u with respect to ζ and ϕ.

Solution

Note first that

$$\frac{\partial \zeta}{\partial x} = 2x \quad \text{and} \quad \frac{\partial \phi}{\partial x} = 2x.$$

Now $\partial^2 u/\partial x^2$ may be written as $\partial/\partial x\,(\partial u/\partial x)$. Consider the first derivative $\partial u/\partial x$; using the Chain Rule (2.2), we have

$$\frac{\partial u}{\partial x} = \frac{\partial u}{\partial \zeta}\frac{\partial \zeta}{\partial x} + \frac{\partial u}{\partial \phi}\frac{\partial \phi}{\partial x} = 2x\frac{\partial u}{\partial \zeta} + 2x\frac{\partial u}{\partial \phi}.$$

This equation not only gives $\partial u/\partial x$ in terms of $\partial u/\partial \zeta$ and $\partial u/\partial \phi$, it also gives a rule for differentiating with respect to x. We have

$$\frac{\partial v}{\partial x} = 2x\left(\frac{\partial v}{\partial \zeta} + \frac{\partial v}{\partial \phi}\right) \qquad (2.3)$$

for any function v of x and y. Thus

$$\frac{\partial^2 u}{\partial x^2} = \frac{\partial}{\partial x}\left(\frac{\partial u}{\partial x}\right) = \frac{\partial}{\partial x}\left[2x\left(\frac{\partial u}{\partial \zeta} + \frac{\partial u}{\partial \phi}\right)\right].$$

Here there is a product to be differentiated. This gives

$$\frac{\partial^2 u}{\partial x^2} = 2\left(\frac{\partial u}{\partial \zeta} + \frac{\partial u}{\partial \phi}\right) + 2x\frac{\partial}{\partial x}\left(\frac{\partial u}{\partial \zeta} + \frac{\partial u}{\partial \phi}\right).$$

Then using Equation (2.3), with $v = \partial u/\partial \zeta + \partial u/\partial \phi$, we have

$$\frac{\partial^2 u}{\partial x^2} = 2\left(\frac{\partial u}{\partial \zeta} + \frac{\partial u}{\partial \phi}\right) + 4x^2\left[\frac{\partial}{\partial \zeta}\left(\frac{\partial u}{\partial \zeta} + \frac{\partial u}{\partial \phi}\right) + \frac{\partial}{\partial \phi}\left(\frac{\partial u}{\partial \zeta} + \frac{\partial u}{\partial \phi}\right)\right]$$

$$= 2\left(\frac{\partial u}{\partial \zeta} + \frac{\partial u}{\partial \phi}\right) + 4x^2\left(\frac{\partial^2 u}{\partial \zeta^2} + \frac{\partial^2 u}{\partial \zeta\partial \phi} + \frac{\partial^2 u}{\partial \phi\partial \zeta} + \frac{\partial^2 u}{\partial \phi^2}\right)$$

$$= 2\left(\frac{\partial u}{\partial \zeta} + \frac{\partial u}{\partial \phi}\right) + 4x^2\left(\frac{\partial^2 u}{\partial \zeta^2} + 2\frac{\partial^2 u}{\partial \zeta\partial \phi} + \frac{\partial^2 u}{\partial \phi^2}\right). \quad \blacksquare$$

Note that
$$\frac{\partial^2 u}{\partial \phi\partial \zeta} = \frac{\partial^2 u}{\partial \zeta\partial \phi}$$
for all the functions u to be considered in the course. (This was called the *Mixed Derivative Theorem* in MST209 *Unit 12*.)

In this example, the final expression looks much more complicated than the original $\partial^2 u/\partial x^2$. However, as the next exercise illustrates, second-order partial differential equations may often be simplified considerably when changing to new variables.

Exercise 2.6

(a) Use the transformation given in Example 2.2 and the Chain Rule (2.2) to write $\partial^2 u/\partial y^2$ in terms of the partial derivatives of u with respect to ζ and ϕ.

(b) Using the results from part (a) and Example 2.2, show that the equation

$$\frac{\partial^2 u}{\partial x^2} - \frac{1}{x}\frac{\partial u}{\partial x} - 4x^2\frac{\partial^2 u}{\partial y^2} = 0 \quad (x \neq 0)$$

reduces to

$$\frac{\partial^2 u}{\partial \zeta\partial \phi} = 0$$

when the variables are changed to ζ and ϕ.

This exercise illustrates a very useful method of transforming second-order partial differential equations. The original equation here is difficult to solve; however, the transformed equation has general solution

$$u(\zeta, \phi) = f(\zeta) + g(\phi),$$

for arbitrary functions f and g. Hence the original equation has the general solution

$$u = f(x^2 + y) + g(x^2 - y).$$

These ideas are developed further in *Unit 9*.

This will be shown in Subsection 4.1.

End-of-section exercises

Exercise 2.7

A function c of x and y is to be transformed to new coordinates (ζ, ϕ), where $x = \zeta$ and $y = \zeta + \phi$.

Calculate $\partial c / \partial \zeta$ and $\partial c / \partial \phi$ in terms of $\partial c / \partial x$ and $\partial c / \partial y$.

Exercise 2.8

If the density ρ is a function of x and y, and the transformation

$$\zeta = x^2 - y^2, \qquad \phi = xy$$

is made, show that the first-order partial differential equation

$$x \frac{\partial \rho}{\partial x} - y \frac{\partial \rho}{\partial y} = 0 \qquad (x^2 + y^2 \neq 0)$$

reduces to

$$\frac{\partial \rho}{\partial \zeta} = 0.$$

Hence find ρ as a function of x and y.

Exercise 2.9

Suppose that u is a function of two variables x and t, satisfying the partial differential equation

$$\frac{\partial^2 u}{\partial t^2} - c^2 \frac{\partial^2 u}{\partial x^2} = 0, \qquad \text{where } c \text{ is a non-zero constant.}$$

This is the wave equation, referred to on page 114.

By transforming to new variables ζ and ϕ, where

$$\zeta = x - ct \quad \text{and} \quad \phi = x + ct,$$

show that the equation can be simplified to

$$\frac{\partial^2 u}{\partial \zeta \partial \phi} = 0.$$

3   *The method of characteristics*

You saw in Subsection 2.2 that a change of variables, and use of the Chain Rule, can simplify a partial differential equation to a form that is solvable using the methods of Section 1. But in Subsection 2.2, the necessary transformations were always given. This section provides a method of *finding* these transformations from the coefficients in a first-order linear partial differential equation.

3.1 What are characteristics?

You saw in Example 2.1 that, using the transformation $\zeta = x$ and $\phi = x - y$, the partial differential equation

$$\frac{\partial u}{\partial x} + \frac{\partial u}{\partial y} = 0 \quad \text{is transformed into} \quad \frac{\partial u}{\partial \zeta} = 0,$$

and hence the general solution is

$$u = f(\phi) = f(x - y), \quad \text{where } f \text{ is an arbitrary function.} \quad (3.1)$$

The following exercise provides another illustration of this approach.

The transformation as given in Example 2.1 was
$$x = \zeta, \quad y = \zeta - \phi.$$
This is equivalent to
$$\zeta = x, \quad \phi = x - y.$$

Exercise 3.1

Consider the partial differential equation

$$\frac{\partial u}{\partial x} - \frac{\partial u}{\partial y} = 0.$$

Using the transformation $\zeta = x$, $\phi = x + y$, together with the Chain Rule (2.2), show that this equation can be written as

$$\frac{\partial u}{\partial \zeta} = 0,$$

and hence that the general solution is

$$u = f(x + y), \quad \text{where } f \text{ is an arbitrary function.} \quad (3.2)$$

The two solutions in Equations (3.1) and (3.2) have a similar form, and may both be written as

$$u(x, y) = f(\phi),$$

where $\phi = \phi(x, y)$ is an appropriate combination of the variables x and y that simplifies the original partial differential equation. The essential feature of this transformation is that it introduces a combination ϕ of the variables x and y, with the special property that derivatives with respect to ϕ are absent from the transformed partial differential equation. When integrating the transformed partial differential equation, ϕ is held constant. In geometrical terms, this is equivalent to integrating the original equation along the contours defined by $\phi(x, y) = \text{constant}$.

Contours are introduced in MST209 *Unit 23*.

These contours are, in general, a family of curves in the (x, y)-plane. In the first of the examples above, with $\partial u/\partial x + \partial u/\partial y = 0$, we have

$$\phi(x, y) = x - y,$$

and the contours, $x - y = \text{constant}$, form a set of straight lines, as shown in Figure 3.1. Here we have identified a special set of straight lines in the (x, y)-plane, connected with the partial differential equation

$$\frac{\partial u}{\partial x} + \frac{\partial u}{\partial y} = 0.$$

In general, given a partial differential equation, we seek a set of *curves*

$$\phi(x, y) = \text{constant},$$

for which the transformed equation includes no partial derivative with respect to ϕ. These are called the *characteristic curves*, or sometimes just *characteristics*, of the partial differential equation. Along these curves, the combination $\phi(x, y)$ of the variables x and y is constant.

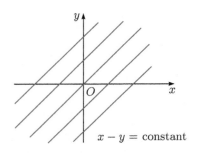

Figure 3.1

Each first-order partial differential equation has a set of characteristic curves associated with it, and for most 'reasonable' equations, there is just one characteristic through each point in the (x, y)-plane.

Exercise 3.2

What are the characteristic curves for the partial differential equation $\partial u / \partial x - \partial u / \partial y = 0$ of Exercise 3.1?

In the examples seen so far, the transformations and hence the equations of the characteristics have been given. We now investigate how to *find* the characteristic curves, $\phi(x, y) = \text{constant}$, in the general case.

Consider a first-order linear partial differential equation,

$$a(x,y)\frac{\partial u}{\partial x}(x,y) + b(x,y)\frac{\partial u}{\partial y}(x,y) + c(x,y)u(x,y) = d(x,y),$$

where a, b, c and d are known functions of x and y. Assuming that $a(x, y) \neq 0$ for any point (x, y) in the region under consideration, we divide by $a(x, y)$ to give

$$\frac{\partial u}{\partial x}(x,y) + \frac{b(x,y)}{a(x,y)}\frac{\partial u}{\partial y}(x,y) + \frac{c(x,y)}{a(x,y)}u(x,y) = \frac{d(x,y)}{a(x,y)}.$$

Now, writing the quotients as single functions in the obvious way, we have (in abbreviated form)

$$\frac{\partial u}{\partial x} + g(x,y)\frac{\partial u}{\partial y} + h(x,y)u = k(x,y). \tag{3.3}$$

We want to transform this equation by defining two new variables,

$$\zeta = \zeta(x, y) \qquad \text{and} \qquad \phi = \phi(x, y),$$

where ζ and ϕ are such that the transformed equation does not contain partial derivatives with respect to ϕ. That is, we want to transform the equation into one of the form

$$\frac{\partial u}{\partial \zeta} + h(\zeta, \phi)u = k(\zeta, \phi), \tag{3.4} \qquad \text{Here } u = u(\zeta, \phi).$$

which can be solved by a known method.

Comparing Equations (3.3) and (3.4), we require

$$\frac{\partial u}{\partial \zeta} = \frac{\partial u}{\partial x} + g(x,y)\frac{\partial u}{\partial y}. \tag{3.5}$$

The Chain Rule (2.1) provides another expression for $\partial u / \partial \zeta$, as

$$\frac{\partial u}{\partial \zeta} = \frac{\partial u}{\partial x}\frac{\partial x}{\partial \zeta} + \frac{\partial u}{\partial y}\frac{\partial y}{\partial \zeta}. \tag{3.6}$$

Comparing Equations (3.5) and (3.6), the aim is achieved if we define ζ such that

$$\frac{\partial x}{\partial \zeta} = 1 \qquad \text{and} \qquad \frac{\partial y}{\partial \zeta} = g(x,y). \tag{3.7}$$

Now, if we *choose* $\zeta = x$, then $\partial x / \partial \zeta = 1$, as required.

The variable y is a function of ζ and ϕ, in general, but on a characteristic, ϕ is constant. So along a particular characteristic, y may be considered as a function of ζ alone. Hence we may write

$$\frac{\partial y}{\partial \zeta} = \frac{dy}{d\zeta} = \frac{dy}{dx} \qquad \text{(on } \phi = \text{constant)},$$

due to the choice $\zeta = x$. From the second of Equations (3.7), we then have

$$\frac{dy}{dx} = g(x,y) \qquad \text{(on } \phi = \text{constant)}.$$

This is a first-order ordinary differential equation. Integrating this equation will introduce an arbitrary constant, and the different values of this constant yield a family of curves in the (x, y)-plane. For example, if $g(x, y) = -x/y$, then integrating the equation $dy/dx = -x/y$ gives (after some rearranging) $x^2 + y^2 = c$, where c is an arbitrary constant. The corresponding curves form a family of circles (see Figure 3.2). According to the way we have defined the function ϕ above, ϕ is a constant along each of these curves. So in this case we *choose* ϕ to be the function $x^2 + y^2$. Clearly, ϕ could be any multiple of $x^2 + y^2$, because when $x^2 + y^2$ is constant then ϕ will be constant, and that is the requirement for the characteristic curves.

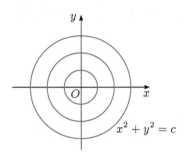

Figure 3.2

More generally, on integrating the equation $dy/dx = g(x, y)$, we introduce an arbitrary constant c, and the result of the integration can always be expressed in the form $\alpha(x, y) = c$ for some function α of x and y. If we define $\phi = \alpha(x, y)$, then the equations $\phi = $ constant define the **characteristic curves** of the original partial differential equation. The following example illustrates how this is done.

The characteristics are given by $\alpha = $ constant, and we take $\phi = \alpha$. Alternatively, we could take $\phi = f(\alpha)$ (for any convenient function f), since the curve $\alpha = c$ is then also described by

$$\phi = f(c) \quad \text{(constant)}.$$

Example 3.1

Find the equations of the characteristic curves for the partial differential equation

$$-2xy\frac{\partial u}{\partial x} + 4x\frac{\partial u}{\partial y} + yu = 4xy \qquad (x > 0, \ y > 0). \qquad (3.8)$$

Hence define the new variable ϕ that could be used to simplify the partial differential equation.

Solution

First we rearrange the equation so that the coefficient of $\partial u/\partial x$ is 1; dividing by $-2xy$, we have

$$\frac{\partial u}{\partial x} - \frac{2}{y}\frac{\partial u}{\partial y} - \frac{1}{2x}u = -2.$$

Hence, in the notation of Equation (3.3),

$$g(x, y) = -\frac{2}{y}, \qquad h(x, y) = -\frac{1}{2x}, \qquad k(x, y) = -2.$$

To find the equations of the characteristics, we need to integrate the ordinary differential equation

$$\frac{dy}{dx} = g(x, y) = -\frac{2}{y}, \qquad \text{that is,} \qquad y\frac{dy}{dx} = -2.$$

Integrating this with respect to x, we obtain

$$\tfrac{1}{2}y^2 = -2x + c, \qquad \text{where } c \text{ is an arbitrary constant.}$$

So in this case, we have $\alpha(x, y) = \tfrac{1}{2}y^2 + 2x$. The curves $\alpha(x, y) = c$ (constant), shown in Figure 3.3, are the characteristic curves for this partial differential equation, so define

$$\phi = \tfrac{1}{2}y^2 + 2x. \quad \blacksquare$$

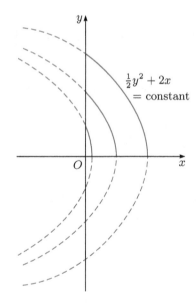

Figure 3.3 The dashed curves indicate whole parabolas, but only the solid portions are characteristics within the solution domain.

Exercise 3.3

Find the equations of the characteristic curves for each of the following partial differential equations. In each case, what is the new variable ϕ?

(a) $\dfrac{\partial u}{\partial x} + \dfrac{\partial u}{\partial y} + u = 2$ (b) $(x+y)\left(\dfrac{\partial u}{\partial x} - \dfrac{\partial u}{\partial y}\right) = u$ $(x+y \neq 0)$

Once the new variable ϕ has been found, we can use it, together with $\zeta = x$, to transform the partial differential equation

$$\frac{\partial u}{\partial x} + g(x,y)\frac{\partial u}{\partial y} + h(x,y)u = k(x,y) \tag{3.3}$$

into a simpler equation that involves only one partial derivative.

The method required is called *the method of characteristics*. To see how it works, consider the partial differential equation from Example 3.1,

$$\frac{\partial u}{\partial x} - \frac{2}{y}\frac{\partial u}{\partial y} - \frac{1}{2x}u = -2 \qquad (x > 0, \ y > 0).$$

Choosing new variables $\phi = \frac{1}{2}y^2 + 2x$ and $\zeta = x$, and using the Chain Rule (2.2), we have

Note that

$$\frac{\partial u}{\partial x} = \frac{\partial u}{\partial \phi}\frac{\partial \phi}{\partial x} + \frac{\partial u}{\partial \zeta}\frac{\partial \zeta}{\partial x} = 2\frac{\partial u}{\partial \phi} + \frac{\partial u}{\partial \zeta},$$

$$\frac{\partial \phi}{\partial x} = 2, \quad \frac{\partial \zeta}{\partial x} = 1,$$

$$\frac{\partial u}{\partial y} = \frac{\partial u}{\partial \phi}\frac{\partial \phi}{\partial y} + \frac{\partial u}{\partial \zeta}\frac{\partial \zeta}{\partial y} = y\frac{\partial u}{\partial \phi} + 0.$$

$$\frac{\partial \phi}{\partial y} = y, \quad \frac{\partial \zeta}{\partial y} = 0.$$

Hence the partial differential equation becomes

$$\frac{\partial u}{\partial x} - \frac{2}{y}\frac{\partial u}{\partial y} - \frac{1}{2x}u = 2\frac{\partial u}{\partial \phi} + \frac{\partial u}{\partial \zeta} - \frac{2}{y}y\frac{\partial u}{\partial \phi} - \frac{1}{2x}u = -2$$

or, in terms of ϕ and ζ only,

$$\frac{\partial u}{\partial \zeta} - \frac{1}{2\zeta}u = -2.$$

This equation is easier to solve than the original partial differential equation. In fact, it can be solved using the integrating factor method. The integrating factor is

$$p(\zeta) = \exp\left(\int\left(-\frac{1}{2\zeta}\right)d\zeta\right) = \exp\left(\ln\left(\zeta^{-1/2}\right)\right) = \zeta^{-1/2}.$$

So the partial differential equation becomes

$$\frac{\partial}{\partial \zeta}\left(\zeta^{-1/2}u\right) = -2\zeta^{-1/2}.$$

Integrating with respect to ζ yields

$$\zeta^{-1/2}u = -4\zeta^{1/2} + f(\phi),$$

where f is an arbitrary function, so that

$$u(\zeta,\phi) = -4\zeta + \zeta^{1/2}f(\phi).$$

Now substitute for ζ and ϕ in terms of x and y, to obtain

$$u(x,y) = -4x + x^{1/2}f\left(\tfrac{1}{2}y^2 + 2x\right), \tag{3.9}$$

which is the general solution of the original equation.

Thus we have taken a rather complicated differential equation and, by using new variables ζ and ϕ, it has been reduced to a type that we know how to solve.

When you solve an ordinary differential equation, you can always check your solution by substituting it back into the original equation. In the same way, for a partial differential equation you can take the general solution, work out the partial derivatives and substitute back into the equation. In the next exercise you are asked to do this.

Exercise 3.4

Calculate $\partial u/\partial x$ and $\partial u/\partial y$ for $u(x, y)$ as given by Equation (3.9).

Using these expressions, together with the expression for $u(x, y)$, substitute into the left-hand side of the original partial differential equation (3.8) of Example 3.1. Show that this is equal to the right-hand side.

The method is summarised below.

Procedure 3.1

To solve a partial differential equation expressed in the form

$$\frac{\partial u}{\partial x}(x, y) + g(x, y)\frac{\partial u}{\partial y}(x, y) + h(x, y)u(x, y) = k(x, y)$$

Observe that the coefficient of $\partial u/\partial x$ is 1.

(where g, h and k are given functions), using the **method of characteristics**, proceed as follows.

(a) Integrate the ordinary differential equation

$$\frac{dy}{dx} = g(x, y),$$

to obtain the equations of the characteristics,

$$\phi(x, y) = \text{constant}.$$

(b) Choose new variables $\zeta = x$ and $\phi = \phi(x, y)$, and use the Chain Rule to write the partial differential equation in terms of ζ and ϕ.

(c) Find the general solution to this equation as a function of ζ and ϕ, if possible.

(d) Perform the inverse transformation, to obtain the general solution of the original equation (as a function of x and y).

In the following exercise, the partial differential equations can be solved using transformations followed by the integrating factor method.

Exercise 3.5

By using the method of characteristics, find the general solution of each of the following partial differential equations.

For each of parts (a) and (b), Step (a) of Procedure 3.1 was done in Exercise 3.3.

(a) $\dfrac{\partial u}{\partial x} + \dfrac{\partial u}{\partial y} + u = 2$ (b) $(x + y)\left(\dfrac{\partial u}{\partial x} - \dfrac{\partial u}{\partial y}\right) = u$ $(x + y \neq 0)$

(c) $x\dfrac{\partial u}{\partial x} + y\dfrac{\partial u}{\partial y} = 2u$ $(x \neq 0)$ (d) $x^2\dfrac{\partial u}{\partial x} - xy\dfrac{\partial u}{\partial y} + y^2 = 0$ $(x \neq 0)$

The method of characteristics can also be viewed more geometrically. Since $\partial u/\partial \zeta$ is a derivative with ϕ held constant, Equation (3.4) gives a condition on a rate of change *along the characteristic* $\phi = \text{constant}$ at each point.

Due to Equation (3.5),

$$\frac{\partial u}{\partial x} + g(x,y)\frac{\partial u}{\partial y}$$

also describes this rate of change along the characteristic. This may be written alternatively as

$$(\mathbf{i} + g\,\mathbf{j}) \cdot \mathbf{grad}\,u,$$

which is recognisable as a multiple of the directional derivative of u along $\mathbf{i} + g\,\mathbf{j}$. With $\phi = $ constant chosen as here to have slope $dy/dx = g$, the vector $\mathbf{i} + g\,\mathbf{j}$ is tangent to the characteristic at each point.

More is said about this in *Unit 9.*

3.2 Partial differential equations with conditions

So far, we have concentrated on finding the general solution of a partial differential equation, which has included an arbitrary function. We turn now to the problem of finding the solution in a specific case, where some extra condition has to be satisfied by the solution.

For example, take the partial differential equation in Exercise 3.5(a),

$$\frac{\partial u}{\partial x} + \frac{\partial u}{\partial y} + u = 2,$$

for which the general solution was found to be

$$u(x,y) = 2 + e^{-x}f(y - x), \qquad \text{where } f \text{ is an arbitrary function.} \quad (3.10)$$

Suppose that $u(x,y)$ must satisfy the additional condition

$$u(x,y) = \sin x \qquad \text{on } y = -x.$$

Consider what this condition means. The characteristics of the partial differential equation were found to be $\phi(x,y) = y - x = $ constant, which are straight lines, and $y = -x$ is the equation of another straight line, which intersects each characteristic once (see Figure 3.4). The condition that $u(x,y) = \sin x$ on this line prescribes u at one point on each characteristic. In fact, by using the given condition, we can find the formula for the arbitrary function in the general solution and hence identify the *particular solution* for this condition.

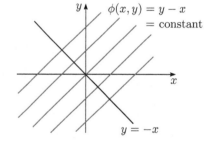

Figure 3.4

We begin by substituting $u(x,y) = \sin x$ on $y = -x$ into Equation (3.10). This gives

$$\sin x = 2 + e^{-x}f(-2x),$$

since $y - x = -2x$ on $y = -x$. We can rewrite this equation as

$$f(-2x) = (\sin x - 2)e^x.$$

To specify the particular solution $u(x,y)$, we need to find the rule for the function f. To do this, replace $-2x$ by a new variable, s; then $x = -\frac{1}{2}s$, and we have

$$f(s) = \left(\sin(-\tfrac{1}{2}s) - 2\right)e^{-s/2},$$

which defines f. Now, putting $y - x$ in place of s, we can write

$$f(y - x) = \left(\sin\left(-\tfrac{1}{2}(y - x)\right) - 2\right)e^{-(y-x)/2}.$$

Hence the particular solution which satisfies both the partial differential equation and the extra condition is

$$u(x,y) = 2 + e^{-x}\left(\sin\left(-\tfrac{1}{2}(y - x)\right) - 2\right)e^{-(y-x)/2}$$

$$= 2 + e^{-(y+x)/2}\left(\sin\left(\tfrac{1}{2}(x - y)\right) - 2\right).$$

As suggested by the text above, the curve on which the additional condition is given should intersect each characteristic only once. Otherwise, it will not usually be possible to find a particular solution.

This is because the partial differential equation itself specifies the rate of change along characteristics, so a value at a single point on each characteristic is what is required to obtain a particular solution.

137

The next example requires a similar approach.

Example 3.2

The partial differential equation

$$(x+y)\left(\frac{\partial u}{\partial x} - \frac{\partial u}{\partial y}\right) = u \qquad (x+y \neq 0)$$

has the general solution

$$u = f(x+y)e^{x/(x+y)}.$$

Find the particular solution which satisfies the condition $u = y$ on $x = 1$.

This general solution was found in Exercise 3.5(b).

Solution

The given condition is that $u = y$ on $x = 1$. Substituting this condition into the general solution of the differential equation gives

$$y = f(1+y)e^{1/(1+y)}, \qquad \text{that is,} \qquad f(1+y) = ye^{-1/(1+y)}.$$

Replacing $1+y$ by a parameter s, we have

$$f(s) = (s-1)e^{-1/s},$$

which is the formula for the unknown function f. Hence, putting $x+y$ in place of s, the particular solution which satisfies the partial differential equation and the given condition is

$$u(x,y) = (x+y-1)e^{-1/(x+y)}e^{x/(x+y)}$$

$$= (x+y-1)e^{(x-1)/(x+y)}. \quad \blacksquare$$

After applying the condition, replace the argument of f by a parameter s, to find the formula for f.

Then replace s by the argument of f in the general solution.

The next two exercises provide the general solution and ask you to find the solution for the given condition. The marginal notes in the solution above indicate the necessary steps in the process.

The end-of-section exercise asks you to undertake the complete solution process, starting from the partial differential equation.

Exercise 3.6

The partial differential equation

$$\frac{\partial u}{\partial x} - 3\frac{\partial u}{\partial y} = u$$

has the general solution

$$u(x,y) = e^x f(y+3x).$$

Find the particular solution that satisfies the condition $u = y$ on $x = 0$.

Exercise 3.7

The partial differential equation

$$-2xy\frac{\partial u}{\partial x} + 2x\frac{\partial u}{\partial y} + yu = 8xy \qquad (x > 0,\ y > 0)$$

has the general solution

$$u(x, y) = -8x + x^{1/2}f(y^2 + 2x).$$

Find the particular solution that satisfies the condition

$$u = 2x^{1/2} \qquad \text{on } y = 0 \ (x > 0).$$

End-of-section exercise

Exercise 3.8

Find the particular solution of the partial differential equation

$$x\frac{\partial u}{\partial x} + y\frac{\partial u}{\partial y} - 3u = 0 \qquad (x \neq 0)$$

that satisfies the condition $u = x^2$ on $y = 1$.

4   Solving simple second-order equations

The main topic of this unit is how to solve first-order partial differential equations. However, you saw at the end of Section 2 that some of the methods involved could potentially be extended to the solution of second-order equations. This section concentrates on a simple class of second-order equations which can be reduced rapidly to first-order equations, and hence solved using the methods seen so far.

See Example 2.2, Exercise 2.6 and Exercise 2.9.

All of these second-order equations have the feature that, if a solution for $u(x, y)$ is sought, then the equation is either 'first-order in $\partial u/\partial x$' or 'first-order in $\partial u/\partial y$'. This means that putting $v = \partial u/\partial x$ or $v = \partial u/\partial y$, respectively, will reduce the original equation for $u(x, y)$ to a first-order equation for $v(x, y)$.

Subsection 4.1 looks at cases where the resulting first-order equation can be solved either by direct integration or by use of an integrating factor. Subsection 4.2 analyses cases where a change of variables as in Section 3 is required. The approaches considered here form the basis for further studies of second-order partial differential equations in *Unit 9*.

4.1   *Using direct integration or an integrating factor*

You have seen that the general solution of a linear first- or second-order *ordinary* differential equation contains respectively one or two arbitrary constants, and that the general solution of a linear first-order *partial* differential equation contains one arbitrary function.

See Subsection 1.1.

This suggests that the general solution of a linear second-order partial differential equation should contain *two* arbitrary functions, which does turn out to be the case. As usual, we speak of the 'general solution' here because *any* solution of a given second-order equation can be expressed by some specific choice of the two arbitrary functions.

As in the first-order case, these arbitrary functions are required to be suitably differentiable; we shall assume that this is the case throughout.

It is not hard to see why the general solution should feature two arbitrary functions. It takes two successive integrations to 'undo' a second-order partial derivative, and an arbitrary function is introduced at each stage. Example 4.1 demonstrates this for a simple case.

Example 4.1

Find the general solution of the equation

$$\frac{\partial^2 u}{\partial x \partial y} = 0, \qquad \text{where } u = u(x, y).$$

Solution

The equation is

$$\frac{\partial}{\partial x} \left(\frac{\partial u}{\partial y} \right) = 0,$$

so that integrating with respect to x gives

$$\frac{\partial u}{\partial y} = f(y), \qquad \text{where } f \text{ is an arbitrary function.}$$

On integrating this equation with respect to y, we obtain

$$u = \int f(y) \, dy + g(x), \qquad \text{where } g \text{ is an arbitrary function.}$$

Writing $h(y) = \int f(y) \, dy$, the general solution is

$$u(x, y) = g(x) + h(y).$$

(This is equivalent to writing the general solution as

$$u(x, y) = f(x) + g(y),$$

where f and g are arbitrary functions.)   ∎

The indefinite integral of an arbitrary function is also an arbitrary function.

The outcome of Example 4.1 verifies the result quoted after Exercise 2.6: the equation

$$\frac{\partial^2 u}{\partial \zeta \partial \phi} = 0$$

has general solution

$$u(\zeta, \phi) = f(\zeta) + g(\phi),$$

where f and g are arbitrary functions.

The mixed partial derivative $\partial^2 u / \partial x \, \partial y$ is the same as $\partial^2 u / \partial y \, \partial x$ for all the functions u considered in the course. Thus we could have started the solution to Example 4.1 by writing the equation as

$$\frac{\partial}{\partial y} \left(\frac{\partial u}{\partial x} \right) = 0.$$

The outcome of doing this is the same as before, since the structure of the solution is unaltered if x and y are exchanged throughout.

Exercise 4.1

Suppose that $u = u(x, y)$.

(a) Find the general solution of the equation

$$\frac{\partial^2 u}{\partial x^2} = 0.$$

(b) Use your answer to part (a) to write down the general solution of the equation

$$\frac{\partial^2 u}{\partial y^2} = 0.$$

As with other types of differential equation, it is always possible to check your solution by substituting it back into the equation.

The straightforward approach of Example 4.1 and Exercise 4.1 can also be applied if the zero right-hand sides of the equations considered there are replaced by non-zero functions. You are asked to look at such a case in Exercise 4.2. For brevity, we shall assume from now on that $u = u(x, y)$ unless otherwise stated, and that the symbols f, g and h represent arbitrary functions of one variable in the current context.

Exercise 4.2

Find the general solution of the equation

$$\frac{\partial^2 u}{\partial x \partial y} = xy^2.$$

This exhausts the types of second-order equation that can be solved by direct integration alone. However, we can make further headway by using the integrating factor method, as described in Subsection 1.3. This method can be applied if the equation contains only one second-order derivative, and if the equation is either 'first-order in $\partial u/\partial x$' or 'first-order in $\partial u/\partial y$', so that putting either $v = \partial u/\partial x$ or $v = \partial u/\partial y$ will produce a first-order equation for v. The following example illustrates the method.

This description includes the equations considered so far in this section, which were simple enough to be solved without putting $v = \partial u/\partial x$ or $v = \partial u/\partial y$.

Example 4.2

Find the general solution of the equation

$$\frac{\partial^2 u}{\partial x^2} - \frac{1}{y}\frac{\partial u}{\partial x} = 1 \qquad (y \neq 0).$$

Solution

Putting $v = \partial u/\partial x$ here gives the first-order equation

$$\frac{\partial v}{\partial x} - \frac{1}{y}v = 1 \qquad (y \neq 0).$$

This equation (with u in place of v) was solved in Example 1.4.

The integrating factor is

$$\exp\left(\int\left(-\frac{1}{y}\right)dx\right) = e^{-x/y},$$

so that the equation for v can be written as

$$\frac{\partial}{\partial x}(e^{-x/y}v) = e^{-x/y}.$$

On integrating with respect to x, we have

$$e^{-x/y}v = -ye^{-x/y} + f(y), \qquad \text{where } f \text{ is an arbitrary function,}$$

so that

$$\frac{\partial u}{\partial x} = v = -y + f(y)e^{x/y}.$$

After a further integration with respect to x, we obtain the general solution

$$u = -xy + yf(y)e^{x/y} + g(y), \qquad \text{where } g \text{ is an arbitrary function.}$$

Since f is arbitrary, so is the function $h(y) = yf(y)$. Thus the general solution of the given equation is

$$u(x, y) = -xy + g(y) + h(y)e^{x/y}. \quad \blacksquare$$

Exercise 4.3

Find the general solution of each of the following equations.

(a) $\dfrac{\partial^2 u}{\partial y^2} - \dfrac{1}{y}\dfrac{\partial u}{\partial y} = 0 \quad (y \neq 0), \qquad$ where $u = u(x, y)$.

(b) $\dfrac{\partial^2 u}{\partial x \partial t} + \dfrac{1}{t}\dfrac{\partial u}{\partial x} = x \quad (t \neq 0), \qquad$ where $u = u(x, t)$.

Even when the methods of this subsection cannot be applied directly, it is sometimes possible to reduce an equation to one of the forms considered here by changing the independent variables. This possibility is investigated in the next subsection.

4.2 Using the Chain Rule again

In Section 2, you saw how an extended version of the Chain Rule could be used to transform first-order partial differential equations into forms more amenable to being solved. In Subsection 3.1, you saw how a suitable transformation of independent variables for this purpose could be derived by applying the method of characteristics. This method applies to equations of the form

See Equations (2.1) or (2.2).

See Procedure 3.1 on page 136.

$$\frac{\partial v}{\partial x} + g(x, y)\frac{\partial v}{\partial y} + h(x, y)v = k(x, y). \tag{4.1}$$

You will now see how the method of characteristics can be applied, as before, in the process of solving certain second-order partial differential equations. Given such an equation for $u(x, y)$, this approach will work provided that putting either $v = \partial u/\partial x$ or $v = \partial u/\partial y$ leads to an equation of the form (4.1) for $v(x, y)$. The following example demonstrates what is involved.

Example 4.3

Find the general solution of the equation

$$\frac{\partial^2 u}{\partial x^2} + \frac{\partial^2 u}{\partial x \partial y} + \frac{\partial u}{\partial x} = 2.$$

Solution

The given equation is 'first-order in $\partial u/\partial x$'; that is, putting $v = \partial u/\partial x$ gives the first-order equation

$$\frac{\partial v}{\partial x} + \frac{\partial v}{\partial y} + v = 2. \tag{4.2}$$

The solution of this equation (with u in place of v) was obtained in Exercise 3.5(a).

Comparing this with the form (4.1), and applying the method of characteristics, we solve the ordinary differential equation

$$\frac{dy}{dx} = 1, \qquad \text{to obtain} \qquad y = x + c,$$

and hence choose $\phi = y - x$. Taking also $\zeta = x$, the Chain Rule (2.2) gives

$$\frac{\partial v}{\partial x} = \frac{\partial v}{\partial \zeta}\frac{\partial \zeta}{\partial x} + \frac{\partial v}{\partial \phi}\frac{\partial \phi}{\partial x} = \frac{\partial v}{\partial \zeta} - \frac{\partial v}{\partial \phi},$$

$$\frac{\partial v}{\partial y} = \frac{\partial v}{\partial \zeta}\frac{\partial \zeta}{\partial y} + \frac{\partial v}{\partial \phi}\frac{\partial \phi}{\partial y} = \frac{\partial v}{\partial \phi}.$$

Hence Equation (4.2) becomes

$$\frac{\partial v}{\partial x} + \frac{\partial v}{\partial y} + v = \frac{\partial v}{\partial \zeta} + v = 2.$$

Using the integrating factor e^ζ, the general solution of this equation is found to be

$$v(\zeta, \phi) = 2 + e^{-\zeta}f(\phi), \qquad \text{where } f \text{ is an arbitrary function,}$$

leading to

$$v(x, y) = 2 + e^{-x}f(y - x). \tag{4.3}$$

Since $\partial u/\partial x = v$, it remains to integrate the right-hand side of
Equation (4.3) with respect to x. To do so, it is helpful to note that

$$e^{-x}f(y-x) = e^{-y}e^{y-x}f(y-x) = e^{-y}f_1(x-y),$$

where the arbitrary function f_1 is defined by

$$f_1(s) = e^{-s}f(-s).$$

Then, from Equation (4.3), we have

$$u = \int v\,dx = \int 2\,dx + e^{-y}\int f_1(x-y)\,dx$$
$$= 2x + e^{-y}g(x-y) + h(y),$$

where g (given by $g(s) = \int f_1(s)\,ds$) and h are arbitrary functions. This is
the general solution of the original equation. ■

Since f is an arbitrary
function, so is f_1.

Using integration by
substitution, with $s = x - y$
and y held constant, we have
$ds/dx = 1$ and

$$\int f_1(s)\,dx = \int f_1(s)\frac{ds}{dx}\,dx$$
$$= \int f_1(s)\,ds.$$

Exercise 4.4

Find the general solution of each of the following equations, for $u = u(x,y)$.

(a) $\dfrac{\partial^2 u}{\partial x\partial y} - 3\dfrac{\partial^2 u}{\partial y^2} - \dfrac{\partial u}{\partial y} = 0$

(b) $xy\dfrac{\partial^2 u}{\partial x^2} - 2x^2\dfrac{\partial^2 u}{\partial x\partial y} - y\dfrac{\partial u}{\partial x} = 0$ $(x > 0,\ y > 0)$

In part (a) you may find the
statement of Exercise 3.6
useful.

In part (b), separation of
variables is required in finding
the equations of the
characteristics.

This section has looked at how to solve linear second-order partial
differential equations which are either 'first-order in $\partial u/\partial x$' or 'first-order
in $\partial u/\partial y$'. This requirement excludes, for example

$$\frac{\partial^2 u}{\partial x\partial y} + u = 0,$$

since putting $v = \partial u/\partial x$ or $v = \partial u/\partial y$ cannot alter the u term into one
that involves v. Also excluded are partial differential equations of the form

$$A\frac{\partial^2 u}{\partial x^2} + B\frac{\partial^2 u}{\partial x\partial y} + C\frac{\partial^2 u}{\partial y^2} = 0 \qquad (A \neq 0,\ C \neq 0),$$

containing both a $\partial^2 u/\partial x^2$ term and a $\partial^2 u/\partial y^2$ term. The solution of
equations of this type will be considered further in *Unit 9*, where a method
of characteristics is developed for second-order equations.

End-of-section exercise

Exercise 4.5

Find the general solution of each of the following equations.

(a) $\dfrac{\partial^2 u}{\partial x^2} - y\dfrac{\partial^2 u}{\partial x\partial y} = 0$ $(y > 0)$,   where $u = u(x,y)$.

(b) $\dfrac{\partial^2 u}{\partial x\partial t} + 3x^2\dfrac{\partial^2 u}{\partial t^2} - 2\dfrac{\partial u}{\partial t} = 0$,   where $u = u(x,t)$.

In part (a), separation of
variables may be used instead
of the integrating factor
method.

Outcomes

After studying this unit you should be able to:

- solve (find the general solution of) first-order linear partial differential equations of simple form using either direct integration or an integrating factor;

- solve for $u(x, y)$ a pair of first-order partial differential equations, one giving an expression for $\partial u / \partial x$ and the other an expression for $\partial u / \partial y$;

- apply appropriate forms of the Chain Rule for a function $u(x, y)$, where $x = x(\zeta, \phi)$ and $y = y(\zeta, \phi)$;

- solve first-order linear partial differential equations using the method of characteristics;

- apply appropriate forms of the Chain Rule to second-order partial derivatives, and by so doing, apply coordinate transformations to second-order partial differential equations;

- in the case of first-order equations, apply a given extra condition to the general solution so as to obtain the corresponding particular solution;

- apply the methods of solution for first-order equations to solve second-order linear equations for $u(x, y)$ that are either 'first-order in $\partial u / \partial x$' or 'first-order in $\partial u / \partial y$'.

Solutions to the exercises

Section 1

Solution 1.1

(a) Here $u(x,y) = \cos(x-y)$, so

$$\frac{\partial u}{\partial x} = -\sin(x-y) \quad \text{and}$$

$$\frac{\partial u}{\partial y} = -\sin(x-y) \times (-1) = \sin(x-y).$$

So $\dfrac{\partial u}{\partial x} + \dfrac{\partial u}{\partial y} = -\sin(x-y) + \sin(x-y) = 0.$

Hence $u(x,y) = \cos(x-y)$ satisfies the partial differential equation, and is therefore a solution.

(b) Here $u(x,y) = \ln(x-y)$, so

$$\frac{\partial u}{\partial x} = \frac{1}{x-y} \quad \text{and}$$

$$\frac{\partial u}{\partial y} = \frac{1}{x-y} \times (-1) = -\frac{1}{x-y}.$$

So $\dfrac{\partial u}{\partial x} + \dfrac{\partial u}{\partial y} = \dfrac{1}{x-y} - \dfrac{1}{x-y} = 0.$

Hence $u(x,y) = \ln(x-y)$ satisfies the partial differential equation, and is therefore a solution.

(c) Here $u(x,y) = x^2 + 2xy + y^2$, so

$$\frac{\partial u}{\partial x} = 2x + 2y \quad \text{and} \quad \frac{\partial u}{\partial y} = 2x + 2y.$$

So $\dfrac{\partial u}{\partial x} + \dfrac{\partial u}{\partial y} = 2x + 2y + 2x + 2y = 4(x+y) \neq 0.$

Hence $u(x,y) = x^2 + 2xy + y^2$ does not satisfy the partial differential equation, and so is not a solution.

(d) Here $u(x,y) = x^2 - 2xy + y^2 + 6$, so

$$\frac{\partial u}{\partial x} = 2x - 2y \quad \text{and} \quad \frac{\partial u}{\partial y} = -2x + 2y.$$

So $\dfrac{\partial u}{\partial x} + \dfrac{\partial u}{\partial y} = 2x - 2y - 2x + 2y = 0.$

Hence $u(x,y) = x^2 - 2xy + y^2 + 6$ satisfies the partial differential equation, and is therefore a solution.

Solution 1.2

(a) If u is a function of x and y, then $\partial u/\partial y = 0$ means that the arbitrary function must be a function of x only. Therefore the general solution is

$$u(x,y) = f(x), \quad \text{where } f \text{ is an arbitrary function.}$$

(b) If u is a function of z and t, then $\partial u/\partial t = 0$ means that the arbitrary function must be a function of z only. Therefore the general solution is

$$u(z,t) = f(z), \quad \text{where } f \text{ is an arbitrary function.}$$

Solution 1.3

(a) Here u is a function of x and y, and the partial derivative in the equation is with respect to y. This means that the arbitrary function is a function of x. Since $\partial u/\partial y = 2$, we have

$$u(x,y) = 2y + f(x),$$

where f is an arbitrary function.

(b) Here $u = u(x,y)$, and the partial derivative is with respect to x. Hence the arbitrary function is a function of y. Since $\partial u/\partial x = \sin x$, we have

$$u(x,y) = -\cos x + f(y),$$

where f is an arbitrary function.

Solution 1.4

(a) Integrating $\partial u/\partial x = y$ with respect to x gives

$$u(x,y) = xy + f(y),$$

where f is an arbitrary function.

(b) Integrating $\partial u/\partial y = xy$ with respect to y gives

$$u(x,y) = \tfrac{1}{2}xy^2 + f(x),$$

where f is an arbitrary function.

(c) Integrating $\partial u/\partial t = x^2 + t^2$ with respect to t gives

$$u(x,t) = x^2 t + \tfrac{1}{3}t^3 + f(x),$$

where f is an arbitrary function.

(d) Since u is a function of x, y, z and t, integrating $\partial u/\partial z = 2ze^{-4t}$ with respect to z gives

$$u(x,y,z,t) = z^2 e^{-4t} + f(x,y,t),$$

where f is an arbitrary function of three variables.

Solution 1.5

(a) Integrating the first equation with respect to x yields

$$u(x,y) = x^3 + f(y), \quad \text{where } f \text{ is arbitrary.}$$

Now differentiating this with respect to y, we have

$$\frac{\partial u}{\partial y} = 0 + \frac{df}{dy} = 8y.$$

Integrating gives

$$f(y) = 4y^2 + c, \quad \text{where } c \text{ is an arbitrary constant.}$$

Therefore $u(x,y) = x^3 + 4y^2 + c.$

(b) Integrating the first equation with respect to x gives

$$u(x,y) = x^3 y + \cos(ax) + f(y),$$

where f is an arbitrary function. Now differentiating this with respect to y, we have

$$\frac{\partial u}{\partial y} = x^3 + 0 + \frac{df}{dy} = x^3 - e^{-y},$$

that is, $df/dy = -e^{-y}$. Integrating, we obtain

$$f(y) = e^{-y} + c, \quad \text{where } c \text{ is an arbitrary constant.}$$

Therefore $u(x,y) = x^3 y + \cos(ax) + e^{-y} + c.$

(c) Integrating the first equation with respect to x gives
$$u(x, y) = x^3 e^y + f(y),$$
where f is an arbitrary function. Now differentiating this with respect to y, we have
$$\frac{\partial u}{\partial y} = x^3 e^y + \frac{df}{dy} = x^3 e^y + y^3 e^y + 3y^2 e^y,$$
that is,
$$\frac{df}{dy} = y^3 e^y + 3y^2 e^y = \frac{d}{dy}\left(y^3 e^y\right).$$
On integrating, we have
$$f(y) = y^3 e^y + c, \quad \text{where } c \text{ is an arbitrary constant.}$$
Therefore $u(x, y) = x^3 e^y + y^3 e^y + c = (x^3 + y^3)e^y + c.$

Solution 1.6

(a) The integrating factor is
$$p(x) = \exp\left(\int (-\lambda)\, dx\right) = e^{-\lambda x}.$$

(b) Multiplying each term of the partial differential equation by $e^{-\lambda x}$ gives
$$e^{-\lambda x}\frac{\partial u}{\partial x} - \lambda e^{-\lambda x} u = 1, \quad \text{or} \quad \frac{\partial}{\partial x}(e^{-\lambda x} u) = 1.$$
Integrating gives
$$e^{-\lambda x} u = x + f(y),$$
where f is an arbitrary function. On rearranging, we have
$$u(x, y) = x e^{\lambda x} + e^{\lambda x} f(y).$$
(As before, we have mostly written u and $\partial u / \partial x$ rather than $u(x, y)$ and $(\partial u / \partial x)(x, y)$ here; this is normal practice, the variables x and y being committed to memory.)

Solution 1.7

(a) The integrating factor is
$$p(y) = \exp\left(\int \frac{3}{y}\, dy\right) = \exp(3\ln y) = y^3.$$

(b) Multiplying each term of the partial differential equation by y^3 gives
$$y^3 \frac{\partial u}{\partial y} + 3y^2 u = y^5, \quad \text{or} \quad \frac{\partial}{\partial y}(y^3 u) = y^5.$$
Integrating yields
$$y^3 u = \tfrac{1}{6} y^6 + f(x),$$
where f is an arbitrary function. So
$$u(x, y) = \tfrac{1}{6} y^3 + \frac{f(x)}{y^3}.$$

Solution 1.8

(a) The integrating factor is
$$p(x, y) = \exp\left(\int \frac{1}{y}\, dx\right) = e^{x/y}.$$
The partial differential equation becomes
$$e^{x/y}\frac{\partial u}{\partial x} + \frac{e^{x/y}}{y} u = e^{x/y}, \quad \text{or} \quad \frac{\partial}{\partial x}(e^{x/y} u) = e^{x/y}.$$

Integrating, we have
$$e^{x/y} u = y\, e^{x/y} + f(y),$$
where f is an arbitrary function. Therefore
$$u(x, y) = y + e^{-x/y} f(y).$$

(b) The integrating factor is
$$p(x, y) = \exp\left(\int (-xy)\, dy\right) = e^{-xy^2/2}.$$
The partial differential equation becomes
$$e^{-xy^2/2}\frac{\partial u}{\partial y} - xy\, e^{-xy^2/2} u = y\, e^{-xy^2/2},$$
that is,
$$\frac{\partial}{\partial y}\left(e^{-xy^2/2} u\right) = y\, e^{-xy^2/2}.$$
Integrating with respect to y, we have
$$e^{-xy^2/2} u = -\frac{1}{x}e^{-xy^2/2} + f(x),$$
where f is an arbitrary function. Therefore
$$u(x, y) = -\frac{1}{x} + e^{xy^2/2} f(x).$$

Solution 1.9

Integrating the first equation gives
$$u(x, y) = x^2 + e^{x-y} + f(y),$$
where f is an arbitrary function.
Differentiating this with respect to y, we have
$$\frac{\partial u}{\partial y} = -e^{x-y} + \frac{df}{dy} = 2y - e^{x-y},$$
that is, $df/dy = 2y$, so that
$$f(y) = y^2 + c, \quad \text{where } c \text{ is an arbitrary constant.}$$
So $u(x, y) = x^2 + y^2 + e^{x-y} + c.$

Solution 1.10

The integrating factor is
$$p(x, y) = \exp\left(\int \frac{1}{x^2(1+y)}\, dx\right) = \exp\left(-\frac{1}{x(1+y)}\right).$$
The partial differential equation becomes
$$\exp\left(-\frac{1}{x(1+y)}\right)\frac{\partial u}{\partial x} + \frac{\exp\left(-\dfrac{1}{x(1+y)}\right)}{x^2(1+y)} u = -2(1-y);$$
that is,
$$\frac{\partial}{\partial x}\left(\exp\left(-\frac{1}{x(1+y)}\right) u\right) = -2(1-y).$$
Integrating with respect to x gives
$$\exp\left(-\frac{1}{x(1+y)}\right) u = -2(1-y)x + f(y),$$
where f is an arbitrary function. So
$$u(x, y) = (-2(1-y)x + f(y))\exp\left(\frac{1}{x(1+y)}\right).$$

Section 2

Solution 2.1

To differentiate $u(r, \theta)$ with respect to r, hold θ constant and differentiate as if u were a function of r alone. Thus,

$$\frac{\partial u}{\partial r} = 2r \sin^2 \theta.$$

Similarly,

$$\frac{\partial u}{\partial \theta} = 2r^2 \sin \theta \cos \theta - 2a^2 \cos \theta \sin \theta$$
$$= 2(r^2 - a^2) \sin \theta \cos \theta.$$

Solution 2.2

We use the Chain Rule diagram below.

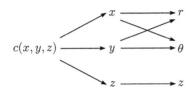

We have

$$\frac{\partial c}{\partial r} = \frac{\partial c}{\partial x}\frac{\partial x}{\partial r} + \frac{\partial c}{\partial y}\frac{\partial y}{\partial r} \qquad \left(\text{since } \frac{\partial z}{\partial r} = 0\right),$$

$$\frac{\partial c}{\partial \theta} = \frac{\partial c}{\partial x}\frac{\partial x}{\partial \theta} + \frac{\partial c}{\partial y}\frac{\partial y}{\partial \theta} \qquad \left(\text{since } \frac{\partial z}{\partial \theta} = 0\right).$$

$$\frac{\partial c}{\partial z} = \frac{\partial c}{\partial z} \qquad \left(\text{since } \frac{\partial z}{\partial z} = 1\right).$$

Now

$$\frac{\partial x}{\partial r} = \cos \theta, \qquad \frac{\partial x}{\partial \theta} = -r \sin \theta,$$

$$\frac{\partial y}{\partial r} = \sin \theta, \qquad \frac{\partial y}{\partial \theta} = r \cos \theta,$$

and

$$\frac{\partial c}{\partial x} = -2c_0 z x = -2c_0 z r \cos \theta,$$

$$\frac{\partial c}{\partial y} = -2c_0 z y = -2c_0 z r \sin \theta,$$

$$\frac{\partial c}{\partial z} = c_0(2z - x^2 - y^2) = c_0(2z - r^2).$$

Therefore

$$\frac{\partial c}{\partial r} = -2c_0 z r \cos^2 \theta - 2c_0 z r \sin^2 \theta = -2c_0 z r,$$

$$\frac{\partial c}{\partial \theta} = -2c_0 z r \cos \theta(-r \sin \theta) - 2c_0 z r \sin \theta(r \cos \theta) = 0,$$

$$\frac{\partial c}{\partial z} = c_0(2z - r^2).$$

Solution 2.3

We use the Chain Rule diagram below.

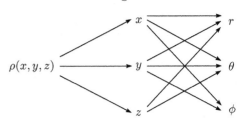

We have

$$\frac{\partial \rho}{\partial r} = \frac{\partial \rho}{\partial x}\frac{\partial x}{\partial r} + \frac{\partial \rho}{\partial y}\frac{\partial y}{\partial r} + \frac{\partial \rho}{\partial z}\frac{\partial z}{\partial r},$$

$$\frac{\partial \rho}{\partial \theta} = \frac{\partial \rho}{\partial x}\frac{\partial x}{\partial \theta} + \frac{\partial \rho}{\partial y}\frac{\partial y}{\partial \theta} + \frac{\partial \rho}{\partial z}\frac{\partial z}{\partial \theta},$$

$$\frac{\partial \rho}{\partial \phi} = \frac{\partial \rho}{\partial x}\frac{\partial x}{\partial \phi} + \frac{\partial \rho}{\partial y}\frac{\partial y}{\partial \phi} + \frac{\partial \rho}{\partial z}\frac{\partial z}{\partial \phi}.$$

Now

$$\frac{\partial \rho}{\partial x} = x\rho_0(x^2 + y^2 + z^2)^{-1/2} = \rho_0 \sin \theta \cos \phi,$$

$$\frac{\partial \rho}{\partial y} = y\rho_0(x^2 + y^2 + z^2)^{-1/2} = \rho_0 \sin \theta \sin \phi,$$

$$\frac{\partial \rho}{\partial z} = z\rho_0(x^2 + y^2 + z^2)^{-1/2} = \rho_0 \cos \theta,$$

and

$$\frac{\partial x}{\partial r} = \sin \theta \cos \phi, \qquad \frac{\partial x}{\partial \theta} = r \cos \theta \cos \phi,$$

$$\frac{\partial x}{\partial \phi} = -r \sin \theta \sin \phi, \qquad \frac{\partial y}{\partial r} = \sin \theta \sin \phi,$$

$$\frac{\partial y}{\partial \theta} = r \cos \theta \sin \phi, \qquad \frac{\partial y}{\partial \phi} = r \sin \theta \cos \phi,$$

$$\frac{\partial z}{\partial r} = \cos \theta, \qquad \frac{\partial z}{\partial \theta} = -r \sin \theta, \qquad \frac{\partial z}{\partial \phi} = 0.$$

Therefore

$$\frac{\partial \rho}{\partial r} = \rho_0 \sin^2\theta \cos^2\phi + \rho_0 \sin^2\theta \sin^2\phi + \rho_0 \cos^2\theta = \rho_0,$$

$$\frac{\partial \rho}{\partial \theta} = r\rho_0 \sin \theta \cos \theta \cos^2\phi + r\rho_0 \sin \theta \cos \theta \sin^2\phi$$
$$- r\rho_0 \cos \theta \sin \theta = 0,$$

$$\frac{\partial \rho}{\partial \phi} = -r\rho_0 \sin^2\theta \cos \phi \sin \phi + r\rho_0 \sin^2\theta \sin \phi \cos \phi = 0.$$

Solution 2.4

(a) We use the Chain Rule diagram below.

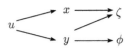

With $x = \zeta$ and $y = \phi - \zeta$, the Chain Rule (2.1) gives

$$\frac{\partial u}{\partial \zeta} = \frac{\partial u}{\partial x}\frac{\partial x}{\partial \zeta} + \frac{\partial u}{\partial y}\frac{\partial y}{\partial \zeta} = \frac{\partial u}{\partial x} - \frac{\partial u}{\partial y},$$

since $\partial x/\partial \zeta = 1$ and $\partial y/\partial \zeta = -1$.

(b) The partial differential equation

$$\frac{\partial u}{\partial x} - \frac{\partial u}{\partial y} + u = 2$$

then becomes

$$\frac{\partial u}{\partial \zeta} + u = 2.$$

(c) This equation is now in a form that can be evaluated by using the integrating factor e^ζ. We have

$$\frac{\partial}{\partial \zeta}(e^\zeta u) = 2e^\zeta.$$

Integrating this with respect to ζ, holding ϕ constant, we obtain

$$e^\zeta u = 2e^\zeta + f(\phi), \quad \text{where } f \text{ is an arbitrary function,}$$

or $u(\zeta, \phi) = 2 + e^{-\zeta} f(\phi)$.

Now, from the transformation $x = \zeta$, $y = \phi - \zeta$, we have $\phi = y + \zeta = y + x$. Hence, in terms of x and y,

$$u(x, y) = 2 + e^{-x} f(x + y).$$

Solution 2.5

Note first that

$$\frac{\partial \zeta}{\partial x} = 1, \qquad \frac{\partial \phi}{\partial x} = \frac{1}{x^2}, \qquad \frac{\partial \zeta}{\partial y} = 0, \qquad \frac{\partial \phi}{\partial y} = -\frac{1}{y^2}.$$

The Chain Rule (2.2) for $\partial u / \partial x$ is

$$\frac{\partial u}{\partial x} = \frac{\partial u}{\partial \zeta} \frac{\partial \zeta}{\partial x} + \frac{\partial u}{\partial \phi} \frac{\partial \phi}{\partial x}$$

$$= \frac{\partial u}{\partial \zeta} + \frac{\partial u}{\partial \phi}\left(\frac{1}{x^2}\right) = \frac{\partial u}{\partial \zeta} + \frac{1}{x^2}\frac{\partial u}{\partial \phi}.$$

The Chain Rule (2.2) for $\partial u / \partial y$ is

$$\frac{\partial u}{\partial y} = \frac{\partial u}{\partial \zeta} \frac{\partial \zeta}{\partial y} + \frac{\partial u}{\partial \phi} \frac{\partial \phi}{\partial y}$$

$$= \frac{\partial u}{\partial \zeta} \times 0 + \frac{\partial u}{\partial \phi}\left(-\frac{1}{y^2}\right) = -\frac{1}{y^2}\frac{\partial u}{\partial \phi}.$$

Hence

$$x^2 \frac{\partial u}{\partial x} + y^2 \frac{\partial u}{\partial y} - x^2 u$$

$$= x^2\left(\frac{\partial u}{\partial \zeta} + \frac{1}{x^2}\frac{\partial u}{\partial \phi}\right) + y^2\left(-\frac{1}{y^2}\frac{\partial u}{\partial \phi}\right) - x^2 u$$

$$= x^2 \frac{\partial u}{\partial \zeta} - x^2 u = \zeta^2 \frac{\partial u}{\partial \zeta} - \zeta^2 u.$$

The given equation transforms to

$$\zeta^2 \frac{\partial u}{\partial \zeta} - \zeta^2 u = 1, \qquad \text{or}$$

$$\frac{\partial u}{\partial \zeta} - u = \frac{1}{\zeta^2} \qquad (\zeta \neq 0).$$

Solution 2.6

(a) Note first that

$$\frac{\partial \zeta}{\partial y} = 1, \qquad \text{and} \qquad \frac{\partial \phi}{\partial y} = -1.$$

The Chain Rule (2.2) for $\partial u / \partial y$ is

$$\frac{\partial u}{\partial y} = \frac{\partial u}{\partial \zeta} \frac{\partial \zeta}{\partial y} + \frac{\partial u}{\partial \phi} \frac{\partial \phi}{\partial y} = \frac{\partial u}{\partial \zeta} - \frac{\partial u}{\partial \phi}.$$

So the rule for differentiating v with respect to y is

$$\frac{\partial v}{\partial y} = \frac{\partial v}{\partial \zeta} - \frac{\partial v}{\partial \phi}. \qquad \text{(S.1)}$$

Now, for $\partial^2 u / \partial y^2$, we have

$$\frac{\partial^2 u}{\partial y^2} = \frac{\partial}{\partial y}\left(\frac{\partial u}{\partial y}\right) = \frac{\partial}{\partial y}\left(\frac{\partial u}{\partial \zeta} - \frac{\partial u}{\partial \phi}\right).$$

Using Equation (S.1), with $v = \partial u / \partial \zeta - \partial u / \partial \phi$, gives

$$\frac{\partial^2 u}{\partial y^2} = \frac{\partial}{\partial \zeta}\left(\frac{\partial u}{\partial \zeta} - \frac{\partial u}{\partial \phi}\right) - \frac{\partial}{\partial \phi}\left(\frac{\partial u}{\partial \zeta} - \frac{\partial u}{\partial \phi}\right)$$

$$= \frac{\partial^2 u}{\partial \zeta^2} - \frac{\partial^2 u}{\partial \zeta \partial \phi} - \frac{\partial^2 u}{\partial \phi \partial \zeta} + \frac{\partial^2 u}{\partial \phi^2}$$

$$= \frac{\partial^2 u}{\partial \zeta^2} - 2\frac{\partial^2 u}{\partial \zeta \partial \phi} + \frac{\partial^2 u}{\partial \phi^2}.$$

(b) Substituting the expressions found (in Example 2.2 and part (a) above) into the partial differential equation, we have

$$2\left(\frac{\partial u}{\partial \zeta} + \frac{\partial u}{\partial \phi}\right) + 4x^2\left(\frac{\partial^2 u}{\partial \zeta^2} + 2\frac{\partial^2 u}{\partial \zeta \partial \phi} + \frac{\partial^2 u}{\partial \phi^2}\right)$$

$$-\frac{1}{x}\left[2x\left(\frac{\partial u}{\partial \zeta} + \frac{\partial u}{\partial \phi}\right)\right] - 4x^2\left(\frac{\partial^2 u}{\partial \zeta^2} - 2\frac{\partial^2 u}{\partial \zeta \partial \phi} + \frac{\partial^2 u}{\partial \phi^2}\right) = 0.$$

On removing the brackets, all terms cancel except two, leaving

$$8x^2 \frac{\partial^2 u}{\partial \zeta \partial \phi} + 8x^2 \frac{\partial^2 u}{\partial \zeta \partial \phi} = 0.$$

Since $x \neq 0$, this is equivalent to

$$\frac{\partial^2 u}{\partial \zeta \partial \phi} = 0.$$

Solution 2.7

Note first that

$$\frac{\partial x}{\partial \zeta} = 1, \qquad \frac{\partial y}{\partial \zeta} = 1, \qquad \frac{\partial x}{\partial \phi} = 0, \qquad \frac{\partial y}{\partial \phi} = 1.$$

The Chain Rule (2.1), with c in place of u, gives

$$\frac{\partial c}{\partial \zeta} = \frac{\partial c}{\partial x} \frac{\partial x}{\partial \zeta} + \frac{\partial c}{\partial y} \frac{\partial y}{\partial \zeta} = \frac{\partial c}{\partial x} + \frac{\partial c}{\partial y}.$$

Similarly,

$$\frac{\partial c}{\partial \phi} = \frac{\partial c}{\partial x} \frac{\partial x}{\partial \phi} + \frac{\partial c}{\partial y} \frac{\partial y}{\partial \phi} = \frac{\partial c}{\partial y}.$$

Solution 2.8

Note first that

$$\frac{\partial \zeta}{\partial x} = 2x, \qquad \frac{\partial \phi}{\partial x} = y, \qquad \frac{\partial \zeta}{\partial y} = -2y, \qquad \frac{\partial \phi}{\partial y} = x.$$

Now express $\partial \rho / \partial x$ and $\partial \rho / \partial y$ in terms of derivatives with respect to ζ and ϕ, using the Chain Rule (2.2). This gives

$$\frac{\partial \rho}{\partial x} = \frac{\partial \rho}{\partial \zeta} \frac{\partial \zeta}{\partial x} + \frac{\partial \rho}{\partial \phi} \frac{\partial \phi}{\partial x} = 2x\frac{\partial \rho}{\partial \zeta} + y\frac{\partial \rho}{\partial \phi},$$

$$\frac{\partial \rho}{\partial y} = \frac{\partial \rho}{\partial \zeta} \frac{\partial \zeta}{\partial y} + \frac{\partial \rho}{\partial \phi} \frac{\partial \phi}{\partial y} = -2y\frac{\partial \rho}{\partial \zeta} + x\frac{\partial \rho}{\partial \phi}.$$

Substituting into the partial differential equation gives

$$x\left(2x\frac{\partial \rho}{\partial \zeta} + y\frac{\partial \rho}{\partial \phi}\right) - y\left(-2y\frac{\partial \rho}{\partial \zeta} + x\frac{\partial \rho}{\partial \phi}\right) = 0,$$

that is,

$$2x^2\frac{\partial \rho}{\partial \zeta} + xy\frac{\partial \rho}{\partial \phi} + 2y^2\frac{\partial \rho}{\partial \zeta} - xy\frac{\partial \rho}{\partial \phi} = 0, \qquad \text{or}$$

$$2(x^2 + y^2)\frac{\partial \rho}{\partial \zeta} = 0.$$

Since $x^2 + y^2 \neq 0$, we have
$$\frac{\partial \rho}{\partial \zeta} = 0.$$
Integrating this equation, holding ϕ constant, gives
$$\rho = f(\phi), \qquad \text{where } f \text{ is an arbitrary function.}$$
Hence $\rho = f(xy)$.

Solution 2.9

Note first that
$$\frac{\partial \zeta}{\partial x} = 1, \qquad \frac{\partial \phi}{\partial x} = 1, \qquad \frac{\partial \zeta}{\partial t} = -c, \qquad \frac{\partial \phi}{\partial t} = c.$$
Now express $\partial^2 u/\partial x^2$ and $\partial^2 u/\partial t^2$ in terms of derivatives with respect to ζ, ϕ. The Chain Rule for $\partial u/\partial x$ is
$$\frac{\partial u}{\partial x} = \frac{\partial u}{\partial \zeta}\frac{\partial \zeta}{\partial x} + \frac{\partial u}{\partial \phi}\frac{\partial \phi}{\partial x} = \frac{\partial u}{\partial \zeta} + \frac{\partial u}{\partial \phi}.$$
So the rule for differentiating a function v with respect to x is
$$\frac{\partial v}{\partial x} = \frac{\partial v}{\partial \zeta} + \frac{\partial v}{\partial \phi}.$$
It follows that
$$\frac{\partial^2 u}{\partial x^2} = \frac{\partial}{\partial x}\left(\frac{\partial u}{\partial x}\right) = \frac{\partial}{\partial x}\left(\frac{\partial u}{\partial \zeta} + \frac{\partial u}{\partial \phi}\right)$$
$$= \frac{\partial}{\partial \zeta}\left(\frac{\partial u}{\partial \zeta} + \frac{\partial u}{\partial \phi}\right) + \frac{\partial}{\partial \phi}\left(\frac{\partial u}{\partial \zeta} + \frac{\partial u}{\partial \phi}\right)$$
$$= \frac{\partial^2 u}{\partial \zeta^2} + 2\frac{\partial^2 u}{\partial \zeta \partial \phi} + \frac{\partial^2 u}{\partial \phi^2}.$$
The Chain Rule for $\partial u/\partial t$ is
$$\frac{\partial u}{\partial t} = \frac{\partial u}{\partial \zeta}\frac{\partial \zeta}{\partial t} + \frac{\partial u}{\partial \phi}\frac{\partial \phi}{\partial t} = -c\frac{\partial u}{\partial \zeta} + c\frac{\partial u}{\partial \phi}.$$
So the rule for differentiating a function v with respect to t is
$$\frac{\partial v}{\partial t} = -c\frac{\partial v}{\partial \zeta} + c\frac{\partial v}{\partial \phi}.$$
It follows that
$$\frac{\partial^2 u}{\partial t^2} = \frac{\partial}{\partial t}\left(\frac{\partial u}{\partial t}\right)$$
$$= -c\frac{\partial}{\partial \zeta}\left(-c\frac{\partial u}{\partial \zeta} + c\frac{\partial u}{\partial \phi}\right) + c\frac{\partial}{\partial \phi}\left(-c\frac{\partial u}{\partial \zeta} + c\frac{\partial u}{\partial \phi}\right)$$
$$= c^2\frac{\partial^2 u}{\partial \zeta^2} - 2c^2\frac{\partial^2 u}{\partial \zeta \partial \phi} + c^2\frac{\partial^2 u}{\partial \phi^2}.$$
Substituting into the partial differential equation, we have
$$\frac{\partial^2 u}{\partial t^2} - c^2\frac{\partial^2 u}{\partial x^2} = c^2\frac{\partial^2 u}{\partial \zeta^2} - 2c^2\frac{\partial^2 u}{\partial \zeta \partial \phi} + c^2\frac{\partial^2 u}{\partial \phi^2}$$
$$- c^2\left(\frac{\partial^2 u}{\partial \zeta^2} + 2\frac{\partial^2 u}{\partial \zeta \partial \phi} + \frac{\partial^2 u}{\partial \phi^2}\right) = 0,$$
or $-4c^2\dfrac{\partial^2 u}{\partial \zeta \partial \phi} = 0.$

Since $c \neq 0$, this is equivalent to
$$\frac{\partial^2 u}{\partial \zeta \partial \phi} = 0.$$

Section 3

Solution 3.1

Note first that
$$\frac{\partial \zeta}{\partial x} = 1, \qquad \frac{\partial \phi}{\partial x} = 1, \qquad \frac{\partial \zeta}{\partial y} = 0, \qquad \frac{\partial \phi}{\partial y} = 1.$$
Hence, by the Chain Rule (2.2),
$$\frac{\partial u}{\partial x} = \frac{\partial u}{\partial \zeta}\frac{\partial \zeta}{\partial x} + \frac{\partial u}{\partial \phi}\frac{\partial \phi}{\partial x} = \frac{\partial u}{\partial \zeta} + \frac{\partial u}{\partial \phi},$$
$$\frac{\partial u}{\partial y} = \frac{\partial u}{\partial \zeta}\frac{\partial \zeta}{\partial y} + \frac{\partial u}{\partial \phi}\frac{\partial \phi}{\partial y} = \frac{\partial u}{\partial \phi}.$$
Substituting into $\partial u/\partial x - \partial u/\partial y = 0$ gives
$$\frac{\partial u}{\partial \zeta} + \frac{\partial u}{\partial \phi} - \frac{\partial u}{\partial \phi} = 0, \qquad \text{or} \qquad \frac{\partial u}{\partial \zeta} = 0.$$
Now, integrating with respect to ζ, keeping ϕ constant, gives $u = f(\phi)$, where f is an arbitrary function.
So $u = f(x + y)$ is the general solution of the original equation.

Solution 3.2

The equation $\partial u/\partial x - \partial u/\partial y = 0$ was simplified to $\partial u/\partial \zeta = 0$ using the transformation $\zeta = x$, $\phi = x + y$. This equation was integrated by holding ϕ constant. So the characteristic curves of $\partial u/\partial x - \partial u/\partial y = 0$ are given by
$$\phi(x, y) = x + y = \text{ constant.}$$
(See Solution 3.5(b) for a sketch of this set of lines.)

Solution 3.3

(a) The given equation is in the form of Equation (3.3), so that $g(x, y) = 1$.
Integrating $dy/dx = 1$ gives
$$y = x + c, \qquad \text{where } c \text{ is an arbitrary constant.}$$
Now $\alpha(x, y) = y - x \; (= c)$, and $\phi = \alpha(x, y)$. The equations of the characteristic curves are
$$y - x = \text{constant},$$
and the new variable is $\phi = y - x$.

(b) Dividing through by $x + y$ puts the equation into the required form,
$$\frac{\partial u}{\partial x} - \frac{\partial u}{\partial y} - \frac{u}{x + y} = 0 \qquad (x + y \neq 0),$$
so that $g(x, y) = -1$.
Integrating $dy/dx = -1$ gives
$$y = -x + c, \qquad \text{where } c \text{ is an arbitrary constant.}$$
Now $\alpha(x, y) = y + x \; (= c)$, and $\phi = \alpha(x, y)$. The equations of the characteristic curves are
$$y + x = \text{constant},$$
and the new variable is $\phi = y + x$.

Solution 3.4

Since $u(x,y) = -4x + x^{1/2} f\left(\frac{1}{2}y^2 + 2x\right)$, we have

$$\frac{\partial u}{\partial x} = -4 + \frac{1}{2}x^{-1/2} f\left(\frac{1}{2}y^2 + 2x\right) + 2x^{1/2} f'\left(\frac{1}{2}y^2 + 2x\right)$$

and

$$\frac{\partial u}{\partial y} = x^{1/2} y\, f'\left(\frac{1}{2}y^2 + 2x\right).$$

Substituting these into the left-hand side of Equation (3.8), we have

$$-2xy\left(-4 + \frac{1}{2}x^{-1/2} f\left(\frac{1}{2}y^2 + 2x\right) + 2x^{1/2} f'\left(\frac{1}{2}y^2 + 2x\right)\right)$$

$$+ 4x\left(x^{1/2} y\, f'\left(\frac{1}{2}y^2 + 2x\right)\right) + y\left(-4x + x^{1/2} f\left(\frac{1}{2}y^2 + 2x\right)\right)$$

$$= 8xy - x^{1/2}y\, f\left(\frac{1}{2}y^2 + 2x\right) - 4x^{3/2}y\, f'\left(\frac{1}{2}y^2 + 2x\right)$$

$$+ 4x^{3/2}y\, f'\left(\frac{1}{2}y^2 + 2x\right) - 4xy + x^{1/2}y\, f\left(\frac{1}{2}y^2 + 2x\right)$$

$$= 4xy, \qquad \text{which equals the right-hand side.}$$

Solution 3.5

(a) The equation is in the required form.

Step (a): Integrating $dy/dx = 1$ gives $y = x + c$, where c is an arbitrary constant; hence $\phi(x,y) = y - x$.

(It is not necessary to write down α explicitly.)

The characteristic curves $\phi(x,y) = \text{constant}$ are sketched below.

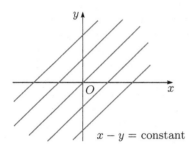

Step (b): The new variables are $\zeta = x$, $\phi = y - x$; so

$$\frac{\partial u}{\partial x} = \frac{\partial u}{\partial \zeta}\frac{\partial \zeta}{\partial x} + \frac{\partial u}{\partial \phi}\frac{\partial \phi}{\partial x} = \frac{\partial u}{\partial \zeta} - \frac{\partial u}{\partial \phi},$$

$$\frac{\partial u}{\partial y} = \frac{\partial u}{\partial \zeta}\frac{\partial \zeta}{\partial y} + \frac{\partial u}{\partial \phi}\frac{\partial \phi}{\partial y} = 0 + \frac{\partial u}{\partial \phi}.$$

Substituting these into the given partial differential equation yields

$$\frac{\partial u}{\partial \zeta} - \frac{\partial u}{\partial \phi} + \frac{\partial u}{\partial \phi} + u = 2, \qquad \text{or}$$

$$\frac{\partial u}{\partial \zeta} + u = 2.$$

Step (c): The integrating factor is

$$p(\zeta) = \exp\left(\int 1\, d\zeta\right) = e^{\zeta},$$

so the equation becomes

$$\frac{\partial}{\partial \zeta}\left(e^{\zeta} u\right) = 2e^{\zeta}.$$

Integrating, we have

$$e^{\zeta} u = 2e^{\zeta} + f(\phi),$$

where f is an arbitrary function, so

$$u(\zeta, \phi) = 2 + e^{-\zeta} f(\phi).$$

Step (d): Performing the inverse transformation gives

$$u(x,y) = 2 + e^{-x} f(y - x).$$

(b) Rearranging the given equation, we obtain

$$\frac{\partial u}{\partial x} - \frac{\partial u}{\partial y} - \frac{u}{x+y} = 0 \qquad (x + y \neq 0).$$

Step (a): Integrating $dy/dx = -1$ gives $y = -x + c$, where c is an arbitrary constant; hence $\phi(x,y) = y + x$.

The characteristic curves $\phi(x,y) = \text{constant}$ are sketched below.

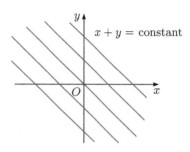

Step (b): The new variables are $\zeta = x$, $\phi = y + x$; so

$$\frac{\partial u}{\partial x} = \frac{\partial u}{\partial \zeta}\frac{\partial \zeta}{\partial x} + \frac{\partial u}{\partial \phi}\frac{\partial \phi}{\partial x} = \frac{\partial u}{\partial \zeta} + \frac{\partial u}{\partial \phi},$$

$$\frac{\partial u}{\partial y} = \frac{\partial u}{\partial \zeta}\frac{\partial \zeta}{\partial y} + \frac{\partial u}{\partial \phi}\frac{\partial \phi}{\partial y} = 0 + \frac{\partial u}{\partial \phi}.$$

Substituting these into the rearranged partial differential equation yields

$$\frac{\partial u}{\partial \zeta} + \frac{\partial u}{\partial \phi} - \frac{\partial u}{\partial \phi} - \frac{u}{\phi} = 0 \quad (\phi \neq 0), \qquad \text{or}$$

$$\frac{\partial u}{\partial \zeta} - \frac{u}{\phi} = 0.$$

Step (c): The integrating factor is

$$p(\zeta, \phi) = \exp\left(\int \left(-\frac{1}{\phi}\right) d\zeta\right) = \exp\left(-\frac{\zeta}{\phi}\right) = e^{-\zeta/\phi},$$

so the equation becomes

$$\frac{\partial}{\partial \zeta}\left(e^{-\zeta/\phi} u\right) = 0.$$

Integrating, we have

$$e^{-\zeta/\phi} u = f(\phi),$$

where f is an arbitrary function, so

$$u(\zeta, \phi) = e^{\zeta/\phi} f(\phi).$$

Step (d): Performing the inverse transformation gives

$$u(x,y) = e^{x/(y+x)} f(y + x).$$

(c) Rearranging the given equation, we obtain

$$\frac{\partial u}{\partial x} + \frac{y}{x}\frac{\partial u}{\partial y} - \frac{2u}{x} = 0 \qquad (x \neq 0).$$

Step (a): Rearranging $dy/dx = y/x$ gives

$$\frac{dy}{dx} - \frac{y}{x} = 0,$$

for which the integrating factor is

$$p(x) = \exp\left(\int\left(-\frac{1}{x}\right)dx\right) = \frac{1}{x}.$$

So we have

$$\frac{d}{dx}\left(\frac{y}{x}\right) = 0,$$

which on integrating yields $y/x = c$, where c is an arbitrary constant. Hence $\phi(x,y) = y/x$.

The curves $\phi(x,y) = $ constant are sketched below.

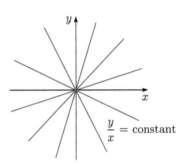

$$\frac{y}{x} = \text{constant}$$

Step (b): The new variables are $\zeta = x$, $\phi = y/x$; so

$$\frac{\partial u}{\partial x} = \frac{\partial u}{\partial\zeta}\frac{\partial\zeta}{\partial x} + \frac{\partial u}{\partial\phi}\frac{\partial\phi}{\partial x} = \frac{\partial u}{\partial\zeta} - \frac{y}{x^2}\frac{\partial u}{\partial\phi},$$

$$\frac{\partial u}{\partial y} = \frac{\partial u}{\partial\zeta}\frac{\partial\zeta}{\partial y} + \frac{\partial u}{\partial\phi}\frac{\partial\phi}{\partial y} = 0 + \frac{1}{x}\frac{\partial u}{\partial\phi}.$$

Substituting these into the rearranged partial differential equation gives

$$\frac{\partial u}{\partial\zeta} - \frac{y}{x^2}\frac{\partial u}{\partial\phi} + \frac{y}{x}\left(\frac{1}{x}\frac{\partial u}{\partial\phi}\right) - \frac{2u}{\zeta} = 0 \qquad (\zeta \neq 0),$$

or $\dfrac{\partial u}{\partial\zeta} - \dfrac{2u}{\zeta} = 0.$

Step (c): The integrating factor is

$$p(\zeta) = \exp\left(\int\left(-\frac{2}{\zeta}\right)d\zeta\right) = \exp(-2\ln\zeta) = \frac{1}{\zeta^2},$$

so the equation becomes

$$\frac{\partial}{\partial\zeta}\left(\frac{1}{\zeta^2}u\right) = 0.$$

Integrating, we have

$$\frac{1}{\zeta^2}u = f(\phi),$$

where f is an arbitrary function, so

$$u(\zeta,\phi) = \zeta^2 f(\phi).$$

Step (d): Performing the inverse transformation gives

$$u(x,y) = x^2 f(y/x).$$

(d) Rearranging the given equation, we obtain

$$\frac{\partial u}{\partial x} - \frac{y}{x}\frac{\partial u}{\partial y} = -\frac{y^2}{x^2} \qquad (x \neq 0).$$

Step (a): Rearranging $dy/dx = -y/x$ gives

$$\frac{dy}{dx} + \frac{y}{x} = 0,$$

for which the integrating factor is

$$p(x) = \exp\left(\int\frac{1}{x}dx\right) = x.$$

So we have

$$\frac{d}{dx}(xy) = 0,$$

which on integrating yields $xy = c$, where c is an arbitrary constant. Hence $\phi(x,y) = xy$.

The curves $\phi(x,y) = $ constant are sketched below.

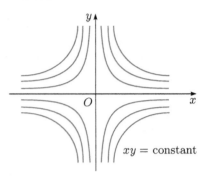

$$xy = \text{constant}$$

Step (b): The new variables are $\zeta = x$, $\phi = xy$; so

$$\frac{\partial u}{\partial x} = \frac{\partial u}{\partial\zeta}\frac{\partial\zeta}{\partial x} + \frac{\partial u}{\partial\phi}\frac{\partial\phi}{\partial x} = \frac{\partial u}{\partial\zeta} + y\frac{\partial u}{\partial\phi},$$

$$\frac{\partial u}{\partial y} = \frac{\partial u}{\partial\zeta}\frac{\partial\zeta}{\partial y} + \frac{\partial u}{\partial\phi}\frac{\partial\phi}{\partial y} = x\frac{\partial u}{\partial\phi}.$$

Substituting these into the rearranged partial differential equation gives

$$\frac{\partial u}{\partial\zeta} + y\frac{\partial u}{\partial\phi} - \frac{y}{x}\left(x\frac{\partial u}{\partial\phi}\right) = -\frac{\phi^2}{\zeta^4} \qquad (\zeta \neq 0), \qquad \text{or}$$

$$\frac{\partial u}{\partial\zeta} = -\phi^2\zeta^{-4}.$$

Step (c): Integrating this equation gives

$$u(\zeta,\phi) = \tfrac{1}{3}\phi^2\zeta^{-3} + f(\phi),$$

where f is an arbitrary function.

Step (d): Performing the inverse transformation gives

$$u(x,y) = \frac{x^2y^2}{3x^3} + f(xy) = \frac{y^2}{3x} + f(xy).$$

Solution 3.6

Substituting the given condition into the general solution gives

$$y = f(y).$$

Hence the particular solution for the given condition is

$$u(x,y) = e^x(y + 3x).$$

(Here the parameter s discussed in the text is just equal to y, so there is no need to introduce s explicitly.)

Solution 3.7

Substituting the given condition into the general solution gives

$$2x^{1/2} = -8x + x^{1/2}f(2x) \qquad (x > 0).$$

Therefore

$$f(2x) = 2 + 8x^{1/2} \qquad (x > 0); \qquad \text{that is,}$$

$$f(s) = 2 + 8\left(\tfrac{1}{2}s\right)^{1/2} \qquad (s > 0).$$

Hence the particular solution for the given condition is

$$u(x,y) = -8x + x^{1/2}\left(2 + 8(\tfrac{1}{2}y^2 + x)^{1/2}\right).$$

Solution 3.8

Rearranging the given equation, we obtain

$$\frac{\partial u}{\partial x} + \frac{y}{x}\frac{\partial u}{\partial y} - \frac{3u}{x} = 0 \qquad (x \neq 0).$$

Step (a): We solve $dy/dx = y/x$ for the characteristic curves. From Solution 3.5(c), the characteristic curves are given by

$$\phi(x,y) = \frac{y}{x} = \text{constant}.$$

Step (b): The new variables are $\zeta = x$, $\phi = y/x$. So

$$\frac{\partial u}{\partial x} = \frac{\partial u}{\partial \zeta} - \frac{y}{x^2}\frac{\partial u}{\partial \phi} \qquad \text{and} \qquad \frac{\partial u}{\partial y} = \frac{1}{x}\frac{\partial u}{\partial \phi},$$

as in Solution 3.5(c). Substituting these into the rearranged partial differential equation gives

$$\frac{\partial u}{\partial \zeta} - \frac{y}{x^2}\frac{\partial u}{\partial \phi} + \frac{y}{x}\left(\frac{1}{x}\frac{\partial u}{\partial \phi}\right) - \frac{3u}{\zeta} = 0 \qquad (\zeta \neq 0),$$

or $\dfrac{\partial u}{\partial \zeta} - \dfrac{3u}{\zeta} = 0.$

Step (c): The integrating factor is

$$p(\zeta) = \exp\left(\int\left(-\frac{3}{\zeta}\right)d\zeta\right) = \frac{1}{\zeta^3},$$

so the equation becomes

$$\frac{\partial}{\partial \zeta}\left(\frac{1}{\zeta^3}u\right) = 0.$$

Integrating, we have

$$\frac{1}{\zeta^3}u = f(\phi),$$

where f is an arbitrary function, so

$$u(\zeta,\phi) = \zeta^3 f(\phi).$$

Step (d): Performing the inverse transformation gives

$$u(x,y) = x^3 f(y/x).$$

Now, if $u = x^2$ when $y = 1$, we have

$$x^2 = x^3 f(1/x); \qquad \text{that is,}$$

$$f\left(\frac{1}{x}\right) = \frac{1}{x} \qquad \text{or} \qquad f(s) = s.$$

Hence the particular solution for the given condition is

$$u(x,y) = x^3\frac{y}{x} = x^2 y.$$

Section 4

Solution 4.1

(a) Integrating $\partial^2 u/\partial x^2 = 0$ once with respect to x gives

$$\frac{\partial u}{\partial x} = f(y),$$

where f is an arbitrary function. Integrating once more with respect to x, we obtain

$$u(x,y) = xf(y) + g(y),$$

where g is also an arbitrary function. This is the general solution for u.

(b) The general solution of the equation $\partial^2 u/\partial y^2 = 0$ can be found by exchanging x and y in the solution to part (a), which gives

$$u(x,y) = yf(x) + g(x),$$

for arbitrary functions f and g.

Solution 4.2

Writing the equation as

$$\frac{\partial}{\partial x}\left(\frac{\partial u}{\partial y}\right) = xy^2,$$

and integrating with respect to x, gives

$$\frac{\partial u}{\partial y} = \frac{1}{2}x^2 y^2 + f(y).$$

Integration of this with respect to y produces

$$u = \frac{1}{6}x^2 y^3 + \int f(y)\,dy + g(x), \qquad \text{or}$$

$$u(x,y) = \frac{1}{6}x^2 y^3 + g(x) + h(y),$$

where $h(y) = \int f(y)\,dy$, and g, h are arbitrary.

Solution 4.3

(a) Putting $v = \partial u/\partial y$ in the equation gives

$$\frac{\partial v}{\partial y} - \frac{1}{y}v = 0 \qquad (y \neq 0).$$

The integrating factor for this is

$$p(y) = \exp\left(\int\left(-\frac{1}{y}\right)dy\right) = \frac{1}{y}, \qquad \text{so that}$$

$$\frac{\partial}{\partial y}\left(\frac{1}{y}v\right) = 0, \qquad \text{or} \qquad \frac{1}{y}v = f(x),$$

where f is an arbitrary function. Then we have

$$\frac{\partial u}{\partial y} = v = yf(x),$$

so another integration gives the general solution

$$u = \frac{1}{2}y^2 f(x) + g(x),$$

where g is an arbitrary function, or

$$u(x,y) = g(x) + y^2 h(x),$$

where we have put $h(x) = \frac{1}{2}f(x)$.

(b) Putting $v = \partial u/\partial x$ in the equation gives

$$\frac{\partial v}{\partial t} + \frac{1}{t}v = x \qquad (t \neq 0).$$

The integrating factor here is

$$p(t) = \exp\left(\int\frac{1}{t}dt\right) = t, \qquad \text{so that}$$

$$\frac{\partial}{\partial t}(tv) = tx, \qquad \text{or} \qquad tv = \frac{1}{2}t^2 x + f(x),$$

where f is an arbitrary function. Then we have

$$\frac{\partial u}{\partial x} = v = \frac{1}{2}tx + \frac{1}{t}f(x).$$

Another integration gives

$$u = \frac{1}{4}tx^2 + \frac{1}{t}\int f(x)\,dx + g(t),$$

where g is an arbitrary function.

Writing $h(x) = \int f(x)\,dx$, the general solution is

$$u = \frac{1}{4}tx^2 + g(t) + \frac{1}{t}h(x).$$

Solution 4.4

(a) Putting $v = \partial u/\partial y$, we have

$$\frac{\partial v}{\partial x} - 3\frac{\partial v}{\partial y} - v = 0. \qquad \text{(S.2)}$$

Comparing this with the form (4.1), and applying the method of characteristics, we solve the ordinary differential equation

$$\frac{dy}{dx} = -3, \qquad \text{to obtain} \qquad y = -3x + c,$$

and hence choose $\phi = y + 3x$. Taking also $\zeta = x$, the Chain Rule (2.2) gives

$$\frac{\partial v}{\partial x} = \frac{\partial v}{\partial \zeta}\frac{\partial \zeta}{\partial x} + \frac{\partial v}{\partial \phi}\frac{\partial \phi}{\partial x} = \frac{\partial v}{\partial \zeta} + 3\frac{\partial v}{\partial \phi},$$

$$\frac{\partial v}{\partial y} = \frac{\partial v}{\partial \zeta}\frac{\partial \zeta}{\partial y} + \frac{\partial v}{\partial \phi}\frac{\partial \phi}{\partial y} = \frac{\partial v}{\partial \phi}.$$

Hence Equation (S.2) becomes

$$\frac{\partial v}{\partial x} - 3\frac{\partial v}{\partial y} - v = \frac{\partial v}{\partial \zeta} - v = 0.$$

Using the integrating factor $e^{-\zeta}$, the general solution of this equation is found to be

$$v(\zeta, \phi) = e^{\zeta} f(\phi),$$

where f is an arbitrary function, leading to

$$v(x, y) = e^{x} f(y + 3x) \qquad \text{(as for Exercise 3.6)}.$$

Now $\partial u/\partial y = v$, so the general solution for u is

$$u(x, y) = e^{x}\int f(y + 3x)\,dy = e^{x}g(y + 3x) + h(x),$$

where g (given by $g(s) = \int f(s)\,ds$) and h are arbitrary functions.

(b) Putting $v = \partial u/\partial x$ and dividing though by xy, we have

$$\frac{\partial v}{\partial x} - \frac{2x}{y}\frac{\partial v}{\partial y} - \frac{1}{x}v = 0. \qquad \text{(S.3)}$$

Comparing this with the form (4.1), and applying the method of characteristics, we solve the ordinary differential equation

$$\frac{dy}{dx} = -\frac{2x}{y},$$

using separation of variables, to obtain

$$\tfrac{1}{2}y^2 = -x^2 + c, \qquad \text{and hence} \qquad \phi = x^2 + \tfrac{1}{2}y^2.$$

Choosing also $\zeta = x$, the Chain Rule (2.2) gives

$$\frac{\partial v}{\partial x} = \frac{\partial v}{\partial \zeta}\frac{\partial \zeta}{\partial x} + \frac{\partial v}{\partial \phi}\frac{\partial \phi}{\partial x} = \frac{\partial v}{\partial \zeta} + 2x\frac{\partial v}{\partial \phi},$$

$$\frac{\partial v}{\partial y} = \frac{\partial v}{\partial \zeta}\frac{\partial \zeta}{\partial y} + \frac{\partial v}{\partial \phi}\frac{\partial \phi}{\partial y} = y\frac{\partial v}{\partial \phi}.$$

Hence Equation (S.3) becomes

$$\frac{\partial v}{\partial x} - \frac{2x}{y}\frac{\partial v}{\partial y} - \frac{1}{x}v = \frac{\partial v}{\partial \zeta} - \frac{1}{\zeta}v = 0.$$

Using the integrating factor $1/\zeta$, the general solution of this equation is found to be

$$v(\zeta, \phi) = \zeta f(\phi),$$

where f is an arbitrary function, leading to

$$v(x, y) = x f(x^2 + \tfrac{1}{2}y^2).$$

Now $\partial u/\partial x = v$, so the general solution for u is

$$u(x, y) = \int x f(x^2 + \tfrac{1}{2}y^2)\,dx = g(x^2 + \tfrac{1}{2}y^2) + h(y),$$

where g (given by $g(s) = \tfrac{1}{2}\int f(s)\,ds$) and h are arbitrary functions. (The last step involves integration by substitution, with $s = x^2 + \tfrac{1}{2}y^2$.)

Solution 4.5

(a) Putting $v = \partial u/\partial x$ gives

$$\frac{\partial v}{\partial x} - y\frac{\partial v}{\partial y} = 0, \qquad \text{(S.4)}$$

for which the characteristics are given by

$$\frac{dy}{dx} = -y, \qquad \text{that is,} \qquad \ln y = -x + c.$$

Hence choose $\zeta = x$ and $\phi = x + \ln y$.

(This is the immediate outcome for ϕ if $dy/dx = -y$ is solved using separation of variables. However, use of the integrating factor method leads instead to $\phi = ye^{x}$. This is equivalent to the choice made above, since $\exp(x + \ln y) = ye^{x}$.)

With $\zeta = x$, $\phi = x + \ln y$, the Chain Rule gives

$$\frac{\partial v}{\partial x} = \frac{\partial v}{\partial \zeta} + \frac{\partial v}{\partial \phi}, \qquad \frac{\partial v}{\partial y} = \frac{1}{y}\frac{\partial v}{\partial \phi},$$

so that Equation (S.4) becomes

$$\frac{\partial v}{\partial \zeta} = 0, \qquad \text{leading to} \qquad v = f(\phi) = f(x + \ln y).$$

Now $\partial u/\partial x = v$, so the general solution for u is

$$u(x, y) = \int f(x + \ln y)\,dx = g(x + \ln y) + h(y),$$

where g (given by $g(s) = \int f(s)\,ds$) and h are arbitrary functions.

(b) Putting $v = \partial u/\partial t$ gives

$$\frac{\partial v}{\partial x} + 3x^2\frac{\partial v}{\partial t} - 2v = 0, \qquad \text{(S.5)}$$

for which the characteristics are given by

$$\frac{dt}{dx} = 3x^2, \qquad \text{that is,} \qquad t = x^3 + c.$$

Hence choose $\zeta = x$ and $\phi = t - x^3$. The Chain Rule then gives

$$\frac{\partial v}{\partial x} = \frac{\partial v}{\partial \zeta} - 3x^2\frac{\partial v}{\partial \phi}, \qquad \frac{\partial v}{\partial t} = \frac{\partial v}{\partial \phi},$$

so that Equation (S.5) becomes

$$\frac{\partial v}{\partial \zeta} - 2v = 0.$$

Using the integrating factor $e^{-2\zeta}$, the general solution of this equation is found to be

$$v(\zeta, \phi) = e^{2\zeta} f(\phi),$$

where f is an arbitrary function, leading to

$$v(x, t) = e^{2x} f(t - x^3).$$

Now $\partial u/\partial t = v$, so the general solution for u is

$$u(x, t) = e^{2x}\int f(t - x^3)\,dt = e^{2x}g(t - x^3) + h(x),$$

where g (given by $g(s) = \int f(s)\,ds$) and h are arbitrary functions.

UNIT 4   *Vector field theory*

Study guide

In starting this unit you should be familiar with the basic ideas in vector calculus and in the calculus of functions of several variables. You should revise these topics, if necessary, by using the *Revision Booklet*. The particular areas of interest are: partial differentiation; Taylor polynomial approximation to functions of several variables; dot product and cross product of vectors; gradient of a scalar field; divergence and curl of a vector field; line, surface and volume integrals.

These topics are the subject of MST209 *Units 4, 12, 23, 24* and *25*. See also Sections 2–4 of the *Revision Booklet*.

This unit is relatively long. You may find that Sections 3–5, in particular, each take longer than usual to study. However, there are many concepts here with which you should already be familiar, and so you may be able to complete some sections more rapidly than expected.

There is an audio session associated with Subsection 3.1.

This unit contains many important formulas and results, to which you will need to refer throughout the rest of the course. In order to help you to do so, these formulas are summarised on the last two pages of the *Handbook*.

Introduction

Fluid mechanics deals continually with *scalar fields*, such as density and pressure, and with *vector fields*, such as velocity and force. In this unit we shall derive some of the important results of the differential and integral calculus of scalar and vector fields.

You should already be familiar with the *gradient* of a scalar field and with the *divergence* and *curl* of a vector field. However, you will see here coordinate-free definitions of the divergence and curl that lead on to the usual expressions in terms of standard coordinate systems.

In *Unit 1* you saw the need to evaluate a *surface integral* to determine the total pressure force on a surface submerged in a fluid. To find the total mass of the fluid, you have to evaluate a *volume integral*. Section 1 considers the evaluation of volume integrals, using cylindrical polar and spherical polar coordinates, whereas in Section 2, these coordinate systems are used to evaluate surface integrals.

Section 3 discusses *Gauss' Divergence Theorem*, which relates a volume integral over a region of space to a surface integral over the bounding surface of the region. One consequence shown here is the *continuity equation* of fluid mechanics, which has a most important role in subsequent units. Section 4 derives *Stokes' Theorem*, which relates a surface integral to a line integral along the curve bounding the surface. As you will see in *Unit 7*, this result links the concepts of *vorticity* and *circulation* in fluid mechanics.

Section 5 presents a number of vector identities and some useful corollaries to Gauss' Divergence Theorem and Stokes' Theorem.

Notation

Scalar fields, f, and vector fields, $\mathbf{F}$, have different values at different points in space. If we need to stress this dependence, then we have previously written the fields as $f(x, y, z)$ and $\mathbf{F}(x, y, z)$, which explicitly show that f and $\mathbf{F}$ are functions of the coordinates (x, y, z) of the point. However, this notation implies that we are using Cartesian coordinates, whereas we might well be using cylindrical polar coordinates or spherical polar coordinates. The values of the fields at a point depend only on the particular point, and not on the chosen coordinate system. So we shall adopt the notations $f(P)$ and $\mathbf{F}(P)$, where P is a general point, to show this dependence on the point. When Cartesian coordinates *are* being used, we shall write the fields as $f(x, y, z)$ and $\mathbf{F}(x, y, z)$, whereas when spherical polar coordinates are used, for example, we shall write them as $f(r, \theta, \phi)$ and $\mathbf{F}(r, \theta, \phi)$.

In each case, the functions concerned may also depend on time. This is not referred to explicitly here.

Although various definitions and theorems are stated concerning scalar and vector fields, we do not formally specify domains for the functions involved, nor are conditions such as differentiability spelt out too precisely. Such matters are not the main concern of this course, which is to develop mathematical models and some methods which can be applied within them. Most of the functions dealt with are defined everywhere and are 'well-behaved' (i.e. they are differentiable). When studying this unit, you should mostly concentrate on using the results, not on their derivations.

1   Cylindrical and spherical polar coordinates

In three dimensions, the most familiar and widely used frame of reference is that of rectangular *Cartesian coordinates*, in which the position of any point, P, in space is specified by an ordered triple (x, y, z). Vectors can be expressed in the form

$$\mathbf{a} = a_1\,\mathbf{i} + a_2\,\mathbf{j} + a_3\,\mathbf{k},$$

where $\mathbf{i}$, $\mathbf{j}$ and $\mathbf{k}$ are the unit vectors at P, normal to the planes $x = $ constant, $y = $ constant and $z = $ constant respectively, as shown in Figure 1.1.

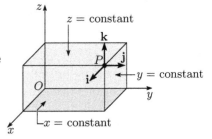

Figure 1.1

However, it is found that in problems which involve cylindrical or spherical symmetry, such as the flow of fluid along a cylindrical pipe, or the flow of fluid past a spherical obstruction, the use of *cylindrical polar coordinates* or *spherical polar coordinates* will frequently simplify the calculations. This section will remind you of these two alternative frames of reference, and of how to use them in the evaluation of volume integrals.

Cylindrical and spherical polar coordinates are discussed in MST209 *Unit 23*, and used to calculate integrals in MST209 *Unit 25*.

One of the factors governing the flow of a fluid through a region is the change in pressure from point to point in the fluid. The spatial rate of change of a scalar field f, such as the pressure of a fluid, is evaluated by using the *gradient* of f,

$$\mathbf{grad}\, f = \frac{\partial f}{\partial x}\mathbf{i} + \frac{\partial f}{\partial y}\mathbf{j} + \frac{\partial f}{\partial z}\mathbf{k}.$$

By 'spatial', we mean with respect to space coordinates; that is, not with respect to time.

The gradient of a scalar field is defined in MST209 *Unit 23*.

So, in order to be able to investigate the flow of fluids using cylindrical polar or spherical polar coordinates, we shall derive expressions for $\mathbf{grad}\, f$ in these two coordinate systems.

1.1 Cylindrical polar coordinates

The *cylindrical polar coordinates* (r, θ, z) of a point P are obtained from the familiar Cartesian coordinates, (x, y, z), by replacing the x and y coordinates by the corresponding plane polar coordinates, r and θ, of the projection of P onto the (x, y)-plane, as shown in Figure 1.2. However, if (r, θ, z) are the cylindrical polar coordinates of a point P, then so are $(r, \theta + 2k\pi, z)$ for $k = 0, \pm1, \pm2, \dots$ (see Figure 1.3). Every point in three-dimensional space may be given *unique* cylindrical polar coordinates (r, θ, z) by restricting the coordinates to the ranges

$$r \geq 0, \qquad -\pi < \theta \leq \pi, \qquad -\infty < z < \infty.$$

The points on the z-axis are slightly anomalous. Each of these points may be given cylindrical polar coordinates $(0, \theta, z)$, where the polar angle θ can take *any* value. However, in order that these points should have unique coordinates, we adopt the convention that they have polar angle $\theta = 0$.

It is quite easy to change from cylindrical polar coordinates to Cartesian coordinates, and vice versa, as follows.

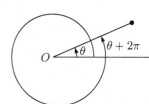

Figure 1.2

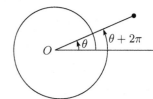

Figure 1.3

If the point P has Cartesian coordinates (x, y, z) and cylindrical polar coordinates (r, θ, z), then

$$x = r\cos\theta,$$
$$y = r\sin\theta,$$
$$z = z.$$

Conversely,

$$r = \sqrt{x^2 + y^2},$$
$$\theta = \begin{cases} \arccos(x/r) & (y \geq 0), \\ -\arccos(x/r) & (y < 0), \end{cases}$$
$$z = z.$$

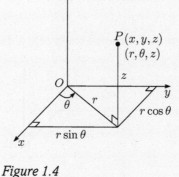

Figure 1.4

In MST209, cylindrical polar coordinates were denoted by $\langle \rho, \theta, z \rangle$. The alternative notation (r, θ, z) is commonly used, and in the context of fluid mechanics it makes sense to avoid using ρ, which typically denotes fluid density.

To find the polar angle θ, it is usually easier to use

$$\tan\theta = y/x,$$

and then to select the value of θ in the correct quadrant by drawing a sketch diagram.

We use '$z = z$' as a shorthand for stating that the two systems have one coordinate in common.

Exercise 1.1

(a) Find the Cartesian coordinates of the point whose cylindrical polar coordinates are $(4, \frac{2}{3}\pi, -3)$.

(b) Find the cylindrical polar coordinates of the point whose Cartesian coordinates are $(-3, -3, -5)$.

The name *'cylindrical* polar coordinates' comes from the fact that the surface $r =$ constant is a circular cylinder whose axis of symmetry is the z-axis. The surface $\theta =$ constant is a half-plane bounded on one edge by the z-axis, and the surface $z =$ constant is a plane perpendicular to the z-axis, just as it is in the Cartesian coordinate system. These surfaces are illustrated in Figure 1.5.

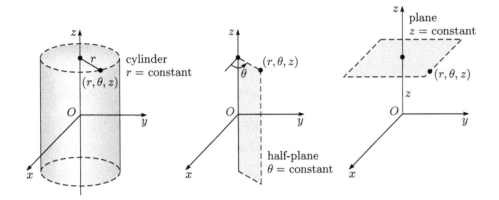

Figure 1.5

Before we can express a vector in terms of cylindrical polar coordinates, we need to specify the unit vectors associated with the system. At a given point, P, we define the unit vectors $\mathbf{e}_r$, $\mathbf{e}_\theta$ and $\mathbf{e}_z$ as follows. Let A be the point on the z-axis with the same z-coordinate as P. Then define $\mathbf{e}_r$ to be the unit vector at P which is perpendicular to the cylindrical surface $r =$ constant through P and in the direction of increasing r; that is, $\mathbf{e}_r$ is in the direction from A to P (see Figure 1.6). Taking the other two coordinates in turn, define $\mathbf{e}_\theta$ to be the unit vector perpendicular to the half-plane $\theta =$ constant through P, in the direction of increasing θ, and define $\mathbf{e}_z$ to be the unit vector perpendicular to the plane $z =$ constant through P, in the direction of increasing z.

By consideration of the angles between the vectors $\mathbf{i}$, $\mathbf{j}$ and the vectors $\mathbf{e}_r$, $\mathbf{e}_\theta$ (see Figure 1.7), we obtain the following.

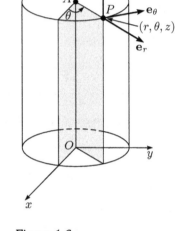

Figure 1.6

If the point P has cylindrical polar coordinates (r, θ, z), then

$$\mathbf{e}_r = \cos\theta\,\mathbf{i} + \sin\theta\,\mathbf{j},$$
$$\mathbf{e}_\theta = -\sin\theta\,\mathbf{i} + \cos\theta\,\mathbf{j},$$
$$\mathbf{e}_z = \mathbf{k},$$

and conversely,

$$\mathbf{i} = \cos\theta\,\mathbf{e}_r - \sin\theta\,\mathbf{e}_\theta,$$
$$\mathbf{j} = \sin\theta\,\mathbf{e}_r + \cos\theta\,\mathbf{e}_\theta,$$
$$\mathbf{k} = \mathbf{e}_z.$$

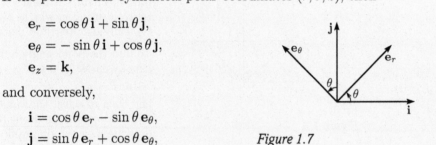

Figure 1.7

The unit vector $\mathbf{e}_z$ is identical to the unit vector $\mathbf{k}$ of the Cartesian coordinate system. We denote it here by $\mathbf{e}_z$ to be consistent with the notation for the other two unit vectors, $\mathbf{e}_r$ and $\mathbf{e}_\theta$.

Exercise 1.2

Express the position vector

$$\mathbf{r} = x\,\mathbf{i} + y\,\mathbf{j} + z\,\mathbf{k}$$

in terms of cylindrical polar coordinates r, θ, z and the associated unit vectors $\mathbf{e}_r$, $\mathbf{e}_\theta$, $\mathbf{e}_z$.

Note that, in contrast to the unit vectors $\mathbf{i}$, $\mathbf{j}$, $\mathbf{k}$, which always have the same directions, the directions of the unit vectors $\mathbf{e}_r$ and $\mathbf{e}_\theta$ vary from point to point.

In Exercise 1.2, you saw that the position vector could be resolved into components parallel to the unit vectors $\mathbf{e}_r$, $\mathbf{e}_\theta$, $\mathbf{e}_z$. Indeed, any vector $\mathbf{a}$ can be expressed in the form

$$\mathbf{a} = a_r\,\mathbf{e}_r + a_\theta\,\mathbf{e}_\theta + a_z\,\mathbf{e}_z.$$

The component of the position vector in the $\mathbf{e}_\theta$-direction is zero.

As seen from Figure 1.6, the unit vectors $\mathbf{e}_r$, $\mathbf{e}_\theta$, $\mathbf{e}_z$ are perpendicular to each other and, what is more, they form a right-handed set of vectors. Algebraically, this means that

$$\begin{array}{lll}
\mathbf{e}_r \cdot \mathbf{e}_r = 1, & \mathbf{e}_\theta \cdot \mathbf{e}_\theta = 1, & \mathbf{e}_z \cdot \mathbf{e}_z = 1, \\
\mathbf{e}_r \cdot \mathbf{e}_\theta = 0, & \mathbf{e}_\theta \cdot \mathbf{e}_z = 0, & \mathbf{e}_z \cdot \mathbf{e}_r = 0, \\
\\
\mathbf{e}_r \times \mathbf{e}_r = \mathbf{0}, & \mathbf{e}_\theta \times \mathbf{e}_\theta = \mathbf{0}, & \mathbf{e}_z \times \mathbf{e}_z = \mathbf{0}, \\
\mathbf{e}_r \times \mathbf{e}_\theta = \mathbf{e}_z, & \mathbf{e}_\theta \times \mathbf{e}_z = \mathbf{e}_r, & \mathbf{e}_z \times \mathbf{e}_r = \mathbf{e}_\theta.
\end{array}$$

A right-handed set of vectors is defined in MST209 *Unit 23*.

The dot product and cross product of two vectors are defined in MST209 *Unit 4*. See also Subsection 3.1 of the *Revision Booklet*.

These relationships can also be obtained algebraically from the expressions above for $\mathbf{e}_r$, $\mathbf{e}_\theta$, $\mathbf{e}_z$ in terms of $\mathbf{i}$, $\mathbf{j}$, $\mathbf{k}$. Also, $\mathbf{a} \times \mathbf{a} = \mathbf{0}$ for any vector $\mathbf{a}$.

Exercise 1.3

For the two vectors

$$\mathbf{a} = a_r\,\mathbf{e}_r + a_\theta\,\mathbf{e}_\theta + a_z\,\mathbf{e}_z \qquad \text{and} \qquad \mathbf{b} = b_r\,\mathbf{e}_r + b_\theta\,\mathbf{e}_\theta + b_z\,\mathbf{e}_z,$$

show that

(a) $\mathbf{a} \cdot \mathbf{b} = a_r b_r + a_\theta b_\theta + a_z b_z$;

(b) $\mathbf{a} \times \mathbf{b} = (a_\theta b_z - a_z b_\theta)\,\mathbf{e}_r + (a_z b_r - a_r b_z)\,\mathbf{e}_\theta + (a_r b_\theta - a_\theta b_r)\,\mathbf{e}_z$.

In Exercise 1.3, recall that
$$\mathbf{b} \cdot \mathbf{a} = \mathbf{a} \cdot \mathbf{b} \quad \text{and}$$
$$\mathbf{b} \times \mathbf{a} = -(\mathbf{a} \times \mathbf{b}),$$
for any vectors $\mathbf{a}$ and $\mathbf{b}$.

From the previous exercise, we have the following result.

Scalar and vector products in cylindrical polar coordinates

If $\mathbf{a} = a_r\,\mathbf{e}_r + a_\theta\,\mathbf{e}_\theta + a_z\,\mathbf{e}_z$ and $\mathbf{b} = b_r\,\mathbf{e}_r + b_\theta\,\mathbf{e}_\theta + b_z\,\mathbf{e}_z$, then

$$\mathbf{a} \cdot \mathbf{b} = a_r b_r + a_\theta b_\theta + a_z b_z \qquad \text{and}$$

$$\mathbf{a} \times \mathbf{b} = \begin{vmatrix} \mathbf{e}_r & \mathbf{e}_\theta & \mathbf{e}_z \\ a_r & a_\theta & a_z \\ b_r & b_\theta & b_z \end{vmatrix}.$$

Notice that the formulas for the dot product and cross product of two vectors have the same form whether the vectors are expressed in terms of their Cartesian components or in terms of their cylindrical polar components.

1.2 Spherical polar coordinates

In order to help in discussing problems with spherical symmetry, we now define the *spherical polar coordinates* (r, θ, ϕ) of a point P. In this system, the coordinate r is the *radial* distance of the point from the origin, θ is the angle which the line OP makes with the positive z-axis, and ϕ is the same angle as that used in cylindrical polar coordinates; see Figure 1.8. (Rather confusingly, this angle was denoted by θ there, and furthermore, the coordinate r had a different meaning too! However, the notation adopted here is fairly standard, though not followed universally.) In order that a

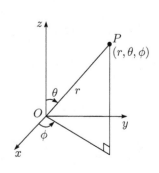

Figure 1.8

point should have unique spherical polar coordinates, we restrict the values of r, θ, ϕ to the ranges

$$r \geq 0, \qquad 0 \leq \theta \leq \pi, \qquad -\pi < \phi \leq \pi.$$

The points on the z-axis are slightly anomalous, just as they were in cylindrical polar coordinates. In order that these points should have unique spherical polar coordinates, we specify that $\phi = 0$ for all points on the z-axis. In addition, we specify that the origin has coordinate $\theta = 0$.

This is identical to the convention adopted for cylindrical polar coordinates.

Exercise 1.4

Find the Cartesian coordinates (x, y, z) of the point P in terms of its spherical polar coordinates (r, θ, ϕ).

In Exercise 1.4 you derived the following relationships.

If the point P has Cartesian coordinates (x, y, z) and spherical polar coordinates (r, θ, ϕ), then

$$x = r \sin\theta \cos\phi,$$
$$y = r \sin\theta \sin\phi,$$
$$z = r \cos\theta.$$

Conversely,

$$r = \sqrt{x^2 + y^2 + z^2},$$
$$\theta = \arccos(z/r),$$
$$\phi = \begin{cases} \arccos\left(x/(r\sin\theta)\right) & (y \geq 0), \\ -\arccos\left(x/(r\sin\theta)\right) & (y < 0). \end{cases}$$

In MST209, spherical polar coordinates were denoted by $\langle r, \theta, \phi \rangle$. As for cylindrical polar coordinates, we use round rather than angled brackets here.

Again, it is easier in practice to use

$$\tan\phi = y/x,$$

and to select the value of ϕ in the correct quadrant by drawing a sketch diagram.

The term '*spherical* polar coordinates' is based on the fact that the surface $r = \text{constant}$ is a sphere with centre at the origin. The surface $\theta = \text{constant}$ is a circular cone with vertex at the origin and axis on the z-axis, and the surface $\phi = \text{constant}$ is a half-plane bounded on one edge by the z-axis. These surfaces are illustrated in Figure 1.9.

As an exception, $\theta = \frac{1}{2}\pi$ is the (x, y)-plane.

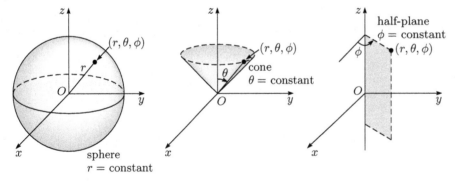

Figure 1.9

Because of the analogy between the surface of a sphere and the Earth's surface, the z-axis is sometimes referred to as the *polar axis*, while θ is called the *colatitude* and ϕ is called the *longitude* or *azimuth*.

We define the unit vectors for this coordinate system in a similar way to those for cylindrical polar coordinates. At the point P with coordinates (r, θ, ϕ), the unit vectors $\mathbf{e}_r$, $\mathbf{e}_\theta$ and $\mathbf{e}_\phi$ are perpendicular to the surfaces $r = \text{constant}$, $\theta = \text{constant}$ and $\phi = \text{constant}$ through the point P,

The colatitude (measured from the north pole) is $\frac{1}{2}\pi$ minus the *latitude* (measured from the equator).

respectively, and in the directions of increasing r, θ and ϕ, respectively, as shown in Figure 1.10.

By considering the components of the unit vectors $\mathbf{e}_r$, $\mathbf{e}_\theta$, $\mathbf{e}_\phi$ in the directions of the Cartesian unit vectors $\mathbf{i}$, $\mathbf{j}$, $\mathbf{k}$, we obtain the following.

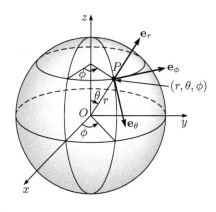

If the point P has spherical polar coordinates (r, θ, ϕ), then

$$\mathbf{e}_r = \sin\theta\cos\phi\,\mathbf{i} + \sin\theta\sin\phi\,\mathbf{j} + \cos\theta\,\mathbf{k},$$
$$\mathbf{e}_\theta = \cos\theta\cos\phi\,\mathbf{i} + \cos\theta\sin\phi\,\mathbf{j} - \sin\theta\,\mathbf{k},$$
$$\mathbf{e}_\phi = -\sin\phi\,\mathbf{i} + \cos\phi\,\mathbf{j},$$

and conversely,

$$\mathbf{i} = \sin\theta\cos\phi\,\mathbf{e}_r + \cos\theta\cos\phi\,\mathbf{e}_\theta - \sin\phi\,\mathbf{e}_\phi,$$
$$\mathbf{j} = \sin\theta\sin\phi\,\mathbf{e}_r + \cos\theta\sin\phi\,\mathbf{e}_\theta + \cos\phi\,\mathbf{e}_\phi,$$
$$\mathbf{k} = \cos\theta\,\mathbf{e}_r - \sin\theta\,\mathbf{e}_\theta.$$

Figure 1.10

You should verify at least one of the formulas in each group of three.

As you can see, from Figure 1.10 or from the above algebraic expressions, the unit vectors $\mathbf{e}_r$, $\mathbf{e}_\theta$ and $\mathbf{e}_\phi$ are mutually perpendicular and form a right-handed set of vectors. This means that we have the usual form for the formulas for the dot and cross products.

Scalar and vector products in spherical polar coordinates

If $\mathbf{a} = a_r\,\mathbf{e}_r + a_\theta\,\mathbf{e}_\theta + a_\phi\,\mathbf{e}_\phi$ and $\mathbf{b} = b_r\,\mathbf{e}_r + b_\theta\,\mathbf{e}_\theta + b_\phi\,\mathbf{e}_\phi$, then

$$\mathbf{a}\cdot\mathbf{b} = a_r b_r + a_\theta b_\theta + a_\phi b_\phi \qquad \text{and}$$

$$\mathbf{a}\times\mathbf{b} = \begin{vmatrix} \mathbf{e}_r & \mathbf{e}_\theta & \mathbf{e}_\phi \\ a_r & a_\theta & a_\phi \\ b_r & b_\theta & b_\phi \end{vmatrix}.$$

1.3   The gradient of a scalar field

The spatial rate of change of a scalar field f can be determined by using the **gradient** of f. In Cartesian coordinates, this vector is defined by

$$\mathbf{grad}\,f = \frac{\partial f}{\partial x}\,\mathbf{i} + \frac{\partial f}{\partial y}\,\mathbf{j} + \frac{\partial f}{\partial z}\,\mathbf{k}.$$

The important properties of the gradient are as follows.

(a) The spatial rate of change of the scalar field f in the direction of the unit vector $\mathbf{e}$ is equal to $\mathbf{e}\cdot\mathbf{grad}\,f$.

(b) The maximum spatial rate of change of the scalar field f at a point P occurs in the direction of $\mathbf{grad}\,f$ at P, and is equal to the magnitude of $\mathbf{grad}\,f$ at P.

(c) The normal to the surface $f = $ constant passing through the point P is given by the direction of $\mathbf{grad}\,f$ at P.

The gradient is defined and these properties derived in MST209 *Unit 23*, where the spatial rate of change of f in the direction of $\mathbf{e}$ was called the *directional derivative* in that direction.

We can derive the expressions for the gradient of a scalar field f in cylindrical and spherical polar coordinates, by using the result that the spatial rate of change of f in the direction of the unit vector $\mathbf{e}$ is $\mathbf{e} \cdot \mathbf{grad}\, f$. For example, in *cylindrical* polar coordinates, if $\mathbf{grad}\, f$ is written in terms of its components,

$$\mathbf{grad}\, f = g_r\, \mathbf{e}_r + g_\theta\, \mathbf{e}_\theta + g_z\, \mathbf{e}_z,$$

where g_r, g_θ, g_z are unknown functions to be found, we see that

$$g_r = \mathbf{e}_r \cdot \mathbf{grad}\, f.$$

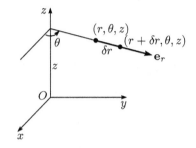

Figure 1.11

This is the (spatial) rate of change of the scalar field $f(r, \theta, z)$ in the direction of the unit vector $\mathbf{e}_r$. At the point (r, θ, z) this is the rate of change of f in the direction of r increasing, with θ and z held constant. Since the distance from the point (r, θ, z) to the point $(r + \delta r, \theta, z)$ is δr (see Figure 1.11), this rate of change is

$$\lim_{\delta r \to 0} \frac{f(r + \delta r, \theta, z) - f(r, \theta, z)}{\delta r} = \frac{\partial f}{\partial r}, \qquad \text{by definition.}$$

Thus, the component of $\mathbf{grad}\, f$ in the $\mathbf{e}_r$-direction is

$$g_r = \frac{\partial f}{\partial r}.$$

Similarly, the component g_θ of $\mathbf{grad}\, f$ in the $\mathbf{e}_\theta$-direction is $\mathbf{e}_\theta \cdot \mathbf{grad}\, f$. But this is the rate of change of the scalar field $f(r, \theta, z)$ in the direction of the unit vector $\mathbf{e}_\theta$, which is equal to

$$\lim_{\delta\theta \to 0} \frac{f(r, \theta + \delta\theta, z) - f(r, \theta, z)}{r\, \delta\theta} = \frac{1}{r}\frac{\partial f}{\partial \theta} \qquad (r \neq 0).$$

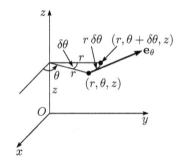

Figure 1.12

The term in the denominator of the above limit arises because the distance from the point (r, θ, z) to the point $(r, \theta + \delta\theta, z)$ is approximately $r\, \delta\theta$ (see Figure 1.12). Hence

$$g_\theta = \frac{1}{r}\frac{\partial f}{\partial \theta}.$$

Finally, the component g_z of $\mathbf{grad}\, f$ in the $\mathbf{e}_z$-direction is $\mathbf{e}_z \cdot \mathbf{grad}\, f$. This is the rate of change of the scalar field $f(r, \theta, z)$ in the direction of $\mathbf{e}_z$, which is equal to

$$\lim_{\delta z \to 0} \frac{f(r, \theta, z + \delta z) - f(r, \theta, z)}{\delta z} = \frac{\partial f}{\partial z},$$

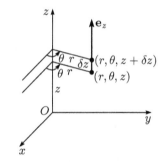

Figure 1.13

since the distance from the point (r, θ, z) to the point $(r, \theta, z + \delta z)$ is δz (see Figure 1.13). Hence

$$g_z = \frac{\partial f}{\partial z}.$$

Collecting together the expressions for g_r, g_θ and g_z, we obtain the following result.

In cylindrical polar coordinates,

$$\mathbf{grad}\, f = \frac{\partial f}{\partial r}\, \mathbf{e}_r + \frac{1}{r}\frac{\partial f}{\partial \theta}\, \mathbf{e}_\theta + \frac{\partial f}{\partial z}\, \mathbf{e}_z.$$

This applies for $r \neq 0$, which is the case also for several later formulas, involving both cylindrical polar and spherical polar coordinates.

Exercise 1.5

Find the gradient of the scalar field

$$f(r, \theta, z) = r^2 \sin \theta \, e^z.$$

We can find the expression for the gradient of a scalar field in *spherical* polar coordinates,

$$\mathbf{grad} \, f = g_r \, \mathbf{e}_r + g_\theta \, \mathbf{e}_\theta + g_\phi \, \mathbf{e}_\phi,$$

by the same method as for cylindrical polar coordinates.

Firstly, we have

$$g_r = \mathbf{e}_r \cdot \mathbf{grad} \, f,$$

which is the rate of change of the function $f(r, \theta, \phi)$ in the direction of $\mathbf{e}_r$. Now, the distance from the point (r, θ, ϕ) to the point $(r + \delta r, \theta, \phi)$ is δr (see Figure 1.14), and so this rate of change is

$$g_r = \lim_{\delta r \to 0} \frac{f(r + \delta r, \theta, \phi) - f(r, \theta, \phi)}{\delta r} = \frac{\partial f}{\partial r}.$$

If you wish to skip this derivation, go straight to the highlighted result on the next page.

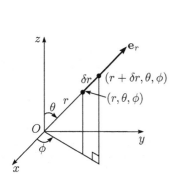

Figure 1.14

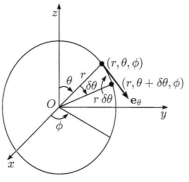

Figure 1.15

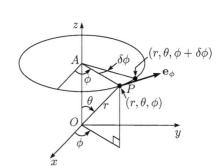

Figure 1.16

Secondly, we have

$$g_\theta = \mathbf{e}_\theta \cdot \mathbf{grad} \, f,$$

which is the rate of change of the function $f(r, \theta, \phi)$ in the direction of the unit vector $\mathbf{e}_\theta$. Now, the distance from the point (r, θ, ϕ) to the point $(r, \theta + \delta\theta, \phi)$ is approximately $r \, \delta\theta$ (see Figure 1.15), and so this rate of change is

$$g_\theta = \lim_{\delta\theta \to 0} \frac{f(r, \theta + \delta\theta, \phi) - f(r, \theta, \phi)}{r \, \delta\theta} = \frac{1}{r} \frac{\partial f}{\partial \theta}.$$

Finally, we have

$$g_\phi = \mathbf{e}_\phi \cdot \mathbf{grad} \, f,$$

which is the rate of change of the function $f(r, \theta, \phi)$ in the direction of the vector $\mathbf{e}_\phi$. The distance from the point (r, θ, ϕ) to the point $(r, \theta, \phi + \delta\phi)$ is approximately (see Figure 1.16)

$$AP \, \delta\phi = (OP \sin \theta) \, \delta\phi = r \sin \theta \, \delta\phi,$$

so this rate of change is

$$g_\phi = \lim_{\delta\phi \to 0} \frac{f(r, \theta, \phi + \delta\phi) - f(r, \theta, \phi)}{r \sin \theta \, \delta\phi} = \frac{1}{r \sin \theta} \frac{\partial f}{\partial \phi}.$$

Collecting together the expressions for g_r, g_θ and g_ϕ, we obtain the following result.

The expressions for **grad** f in cylindrical and spherical polar coordinates are given at the back of the *Handbook*. You are not expected to be able to reproduce their derivations.

In spherical polar coordinates,

$$\mathbf{grad}\, f = \frac{\partial f}{\partial r}\,\mathbf{e}_r + \frac{1}{r}\frac{\partial f}{\partial \theta}\,\mathbf{e}_\theta + \frac{1}{r \sin\theta}\frac{\partial f}{\partial \phi}\,\mathbf{e}_\phi.$$

Exercise 1.6

Find the gradient of the scalar field
$$f(r, \theta, \phi) = r^2 \sin^2\theta \sin(2\phi).$$

1.4 Evaluation of volume integrals

One of the major tools required in order to evaluate quantities such as the mass of fluid in a region is the volume integral. This subsection will remind you of the definition of the volume integral and of how to evaluate such integrals. In particular, we shall concentrate on the evaluation of volume integrals using cylindrical polar and spherical polar coordinates.

Volume integrals are discussed in MST209 *Unit 25*.

Start by recalling the definition of the volume integral $\int_B f\, dV$ of a scalar field f over a region B of three-dimensional space. This involves dividing the region B into N volume elements. (If Cartesian coordinates are required to evaluate the integral, we would normally do the division by using planes parallel to the (x, y)-plane, the (y, z)-plane and the (z, x)-plane. However, any method of dividing up the region can be used.) Now label the volume elements $1, 2, 3, \ldots, N$. Suppose that the ith element has volume δV_i, and that in this element we select a point P_i with position vector $\mathbf{r}_i$ (see Figure 1.17). We now form the sum

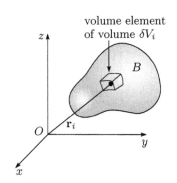

Figure 1.17

$$\sum_{i=1}^{N} f(P_i)\, \delta V_i = f(P_1)\, \delta V_1 + f(P_2)\, \delta V_2 + \cdots + f(P_N)\, \delta V_N.$$

The limit of this sum, as the number of volume elements increases, is defined to be the **volume integral of a scalar field** f over the region B, denoted by $\int_B f\, dV$. That is,

$$\int_B f\, dV = \lim_{N \to \infty} \sum_{i=1}^{N} f(P_i)\, \delta V_i.$$

Similarly, the **volume integral of a vector field** $\mathbf{F}$ over a region B, denoted by $\int_B \mathbf{F}\, dV$, is defined by

$$\int_B \mathbf{F}\, dV = \lim_{N \to \infty} \sum_{i=1}^{N} \mathbf{F}(P_i)\, \delta V_i.$$

The limiting process in these definitions is a complicated one. We require that the limit should not depend on the precise method of dividing the region into its elements or on which point P_i we select in the ith element. However, the number of elements, N, must increase in such a way that the diameter of each element approaches zero. The use of the word 'diameter', referring to regions other than circles or spheres, may be unfamiliar. The *diameter* of a region is just the maximum distance across the region (see Figure 1.18). With all these conditions on the limiting process, it is perhaps quite surprising that the limit ever exists! In fact, it can be shown that the limit always exists as long as the function f (or $\mathbf{F}$) and the boundary of the region B are 'sufficiently smooth'.

The definition above is not of practical use when it comes to evaluating a volume integral. Instead, we express the volume integral $\int_B f \, dV$ as a repeated integral, of the type

$$\int_B f \, dV = \int_{x=a}^{x=b} \left(\int_{y=\alpha(x)}^{y=\beta(x)} \left(\int_{z=\gamma(x,y)}^{z=\delta(x,y)} f(x,y,z) \, dz \right) dy \right) dx,$$

which can be evaluated by three successive ordinary integrations. On the other hand, the definition is useful in expressing physical quantities, such as the volume and mass of a rigid body, in terms of a volume integral.

If a body occupying a region B has density ρ, then the volume and mass of the ith element are δV_i and approximately $\rho(P_i) \, \delta V_i$, respectively. Adding the contributions from all of the elements, the total volume of the body is

$$V = \lim_{N \to \infty} \sum_{i=1}^{N} \delta V_i = \int_B dV,$$

and its total mass is

$$M = \lim_{N \to \infty} \sum_{i=1}^{N} \rho(P_i) \, \delta V_i = \int_B \rho \, dV.$$

To evaluate a volume integral using *cylindrical polar coordinates*, we must divide the region of integration into volume elements whose surfaces are of the form $r = $ constant, $\theta = $ constant and $z = $ constant. A typical such internal volume element is shown in Figure 1.19; it is approximately a rectangular box of sides δr, $r \, \delta\theta$, δz, and so its volume, δV, is given by

$$\delta V \simeq r \, \delta r \, \delta\theta \, \delta z.$$

In terms of integration this means, for example, that

$$\int_B f \, dV = \int_B f(r, \theta, z) \, r \, dr \, d\theta \, dz.$$

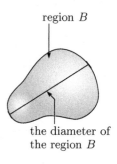

region B

the diameter of the region B

Figure 1.18

Just what these conditions are is not of concern here; in all the problems to be considered, the conditions are satisfied.

This corresponds to choosing the volume element for the integral to be a rectangular box, with volume
$$\delta V \simeq \delta x \, \delta y \, \delta z.$$
This may be compared with the cylindrical and spherical polar cases that follow.

The function being integrated in $\int_B dV$ is the constant function, 1; that is,
$$\int_B dV = \int_B 1 \, dV.$$

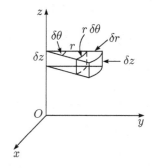

Figure 1.19

The next example should serve as a reminder of how this works in practice.

Example 1.1

Evaluate the integral

$$\int_B (x^2 + y^2)z \, dV,$$

where the region B is a circular cone with height h and vertical angle α, with apex at the origin and axis along the positive z-axis (see Figure 1.20).

Solution

Because of the rotational symmetry of the region of integration, we use cylindrical polar coordinates to evaluate this volume integral. The integrand is

$$(x^2 + y^2)z = [(r\cos\theta)^2 + (r\sin\theta)^2]z = r^2 z.$$

The volume element has volume $\delta V \simeq r \, \delta r \, \delta\theta \, \delta z$. Hence the integral is

$$\int_B (x^2 + y^2)z \, dV = \int_B (r^2 z)r \, dr \, d\theta \, dz = \int_B r^3 z \, dr \, d\theta \, dz.$$

We now have to decide on the order of integration and the corresponding limits of integration. (In any example, the choice of the order of integration can affect the limits for the integrations, and some choices may lead to easier calculations than others. However, there is little to choose between the different orders in this case.)

We begin with the θ integral. For fixed r and z, the variable θ can take values between $\theta = -\pi$ and $\theta = \pi$, so the lower and upper limits of the θ integration will be $-\pi$ and π, respectively.

Next, take the r integral. For fixed z, the variable r can take values between $r = 0$ and $r = z\tan\alpha$ (see Figure 1.21), so these are the limits on the r integration.

Finally, we must integrate with respect to z. The smallest value of z is 0 and the largest is h. So we have

$$\int_B (x^2 + y^2)z \, dV = \int_{z=0}^{z=h} \left(\int_{r=0}^{r=z\tan\alpha} \left(\int_{\theta=-\pi}^{\theta=\pi} r^3 z \, d\theta \right) dr \right) dz$$

$$= \int_{z=0}^{z=h} \left(\int_{r=0}^{r=z\tan\alpha} 2\pi r^3 z \, dr \right) dz$$

$$= \int_{z=0}^{z=h} \tfrac{1}{2}\pi \tan^4\alpha \, z^5 \, dz = \tfrac{1}{12}\pi h^6 \tan^4\alpha. \quad \blacksquare$$

Exercise 1.7

Use cylindrical polar coordinates to calculate the volume of the region B bounded by the paraboloid

$$x^2 + y^2 = z$$

and the plane $z = 1$, as shown in Figure 1.22.

A discussion of the evaluation of volume integrals in terms of cylindrical and spherical polar coordinates is given in MST209 *Unit 25*.

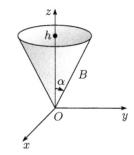

Figure 1.20

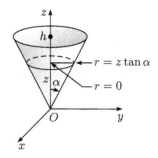

Figure 1.21

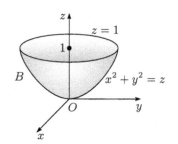

Figure 1.22

Now we turn attention to evaluating volume integrals in *spherical polar coordinates*. To do so, we need to find the volume δV of the volume element shown in Figure 1.23.

This volume element is approximately a rectangular box with sides PQ, PR and PS. Hence

$$\delta V \simeq PQ \times PR \times PS.$$

Now, PQ is the incremental increase in r, the radial distance to P; that is, $PQ = \delta r$. Also, $PR = OP\,\delta\theta = r\,\delta\theta$. Finally,

$$PS = AP\,\delta\phi = (OP\sin\theta)\,\delta\phi = r\sin\theta\,\delta\phi.$$

Therefore,

$$\delta V \simeq r^2 \sin\theta\,\delta r\,\delta\theta\,\delta\phi.$$

In terms of integration this means, for example, that

$$\int_B f\,dV = \int_B f(r,\theta,\phi)\,r^2 \sin\theta\,dr\,d\theta\,d\phi.$$

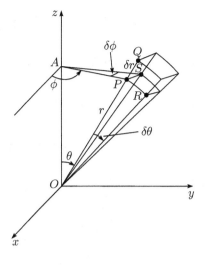

Figure 1.23

Exercise 1.8

By evaluating a volume integral, find the volume of a sphere of radius R whose centre is at the origin.

This section included definitions of cylindrical and spherical polar coordinates. You saw how to express vectors and the gradient of a scalar field in these coordinate systems, and how to evaluate volume integrals using these systems. In the next section, you will see how to use cylindrical and spherical polar coordinates to evaluate surface integrals for surfaces such as cylinders, spheres and cones.

End-of-section exercises

Exercise 1.9

Use spherical polar coordinates to evaluate the volume integral of the scalar field $f(x,y,z) = xyz$, over the region B for which $x > 0$, $y > 0$, $z > 0$, bounded by the coordinate planes and by the sphere $x^2 + y^2 + z^2 = 1$, as shown in Figure 1.24.

Exercise 1.10

(a) Determine the gradients of the scalar fields

$$f_1(r,\theta,z) = r^3 \sin^2\theta\,z^5 \qquad \text{and} \qquad f_2(r,\theta,z) = r^4 \cos^6\theta,$$

where r, θ, z are cylindrical polar coordinates.

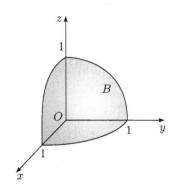

Figure 1.24

(b) Hence show that the surfaces

$$r^3 \sin^2\theta\,z^5 = \text{constant} \qquad \text{and} \qquad r^4 \cos^6\theta = \text{constant}$$

intersect orthogonally (at right angles).

2 Surface integrals

2.1 Surface integrals over curved surfaces

In *Unit 1* Subsection 4.3, you saw that the total force on a flat surface S submerged in a fluid is

$$\mathbf{F}_S = -\int_S p\,\mathbf{n}\,dA,$$

where p is the pressure distribution in the fluid and $\mathbf{n}$ is the unit normal to the surface pointing *into* the fluid. We were able to evaluate such surface integrals in *Unit 1* (for a given pressure distribution) because the surfaces chosen were *flat*; had the surface been curved, the approach used would not have worked. In order to remedy this unsatisfactory situation, we shall now consider *surface integrals over curved surfaces*. Surface integrals have wide application in science and technology. In fluid mechanics, they have uses other than the calculation of the net force on a surface; you will see shortly that they can be used to calculate the rate at which a fluid flows into a given region. A third example of their application is to calculate the rate of heat loss through the walls, windows, roof and floor of a house.

Surface integrals over flat surfaces (also called *area integrals*) are defined in MST209 *Unit 25*.

Consider a general, smooth, two-sided surface S, not necessarily flat, such as is shown in Figure 2.1. The surface may be *closed*, such as the shell of a whole egg, or it may be *open*, such as one piece of the shell of an opened egg. We arbitrarily choose one side of the surface S to be the positive side. If the surface S is closed, the outer surface is conventionally taken to be the positive side. A unit normal vector $\mathbf{n}$, directed away from the surface at any point on the positive side of S, is called a *positive* or *outward* unit normal to the surface S.

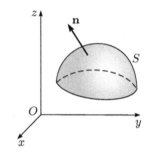

Figure 2.1

The definition of a surface integral over a curved surface S is identical to that for a surface integral over a flat surface. We subdivide the curved surface S into N surface elements of area δA_i, where $i = 1, 2, 3, \ldots, N$, and choose any point P_i on the ith element (see Figure 2.2). We form the sum

$$\sum_{i=1}^{N} f(P_i)\,\delta A_i.$$

The **surface integral of a scalar field** f over S, denoted by $\int_S f\,dA$, is defined to be the limit of this sum as N increases in such a way that the diameter of each surface element approaches zero, provided that this limit exists; that is,

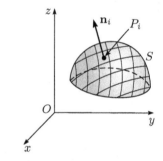

Figure 2.2

$$\int_S f\,dA = \lim_{N\to\infty} \sum_{i=1}^{N} f(P_i)\,\delta A_i.$$

We can similarly define the **surface integral of a vector field** $\mathbf{F}$ over the surface S by

$$\int_S \mathbf{F}\,dA = \lim_{N\to\infty} \sum_{i=1}^{N} \mathbf{F}(P_i)\,\delta A_i.$$

If the surface S of integration is *closed*, then this fact is indicated by adding a small circle onto the integral sign. For example, the surface integral of the scalar field f over the closed surface S is written as

$$\oint_S f \, dA.$$

This notation is similar to the one used for a line integral along a closed curve C.

In *Unit 1*, you saw that the force on a surface element of area δA_i due to the pressure distribution p is approximately $-p(P_i)\,\mathbf{n}_i\,\delta A_i$, where $\mathbf{n}_i$ is the unit normal to the ith element pointing into the fluid, and P_i is a point in the ith element (see Figure 2.2).

For a *curved* surface, the unit normal varies in direction from point to point. In order to associate a unique direction with the unit normal for a surface element, we must take a sufficiently small surface element. So in this case, adding up the contributions from all the surface elements and taking the limit of smaller and smaller surface elements, we find that the total force on the surface S is

$$\lim_{N\to\infty}\sum_{i=1}^{N}\left(-p(P_i)\,\mathbf{n}_i\,\delta A_i\right),$$

which is the surface integral

$$-\int_S p\,\mathbf{n}\,dA.$$

This is the same form as derived in *Unit 1* for a flat surface, except that here the direction of the unit normal $\mathbf{n}$ varies from point to point on the surface S, and therefore cannot be taken outside the integral sign.

This is one example of an integral over a curved surface. Another example is provided by the 'volume flow rate' of a fluid. In engineering applications, it is not necessarily the velocity of the fluid at particular points that is required, but rather the amount of fluid that passes through a given surface per unit time, which is the *volume flow rate*.

Suppose that the fluid has velocity at any point P and at time t given by the vector field $\mathbf{u}(P)$. Imagine a small fixed arbitrary surface element δS, of area δA, within the fluid. Let $\mathbf{n}$ be the unit normal to this surface element. Then, if δt is a sufficiently small time interval, and $\mathbf{u}$ is the velocity at some point on the surface element, the fluid particles initially on the surface element will be displaced approximately by $\mathbf{u}\,\delta t$, as shown in Figure 2.3. (There are, of course, correction terms of order $(\delta t)^2$ which arise because the velocity of the fluid is not quite constant on the surface element.) Indeed, during the time interval of length δt, the fluid flowing through the surface element will be contained in the oblique cylinder illustrated. This cylinder contains the total amount of fluid which has passed through the surface element in time δt.

Now, the volume of an oblique cylinder is the area of the base times the perpendicular height. So the volume of fluid flowing through the surface element δS in time δt is

$$\delta A \times |\mathbf{u}|\,\delta t \cos\theta = \mathbf{u}\cdot\mathbf{n}\,\delta A\,\delta t.$$

The *scalar line integral* of a vector field $\mathbf{F}$ along a closed curve C is denoted by

$$\oint_C \mathbf{F}\cdot d\mathbf{r};$$

see MST209 *Unit 24*.

This is the integral of the vector field $\mathbf{F} = -p\,\mathbf{n}$ over the surface S.

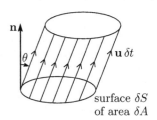

Figure 2.3

Here θ is the angle between $\mathbf{n}$ and $\mathbf{u}$, as shown in Figure 2.3.

Hence, the volume of fluid per unit time flowing through the surface element is $\mathbf{u} \cdot \mathbf{n} \, \delta A$. Adding up the contributions of the fluid flowing through a finite surface S from each surface element, the net volume flow rate of fluid through the surface S is

$$\lim_{N \to \infty} \sum_{i=1}^{N} \mathbf{u}(P_i) \cdot \mathbf{n}_i \, \delta A_i = \int_S \mathbf{u} \cdot \mathbf{n} \, dA.$$

This is the integral of the scalar field $f = \mathbf{u} \cdot \mathbf{n}$ over the surface S.

The volume flow rate of a fluid with velocity $\mathbf{u}$ through a surface S is

$$\int_S \mathbf{u} \cdot \mathbf{n} \, dA.$$

This volume flow rate of fluid through a surface S is sometimes called the *flux* of the fluid through the surface. By analogy, we call the surface integral $\int_S \mathbf{F} \cdot \mathbf{n} \, dA$, for a general vector field $\mathbf{F}$, the *flux* of $\mathbf{F}$ through the surface S. If we are dealing with a plane surface S, of area A, and the velocity is constant across S and perpendicular to S, then the volume flow rate is

$$\int_S \mathbf{u} \cdot \mathbf{n} \, dA = uA, \qquad \text{where } u = |\mathbf{u}|.$$

This result will be used in Block 2.

This formula may be used within the inviscid model to evaluate the volume flow rate in pipes, for example.

2.2 Evaluation of surface integrals

Having considered the definition of surface integrals over curved surfaces, and seen some physical applications of such integrals, the next step is to look at the evaluation of surface integrals using cylindrical polar coordinates and spherical polar coordinates.

We can use *cylindrical polar coordinates* to evaluate surface integrals over each of the surfaces $r =$ constant, $\theta =$ constant and $z =$ constant. For example, to evaluate a surface integral over the curved surface of the cylinder $r = R$, the surface element (see Figure 2.4) has area

These surfaces are described in Subsection 1.1.

$$\delta A = R \, \delta\theta \, \delta z.$$

In terms of integration this means, for example, that the surface integral of the scalar field f over the cylindrical surface $r = R$ is

$$\int_S f \, dA = \int_S f(R, \theta, z) \, R \, d\theta \, dz.$$

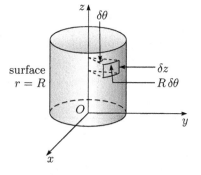

Figure 2.4

Example 2.1

Evaluate the surface integral

$$\int_S f \, dA,$$

where the scalar field f is defined (in terms of Cartesian coordinates) by

$$f(x, y, z) = x^2,$$

and S is the curved surface of the cylinder $x^2 + y^2 = R^2$ between $z = 0$ and $z = h$, as shown in Figure 2.5.

Solution

Because of the rotational symmetry of the surface of integration, we use cylindrical polar coordinates. The integrand is

$$f(x, y, z) = x^2 = r^2 \cos^2\theta.$$

The surface of integration has equation $r = R$, so that the integrand becomes $R^2 \cos^2\theta$. The surface element has area

$$\delta A = R\,\delta\theta\,\delta z.$$

Hence the surface integral is

$$\int_S f\,dA = \int_S (R^2 \cos^2\theta)\,R\,d\theta\,dz = \int_S R^3 \cos^2\theta\,d\theta\,dz.$$

Each of the (two) possible orders of integration leads to the same limits for the integrals in this example. For definiteness, we first integrate with respect to z. For fixed θ, the variable z can take values between $z = 0$ and $z = h$. Then we take the θ integral. The smallest value of θ is $-\pi$ and the largest is π. So we have

$$\int_S f\,dA = \int_{\theta=-\pi}^{\theta=\pi} \left(\int_{z=0}^{z=h} R^3 \cos^2\theta\,dz \right) d\theta$$

$$= \int_{\theta=-\pi}^{\theta=\pi} R^3 h \cos^2\theta\,d\theta$$

$$= \int_{\theta=-\pi}^{\theta=\pi} \tfrac{1}{2} R^3 h\,(1 + \cos(2\theta))\,d\theta$$

$$= \left[\tfrac{1}{2} R^3 h \left(\theta + \tfrac{1}{2}\sin(2\theta) \right) \right]_{\theta=-\pi}^{\theta=\pi}$$

$$= \pi R^3 h. \quad \blacksquare$$

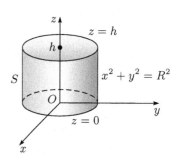

Figure 2.5

Recall that
$$\cos^2\theta = \tfrac{1}{2}\,(1 + \cos(2\theta)).$$

Exercise 2.1

The velocity of a fluid is given by the vector field

$$\mathbf{u}(r, \theta, z) = \frac{1}{r}\,\mathbf{e}_r \qquad (r \neq 0).$$

Find $\int_S \mathbf{u} \cdot \mathbf{n}\,dA$, the flux of fluid through the curved surface S of the cylinder $r = R$ between $z = 0$ and $z = 1$, where $\mathbf{n}$ is the outward unit normal to the surface S (see Figure 2.6).

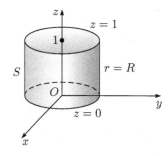

Figure 2.6

We can also use *spherical polar coordinates* to evaluate surface integrals over each of the surfaces $r = $ constant, $\theta = $ constant and $\phi = $ constant. For example, on the surface of the sphere $r = R$, the surface element (see Figure 2.7 overleaf) has area

$$\delta A \simeq R^2 \sin\theta\,\delta\theta\,\delta\phi.$$

In terms of integration this means, for example, that the surface integral of the scalar field f over the surface of the sphere $r = R$ is

$$\int_S f\,dA = \int_S f(R, \theta, \phi)\,R^2 \sin\theta\,d\theta\,d\phi.$$

These surfaces are described in Subsection 1.2.

171

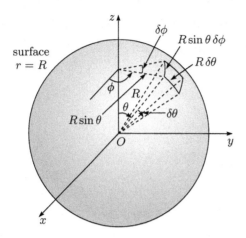

Figure 2.7

Exercise 2.2

By evaluating a surface integral, find the surface area of a sphere of radius R whose centre is at the origin.

Exercise 2.3

Evaluate the surface integral $\int_S \mathbf{F} \cdot \mathbf{n} \, dA$, where $\mathbf{F}$ is the vector field $\mathbf{F} = z \, \mathbf{k}$ and S is the curved surface of the hemisphere

$$x^2 + y^2 + z^2 \leq R^2, \qquad z \geq 0.$$

End-of-section exercises

Exercise 2.4

By evaluating a surface integral, find the area of the curved surface of a circular cone with height h and vertical angle α, as shown in Figure 2.8.

Exercise 2.5

Find the flux of the vector field

$$\mathbf{F} = |\mathbf{r}|^2 \, \mathbf{r},$$

Figure 2.8

where $\mathbf{r}$ is the position vector, through the curved surface of the cylinder $x^2 + y^2 = R^2$ between $z = 0$ and $z = h$.

3 The divergence of a vector field and Gauss' Divergence Theorem

3.1 The divergence of a vector field (audio)

In Subsection 2.1, you saw that the volume flow rate of fluid through a surface S is given by the surface integral $\int_S \mathbf{u} \cdot \mathbf{n} \, dA$. Consideration of this surface integral over a *closed* surface will lead to a definition of the *divergence* of a vector field at a point, which is a measure of how much the vector field is 'expanding' at that point.

Consider a fixed point, P, in the fluid, contained within a small region, B, of volume V (see Figure 3.1). If S is the surface of the region B, then the total volume flow rate of fluid out of the region B is $\oint_S \mathbf{u} \cdot \mathbf{n} \, dA$, where at each point $\mathbf{n}$ is the outward unit normal to the closed surface S. If this volume flow rate from the region B is positive, then either there must be a 'source' of fluid within the region, or the fluid has been compressed and is now 'expanding' within the region (at the instant considered). On the other hand, if the volume flow rate from the region B is negative, then either there must be a 'sink' of fluid within the region, or the fluid must be 'contracting'. The rate of expansion (or contraction) of the fluid within the region B, per unit volume, is

$$\frac{1}{V} \oint_S \mathbf{u} \cdot \mathbf{n} \, dA.$$

This expression will be positive if the fluid is expanding, and negative if the fluid is contracting.

We can find the rate of expansion of the fluid per unit volume *at the point P* by letting the region B shrink to the point P. This rate of expansion of the fluid at the point P is called the *divergence* of the vector field $\mathbf{u}$ at P. It is a scalar field, and is written $\operatorname{div} \mathbf{u}$; thus,

$$\operatorname{div} \mathbf{u} = \lim_{V \to 0} \left(\frac{1}{V} \oint_S \mathbf{u} \cdot \mathbf{n} \, dA \right).$$

By analogy, we can define the divergence of any vector field $\mathbf{F}$, written as $\operatorname{div} \mathbf{F}$, in the following way.

Definition

Let $\mathbf{F}$ be a vector field and P be a point in the domain of $\mathbf{F}$. Let V be the volume of a small region B containing the point P, and let S be the surface of that region. Then the scalar field

$$\operatorname{div} \mathbf{F} = \lim_{V \to 0} \left(\frac{1}{V} \oint_S \mathbf{F} \cdot \mathbf{n} \, dA \right)$$

is called the **divergence** of the vector field $\mathbf{F}$ at the point P.

This definition shows that $\operatorname{div} \mathbf{F}$ is independent of the coordinate system we are using, and clearly illustrates its physical interpretation. The limiting process is, however, a complicated one, in that the limit must be independent of the shapes of the regions B which are used.

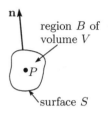

Figure 3.1

The 'source' referred to here is a mathematical concept, not a physical one. As you will see in *Unit 5*, it is a useful model. Similar remarks apply to 'sink'.

It is possible to calculate the divergence of a vector field directly from this definition, but it is rather tedious. Fortunately, there is a more practical method, which we now develop.

We shall derive an expression for div $\mathbf{F}$ in terms of the components of the vector field

$$\mathbf{F} = F_1(x, y, z)\,\mathbf{i} + F_2(x, y, z)\,\mathbf{j} + F_3(x, y, z)\,\mathbf{k}.$$

To do this, consider a small cube with surface S and sides of length $2l$, centred on the point P whose coordinates are (x, y, z), as shown in Figure 3.2.

The surface integral $\oint_S \mathbf{F} \cdot \mathbf{n}\, dA$ in the definition of div $\mathbf{F}$ will have contributions from all six faces of the cube. Consider first the top face, $EFGH$. The outward unit normal to the top face is $\mathbf{n} = \mathbf{k}$, and so

$$\mathbf{F} \cdot \mathbf{n} = \mathbf{F} \cdot \mathbf{k} = F_3.$$

Hence the contribution to the surface integral of $\mathbf{F} \cdot \mathbf{n}$ from the top face is $\int_{EFGH} F_3\, dA$. For a *small* cube, this surface integral is approximately the value of F_3 at the centre of the face, $(x, y, z + l)$, multiplied by the area of the face, $4l^2$; that is,

$$\int_{EFGH} \mathbf{F} \cdot \mathbf{n}\, dA \simeq 4l^2 F_3(x, y, z + l).$$

As the value of F_3 varies from point to point on the face, there are corrections to this approximation. However, because of the symmetries of the face about its centre, these corrections are of fourth order in the small quantity l. Algebraically, this is written

$$\int_{EFGH} \mathbf{F} \cdot \mathbf{n}\, dA = 4l^2 F_3(x, y, z + l) + O(l^4).$$

Using the Taylor polynomial of first order for F_3 at (x, y, z), we have

$$F_3(x, y, z + l) = F_3(x, y, z) + l\frac{\partial F_3}{\partial z}(x, y, z) + O(l^2).$$

So the contribution to the surface integral from the top face is now

$$\int_{EFGH} \mathbf{F} \cdot \mathbf{n}\, dA = 4l^2 F_3(x, y, z) + 4l^3\frac{\partial F_3}{\partial z}(x, y, z) + O(l^4).$$

Next, consider the bottom face, $ABCD$. On the bottom face, the outward unit normal is $\mathbf{n} = -\mathbf{k}$, and so

$$\mathbf{F} \cdot \mathbf{n} = -\mathbf{F} \cdot \mathbf{k} = -F_3.$$

Hence the contribution to the surface integral of $\mathbf{F} \cdot \mathbf{n}$ from the bottom face is $-\int_{ABCD} F_3\, dA$. For a *small* cube, this surface integral is the value of F_3 at the centre of the face, $(x, y, z - l)$, multiplied by the area of the face, $4l^2$, with corrections of fourth order in the small quantity l. Therefore

$$\int_{ABCD} \mathbf{F} \cdot \mathbf{n}\, dA = -4l^2 F_3(x, y, z - l) + O(l^4).$$

Using the Taylor polynomial of first order for F_3 at (x, y, z), we have

$$F_3(x, y, z - l) = F_3(x, y, z) - l\frac{\partial F_3}{\partial z}(x, y, z) + O(l^2).$$

The contribution to the surface integral from the bottom face becomes

$$\int_{ABCD} \mathbf{F} \cdot \mathbf{n}\, dA = -4l^2 F_3(x, y, z) + 4l^3\frac{\partial F_3}{\partial z}(x, y, z) + O(l^4).$$

If you wish to skip this derivation, go straight to Equation (3.1) on page 175.

This is just one convenient shape of region. It is the most natural choice when dealing with Cartesian coordinates.

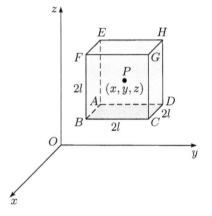

Figure 3.2

The notation $O(h^n)$ for a quantity of order h^n, for small h, was introduced in MST209 *Unit 26*.

For Taylor polynomials, see MST209 *Units 12* and *26*, or Subsection 2.2 of the *Revision Booklet*.

Hence the net contribution to the surface integral over the whole cube from the bottom and top faces is

$$\int_{ABCD} \mathbf{F} \cdot \mathbf{n} \, dA + \int_{EFGH} \mathbf{F} \cdot \mathbf{n} \, dA$$

$$= \left(-4l^2 F_3(x, y, z) + 4l^3 \frac{\partial F_3}{\partial z}(x, y, z) + O(l^4) \right)$$

$$+ \left(4l^2 F_3(x, y, z) + 4l^3 \frac{\partial F_3}{\partial z}(x, y, z) + O(l^4) \right)$$

$$= 8l^3 \frac{\partial F_3}{\partial z}(x, y, z) + O(l^4).$$

We can evaluate similarly the contributions to the surface integral $\oint_S \mathbf{F} \cdot \mathbf{n} \, dA$ from the other two pairs of opposite faces. Rather than repeat the somewhat involved calculations above, notice that the result obtained for the two faces with $z = $ constant involves the partial derivative of the z-component of $\mathbf{F}$ with respect to z. In a similar way, the net contribution from the left and right faces (for which $y = $ constant) is

$$8l^3 \frac{\partial F_2}{\partial y}(x, y, z) + O(l^4),$$

and the net contribution from the front and back faces is

$$8l^3 \frac{\partial F_1}{\partial x}(x, y, z) + O(l^4).$$

Adding up all of these contributions, the surface integral of $\mathbf{F} \cdot \mathbf{n}$ over the whole surface of the cube is

$$\oint_S \mathbf{F} \cdot \mathbf{n} \, dA = 8l^3 \left(\frac{\partial F_1}{\partial x}(x, y, z) + \frac{\partial F_2}{\partial y}(x, y, z) + \frac{\partial F_3}{\partial z}(x, y, z) \right) + O(l^4).$$

Now, the volume of the cube is $V = 8l^3$ and so, using the definition of the divergence, we have

$$\text{div} \, \mathbf{F}(x, y, z) = \lim_{V \to 0} \left(\frac{1}{V} \oint_S \mathbf{F} \cdot \mathbf{n} \, dA \right)$$

$$= \lim_{l \to 0} \frac{1}{8l^3} \left[8l^3 \left(\frac{\partial F_1}{\partial x}(x, y, z) + \frac{\partial F_2}{\partial y}(x, y, z) + \frac{\partial F_3}{\partial z}(x, y, z) \right) + O(l^4) \right]$$

$$= \lim_{l \to 0} \left[\left(\frac{\partial F_1}{\partial x}(x, y, z) + \frac{\partial F_2}{\partial y}(x, y, z) + \frac{\partial F_3}{\partial z}(x, y, z) \right) + O(l) \right]$$

$$= \frac{\partial F_1}{\partial x}(x, y, z) + \frac{\partial F_2}{\partial y}(x, y, z) + \frac{\partial F_3}{\partial z}(x, y, z).$$

We have derived this expression using a region which is a cube. However, the same result is obtained regardless of the shape of the region used.

This result means that we can evaluate div $\mathbf{F}$ by partial differentiation, rather than by integration over a surface.

In Cartesian coordinates, the divergence of $\mathbf{F} = F_1 \mathbf{i} + F_2 \mathbf{j} + F_3 \mathbf{k}$ is

$$\text{div} \, \mathbf{F}(x, y, z) = \frac{\partial F_1}{\partial x} + \frac{\partial F_2}{\partial y} + \frac{\partial F_3}{\partial z}. \tag{3.1}$$

In MST209 *Unit 24*, Equation (3.1) was taken as the *definition* of div $\mathbf{F}$.

Exercise 3.1

Use Equation (3.1) to evaluate the divergence of the vector field

$$\mathbf{F}(x, y, z) = x \, \mathbf{i} + x^2 y^2 \, \mathbf{j} + x^3 y^3 z^3 \, \mathbf{k}$$

(a) at the point (x, y, z);   (b) at the point $(1, 2, 3)$.

Equation (3.1) is very useful for evaluating the divergence of a vector field specified in terms of Cartesian coordinates. Equivalent expressions in terms of cylindrical and spherical polar coordinates can be derived by arguments very similar to that above. The only difference is that the small region surrounding the point P is chosen to have the shape constructed by drawing the surfaces $r =$ constant, $\theta =$ constant and $z =$ constant, in the case of cylindrical polar coordinates, and by drawing the surfaces $r =$ constant, $\theta =$ constant and $\phi =$ constant, in the case of spherical polar coordinates. The algebra is rather tedious (but no more difficult than for Cartesian coordinates), and so we shall just quote the results.

These shapes were illustrated in Subsection 1.4.

The divergence of $\mathbf{F} = F_r\,\mathbf{e}_r + F_\theta\,\mathbf{e}_\theta + F_z\,\mathbf{e}_z$ in cylindrical polar coordinates is

$$\operatorname{div}\mathbf{F}(r,\theta,z) = \frac{1}{r}\frac{\partial}{\partial r}(rF_r) + \frac{1}{r}\frac{\partial F_\theta}{\partial\theta} + \frac{\partial F_z}{\partial z}. \tag{3.2}$$

The divergence of $\mathbf{F} = F_r\,\mathbf{e}_r + F_\theta\,\mathbf{e}_\theta + F_\phi\,\mathbf{e}_\phi$ in spherical polar coordinates is

$$\operatorname{div}\mathbf{F}(r,\theta,\phi) = \frac{1}{r^2}\frac{\partial}{\partial r}(r^2 F_r) + \frac{1}{r\sin\theta}\frac{\partial}{\partial\theta}(\sin\theta\,F_\theta) + \frac{1}{r\sin\theta}\frac{\partial F_\phi}{\partial\phi}. \tag{3.3}$$

Exercise 3.2

Evaluate the divergence of the vector fields

(a) $\mathbf{F}(r,\theta,\phi) = r^n\,\mathbf{e}_r + r\sin\theta\,\mathbf{e}_\theta$,
    where r, θ and ϕ are spherical polar coordinates;

(b) $\mathbf{F}(r,\theta,z) = (1/r)\,\mathbf{e}_r + (z^2 - 1)\,\mathbf{e}_z$,
    where r, θ and z are cylindrical polar coordinates.

The audio session that follows will look in some detail at the different methods we now have available for evaluating the divergence of a particular vector field; you will see that, whichever method is chosen, the answer is the same. Before starting the audio, do the following exercise.

Exercise 3.3

Express $\mathbf{u} = x\,\mathbf{i} + y\,\mathbf{j} + z\,\mathbf{k}$ in terms of spherical polar coordinates.

Hint: Use the expressions given in Subsection 1.2 for Cartesian coordinates x, y, z in terms of spherical polar coordinates r, θ, ϕ. But before using the expressions for $\mathbf{i}$, $\mathbf{j}$, $\mathbf{k}$ in terms of $\mathbf{e}_r$, $\mathbf{e}_\theta$, $\mathbf{e}_\phi$, θ, ϕ, look for a short cut!

The solution to this exercise is given on the audio.

When you are ready, start the audio at Track 25 of CD1.

1   **Hubble's model of the universe**

$\underline{u} = x\underline{i} + y\underline{j} + z\underline{k}$ (Cartesian)

$\quad = r\underline{e}_r$ (spherical polar)

$\quad = \overrightarrow{OP}$

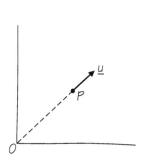

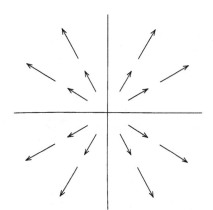

2   **The divergence**

Definition

$$\text{div}\,\underline{F} = \lim_{V \to 0}\left(\frac{1}{V}\oint_S \underline{F}\cdot\underline{n}\,dA\right)$$

The definition is independent
of the shape of the region.

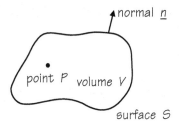

Formulas

$$\text{div}\,\underline{F} = \frac{\partial F_1}{\partial x} + \frac{\partial F_2}{\partial y} + \frac{\partial F_3}{\partial z} \quad \text{(Cartesian)}$$

$$\text{div}\,\underline{F} = \frac{1}{r^2}\frac{\partial}{\partial r}(r^2 F_r) + \frac{1}{r\sin\theta}\frac{\partial}{\partial\theta}(\sin\theta\, F_\theta) + \frac{1}{r\sin\theta}\frac{\partial F_\phi}{\partial\phi} \quad \text{(spherical polar)}$$

3   Divergence at the origin using cubes

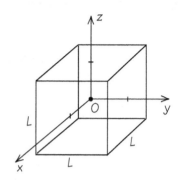

$$\underline{u} = x\underline{i} + y\underline{j} + z\underline{k}$$

$$\operatorname{div}\underline{u} = \lim_{V \to 0} \left(\frac{1}{V} \oint_S \underline{u} \cdot \underline{n}\, dA \right)$$

For top face of cube

Equation $z = $ [　　　　]

Normal $\underline{n} = $ [　　　　]

Vector field $\underline{u} = $ [　　　　　　　　　]

            $\underline{u} \cdot \underline{n} = $ [　　　　]

Integral over top face

$$\int_{\text{top face}} \underline{u} \cdot \underline{n}\, dA = \int_{\text{top face}} [\qquad]\, dA$$

$$= [\qquad]$$

Integral over whole cube

$$\oint_S \underline{u} \cdot \underline{n}\, dA = [\qquad]$$

$$\operatorname{div}\underline{u} = \lim_{V \to 0} \left(\frac{1}{V} \oint_S \underline{u} \cdot \underline{n}\, dA \right)$$

$$= \lim_{L \to 0} \left([\qquad] \right) = [\qquad]$$

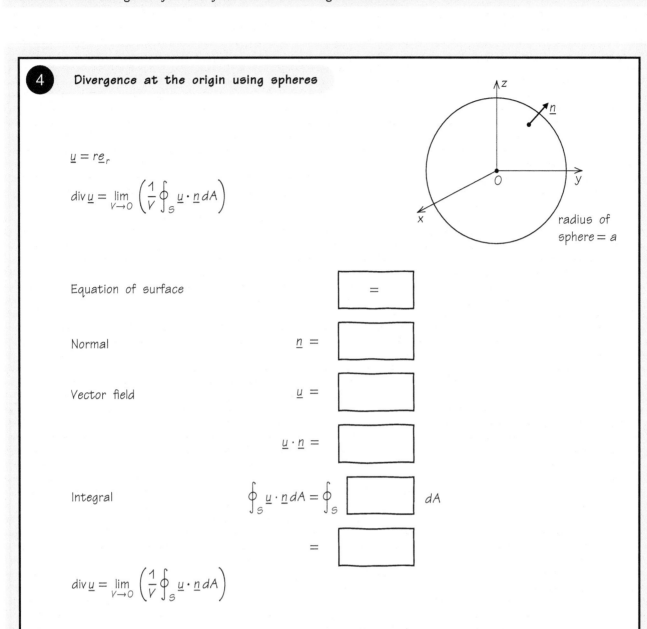

4   **Divergence at the origin using spheres**

radius of sphere $= a$

$\underline{u} = r\underline{e}_r$

$\operatorname{div}\underline{u} = \lim\limits_{V\to O}\left(\dfrac{1}{V}\oint_S \underline{u}\cdot\underline{n}\,dA\right)$

Equation of surface $\boxed{\qquad = \qquad}$

Normal $\underline{n} = \boxed{\qquad\qquad}$

Vector field $\underline{u} = \boxed{\qquad\qquad}$

$\underline{u}\cdot\underline{n} = \boxed{\qquad\qquad}$

Integral $\oint_S \underline{u}\cdot\underline{n}\,dA = \oint_S \boxed{\qquad\qquad}\, dA$

$= \boxed{\qquad\qquad}$

$\operatorname{div}\underline{u} = \lim\limits_{V\to O}\left(\dfrac{1}{V}\oint_S \underline{u}\cdot\underline{n}\,dA\right)$

$= \lim\limits_{a\to O}\left(\boxed{\qquad\qquad\qquad}\right) = \boxed{\qquad\qquad\qquad}$

---

5   **Divergence using formula (Cartesian)**

$$\underline{u} = x\underline{i} + y\underline{j} + z\underline{k}$$

$$\text{div}\,\underline{u} = \frac{\partial u_1}{\partial x} + \frac{\partial u_2}{\partial y} + \frac{\partial u_3}{\partial z}$$

$$= \frac{\partial}{\partial x}\boxed{} + \frac{\partial}{\partial y}\boxed{} + \frac{\partial}{\partial z}\boxed{}$$

$$= \boxed{ + + } = \boxed{}$$

---

6   **Divergence using formula (spherical polar)**

$$\underline{u} = r\underline{e}_r$$

$$\text{div}\,\underline{u} = \frac{1}{r^2}\frac{\partial}{\partial r}(r^2 u_r) + \frac{1}{r\sin\theta}\frac{\partial}{\partial\theta}(\sin\theta\,u_\theta) + \frac{1}{r\sin\theta}\frac{\partial}{\partial\phi}(u_\phi)$$

$$= \frac{1}{r^2}\frac{\partial}{\partial r}\boxed{} + \frac{1}{r\sin\theta}\frac{\partial}{\partial\theta}\boxed{} + \frac{1}{r\sin\theta}\frac{\partial}{\partial\phi}\boxed{}$$

$$= \boxed{}$$

Exercise 3.4

The vector field $\mathbf{u} = x\,\mathbf{i} + y\,\mathbf{j} + z\,\mathbf{k}$ is given in terms of cylindrical polar coordinates by $\mathbf{u} = r\,\mathbf{e}_r + z\,\mathbf{e}_z$ (see Exercise 1.2). Evaluate div $\mathbf{u}$ at the origin, by using the definition,

$$\operatorname{div}\mathbf{u} = \lim_{V \to 0}\left(\frac{1}{V}\oint_S \mathbf{u}\cdot\mathbf{n}\,dA\right),$$

taking regions which are cylinders given by

$$r \le a, \qquad -a \le z \le a,$$

in cylindrical polar coordinates.

Exercise 3.5

For the vector field $\mathbf{u}$ defined in Exercise 3.4, use Equation (3.2) to evaluate div $\mathbf{u}$.

3.2 Gauss' Divergence Theorem

You have seen that the volume flow rate of fluid through a closed surface S, that surrounds a region B, is given by a *surface integral*. If this is negative, the total amount of fluid in the region must be increasing. However, the amount of fluid in the region B is given by a *volume integral*. This means that, in this particular case, there is a connection between a volume integral over the region B and a surface integral over the surface S. This relationship can be generalised from the velocity field to any vector field $\mathbf{F}$, and is called Gauss' Divergence Theorem.

This connection is considered in the next subsection. From it we shall derive the *continuity equation*.

Consider a finite region B which is bounded by a closed surface S. We can divide the region B into N volume elements labelled $1, 2, \ldots, N$, where the ith element δB_i has volume δV_i and is bounded by the surface δS_i. In the ith element, choose a point P_i whose position vector is $\mathbf{r}_i$ (see Figure 3.3).

In Subsection 3.1 the divergence of the vector field $\mathbf{F}$ was defined as

$$\operatorname{div}\mathbf{F} = \lim_{V \to 0}\left(\frac{1}{V}\oint_S \mathbf{F}\cdot\mathbf{n}\,dA\right).$$

For the small element which contains the point P_i, this definition leads directly to the approximation

$$\operatorname{div}\mathbf{F}(P_i) \simeq \frac{1}{\delta V_i}\oint_{\delta S_i} \mathbf{F}\cdot\mathbf{n}\,dA. \tag{3.4}$$

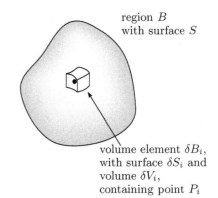

region B
with surface S

volume element δB_i,
with surface δS_i and
volume δV_i,
containing point P_i

Figure 3.3

The error in this approximation will tend to zero as δV_i tends to zero. Adding up these approximations for all of the volume elements gives

$$\sum_{i=1}^{N}\operatorname{div}\mathbf{F}(P_i)\,\delta V_i \simeq \sum_{i=1}^{N}\oint_{\delta S_i}\mathbf{F}\cdot\mathbf{n}\,dA. \tag{3.5}$$

The sum on the right includes contributions from the surfaces of all the subregions, whether these surfaces are 'interior' or 'exterior' to the whole region B. However, whenever two subregions are adjacent to one another, so that a face of one of the subregions coincides wholly or in part with a face of the other, the surface integrals over the coincident parts cancel because their associated outward unit normals point in opposite directions (see Figure 3.4). Therefore, after all such cancellations have taken place, only the surface integrals over the faces of the subregions which are *exterior*

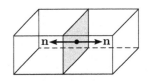

Figure 3.4

181

to region B remain in the summation. Hence the sum of all the surface integrals is equal to an integral over the surface of the region B; that is,

$$\sum_{i=1}^{N} \oint_{\delta S_i} \mathbf{F} \cdot \mathbf{n}\, dA = \oint_S \mathbf{F} \cdot \mathbf{n}\, dA.$$

Substituting this in Equation (3.5), we have

$$\sum_{i=1}^{N} \operatorname{div} \mathbf{F}(P_i)\, \delta V_i \simeq \oint_S \mathbf{F} \cdot \mathbf{n}\, dA. \qquad (3.6)$$

Now N, the number of terms in the sum, is inversely proportional to the mean volume, δV, of the volume elements. However, Equation (3.6) was obtained from Equation (3.4) by multiplying by δV_i and then summing from 1 to N (which is inversely proportional to δV). Hence the error in approximation (3.6) will be of the same order as the error in approximation (3.4), and so tends to zero as N tends to infinity; that is,

$$\lim_{N \to \infty} \left(\sum_{i=1}^{N} \operatorname{div} \mathbf{F}(P_i)\, \delta V_i \right) = \oint_S \mathbf{F} \cdot \mathbf{n}\, dA.$$

The limit of the sum on the left-hand side is by definition the volume integral of $\operatorname{div} \mathbf{F}$ over the region B; that is,

$$\lim_{N \to \infty} \left(\sum_{i=1}^{N} \operatorname{div} \mathbf{F}(P_i)\, \delta V_i \right) = \int_B \operatorname{div} \mathbf{F}\, dV.$$

So we conclude that

$$\int_B \operatorname{div} \mathbf{F}\, dV = \oint_S \mathbf{F} \cdot \mathbf{n}\, dA.$$

This is called *Gauss' Divergence Theorem* or, more concisely, either the *Divergence Theorem* or *Gauss' Theorem*.

Theorem 3.1   Gauss' Divergence Theorem

Let $\mathbf{F}$ be a vector field defined in a region B that is bounded by the surface S. Then

$$\int_B \operatorname{div} \mathbf{F}\, dV = \oint_S \mathbf{F} \cdot \mathbf{n}\, dA.$$

Example 3.1

Verify Gauss' (Divergence) Theorem for the vector field

$$\mathbf{F} = xy\,\mathbf{i} + yz\,\mathbf{j} + zx\,\mathbf{k}$$

and for the region B defined by

$$0 \le x \le 1, \qquad 0 \le y \le 1, \qquad 0 \le z \le 1 \qquad \text{(see Figure (3.5))}.$$

Solution

We have

$$\operatorname{div} \mathbf{F} = \frac{\partial}{\partial x}(xy) + \frac{\partial}{\partial y}(yz) + \frac{\partial}{\partial z}(zx) = y + z + x.$$

Figure 3.4 indicates the situation in which two adjacent subregions are rectangular boxes, but the argument is valid for adjacent subregions of any shape.

The mean volume is

$$\delta V = \frac{1}{N} \sum_{i=1}^{N} \delta V_i.$$

Do not worry about this error argument; just follow the general development to the statement of the theorem below.

The surface integral $\oint_S \mathbf{F} \cdot \mathbf{n}\, dA$ is independent of N.

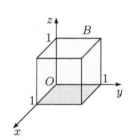

Figure 3.5

Therefore

$$\int_B \operatorname{div} \mathbf{F} \, dV = \int_{z=0}^{z=1} \left(\int_{y=0}^{y=1} \left(\int_{x=0}^{x=1} (x + y + z) \, dx \right) dy \right) dz$$

$$= \int_{z=0}^{z=1} \left(\int_{y=0}^{y=1} \left(\tfrac{1}{2} + y + z \right) dy \right) dz$$

$$= \int_{z=0}^{z=1} (1 + z) \, dz = \tfrac{3}{2}.$$

The surface integral $\oint_S \mathbf{F} \cdot \mathbf{n} \, dA$ has contributions from all six faces of the cube. On the face $x = 0$, the outward normal is $\mathbf{n} = -\mathbf{i}$, and $\mathbf{F} = yz\,\mathbf{j}$. Hence, $\mathbf{F} \cdot \mathbf{n} = 0$ and

$$\int_{\text{face } x=0} \mathbf{F} \cdot \mathbf{n} \, dA = 0.$$

On the face $x = 1$, the outward normal is $\mathbf{n} = \mathbf{i}$, and $\mathbf{F} = y\,\mathbf{i} + yz\,\mathbf{j} + z\,\mathbf{k}$. Hence, $\mathbf{F} \cdot \mathbf{n} = y$. Now $\delta A = \delta y \, \delta z$, and

$$\int_{\text{face } x=1} \mathbf{F} \cdot \mathbf{n} \, dA = \int_{z=0}^{z=1} \left(\int_{y=0}^{y=1} y \, dy \right) dz$$

$$= \int_{z=0}^{z=1} \tfrac{1}{2} \, dz = \tfrac{1}{2}.$$

Similarly, for the other four faces, we find

$$\int_{\text{face } y=0} \mathbf{F} \cdot \mathbf{n} \, dA = 0, \qquad \int_{\text{face } y=1} \mathbf{F} \cdot \mathbf{n} \, dA = \tfrac{1}{2},$$

$$\int_{\text{face } z=0} \mathbf{F} \cdot \mathbf{n} \, dA = 0, \qquad \int_{\text{face } z=1} \mathbf{F} \cdot \mathbf{n} \, dA = \tfrac{1}{2}.$$

Adding the contributions from all of the faces, we obtain

$$\oint_S \mathbf{F} \cdot \mathbf{n} \, dA = 0 + \tfrac{1}{2} + 0 + \tfrac{1}{2} + 0 + \tfrac{1}{2} = \tfrac{3}{2}.$$

Therefore,

$$\int_B \operatorname{div} \mathbf{F} \, dV = \oint_S \mathbf{F} \cdot \mathbf{n} \, dA,$$

as predicted by Gauss' Theorem. ∎

Exercise 3.6

Verify Gauss' (Divergence) Theorem for the vector field

$$\mathbf{F} = x^2 yz \, \mathbf{i} + xy^2 z \, \mathbf{j} + xyz^2 \, \mathbf{k}$$

and for the region B given by

$$0 \le x \le a, \qquad 0 \le y \le b, \qquad 0 \le z \le c.$$

Exercise 3.7

Use Gauss' Theorem to show that

$$\oint_S \mathbf{r} \cdot \mathbf{n} \, dA = 3V,$$

where $\mathbf{r}$ is the position vector and S is a closed surface enclosing a region B of volume V.

3.3   *The continuity equation*

In classical physics, the law of conservation of mass asserts that matter cannot be created or destroyed. In particular, this law may be applied to a fluid in motion, leading to the *continuity equation*. This equation is derived by finding two expressions for the rate of increase of the mass of fluid inside an arbitrary fixed region within the fluid.

Suppose that the fluid has density given by the scalar field ρ and velocity given by the vector field $\mathbf{u}$. Consider the fluid contained in an arbitrary fixed stationary region B, whose surface is S. The mass m_B of the fluid inside B at time t is given by

In general, both ρ and $\mathbf{u}$ may depend on position and time.

$$m_B = \int_B \rho \, dV,$$

and so the rate of increase of the mass inside B is

$$\dot{m}_B = \frac{d}{dt}\left(\int_B \rho \, dV\right) = \int_B \frac{\partial \rho}{\partial t} \, dV,$$

where we are able to take the derivative with respect to t inside the integral sign because the region B is fixed.

We use the ordinary derivative d/dt on the left, because $\int_B \rho \, dV$ is a function of t only. However, ρ is a function of position as well as time, and so we use the partial derivative $\partial/\partial t$ on the right.

Now, the volume flowing through an element of surface of area δA, in a time interval δt, is approximately $\mathbf{u} \cdot \mathbf{n} \, \delta A \, \delta t$, as you saw in Subsection 2.1. So the mass of fluid flowing through this element of surface in a time δt is $\rho \, \mathbf{u} \cdot \mathbf{n} \, \delta A \, \delta t$. Adding the contributions from all of the surface elements, the mass of fluid flowing out of the region B in the time δt is approximately

$$\delta t \oint_S \rho \, \mathbf{u} \cdot \mathbf{n} \, dA.$$

Hence, the rate of *decrease* of mass in the region B, due to fluid flowing out through the surface S, is given by the surface integral

$$\oint_S \rho \, \mathbf{u} \cdot \mathbf{n} \, dA.$$

The rate of *increase* of mass of the fluid in the region B, which is $\dot{m}_B$, is just the negative of this expression; that is,

$$\dot{m}_B = -\oint_S \rho \, \mathbf{u} \cdot \mathbf{n} \, dA.$$

We now have two expressions for the rate of increase of mass of fluid in the region B, and so, by the law of conservation of mass, they must be equal (assuming that there are no sources or sinks within the region). Hence

$$\int_B \frac{\partial \rho}{\partial t} \, dV = -\oint_S \rho \, \mathbf{u} \cdot \mathbf{n} \, dA$$

$$= -\int_B \operatorname{div}(\rho \, \mathbf{u}) \, dV, \qquad \text{using Gauss' Theorem.}$$

It follows that

$$\int_B \left(\frac{\partial \rho}{\partial t} + \operatorname{div}(\rho \, \mathbf{u})\right) dV = 0.$$

Now, the fixed region B can be chosen arbitrarily, and any continuous function whose integral is zero over any arbitrary region B must be the zero function. (If this were not the case, the function would be non-zero at *some* point P in the region. For definiteness, suppose that the function is positive at the point P. As the function is continuous, there must be some region surrounding the point P at all points of which the function is positive. Since the function is positive throughout this region, integrating the function over the region will give a positive result. But this contradicts

the fact that the integral over any region is zero, and so the assertion that
the function is identically zero must be true.) Therefore,

$$\frac{\partial \rho}{\partial t} + \text{div}(\rho\,\mathbf{u}) = 0,$$

which is called the *continuity equation*.

If a fluid has density ρ and velocity $\mathbf{u}$, then

$$\frac{\partial \rho}{\partial t} + \text{div}(\rho\,\mathbf{u}) = 0.$$

This is the **continuity equation**.

For a prescribed fluid motion to be possible, the continuity equation must
be satisfied, otherwise the law of conservation of mass would be violated.
Thus the continuity equation expresses a necessary condition for the
motion of a fluid.

The continuity equation is one of the basic equations of fluid mechanics.
You have seen how it is derived from the law of conservation of mass with
the aid of Gauss' Theorem. We return to this equation in *Unit 5*.

Exercise 3.8

(a) Show that, for an incompressible fluid of uniform constant density, the
continuity equation reduces to

$$\text{div}\,\mathbf{u} = 0.$$

(b) Hence show that the flow specified by the velocity field

$$\mathbf{u} = cx\,\mathbf{i} + cy\,\mathbf{j} - 2cz\,\mathbf{k}, \qquad \text{where } c \text{ is a constant,}$$

is possible for an incompressible fluid of uniform constant density.

End-of-section exercises

Exercise 3.9

Use Gauss' Theorem to evaluate the surface integral

$$\oint_S (\mathbf{grad}\,f) \cdot \mathbf{n}\,dA,$$

where f is the scalar field

$$f(x, y, z) = x^4 + y^4 + z^4,$$

and S is the spherical surface

$$x^2 + y^2 + z^2 = a^2.$$

Exercise 3.10

For a region B bounded by a surface S, show that

$$\oint_S \frac{\mathbf{r} \cdot \mathbf{n}}{r^2}\,dA = \int_B \frac{1}{r^2}\,dV,$$

where $\mathbf{r}$ is the position vector and $r = |\mathbf{r}|$.

4 Stokes' Theorem and irrotational vector fields

4.1 The curl of a vector field

The divergence of a vector field was defined in the previous section. This, when applied to the velocity field of a fluid, gives a measure of the amount of expansion of the fluid at any point. Another important property of a fluid is the rate of (local) *rotation* of the fluid at each point. (In contrast to a rigid body, the rotation of a fluid will generally vary from point to point.) A measure of this rotation is given by the *curl* of the velocity vector field. We now define the curl of a vector field.

The link between the curl and the local rotation of a velocity field was discussed in MST209 *Unit 24*.

Definition

Let $\mathbf{F}$ be a vector field defined over a region B, and let P be a point of B. The **curl** of $\mathbf{F}$, written $\mathbf{curl\,F}$, is a vector field whose components at the point P are defined by

$$(\mathbf{curl\,F}) \cdot \mathbf{n} = \lim_{A \to 0} \left(\frac{1}{A} \oint_C \mathbf{F} \cdot d\mathbf{r} \right),$$

where C is a small closed curve lying in a plane with unit normal $\mathbf{n}$, which encloses the point P, and A is the area enclosed by the curve C (see Figure 4.1). The direction of $\mathbf{n}$ and the direction of traversing the perimeter C are connected by the right-hand screw rule.

Here $(\mathbf{curl\,F}) \cdot \mathbf{n}$ is the component of $\mathbf{curl\,F}$ in the direction of $\mathbf{n}$.

This screw rule states that if a screw, pointed in the direction of $\mathbf{n}$, is rotated in the sense of travel around C, then the screw advances along $\mathbf{n}$.

This definition of the curl, as a limit of line integrals, is not particularly convenient when finding the curl of a vector field. However, any shape can be used for C, the curve of integration. Taking a rectangular shape leads to an expression for $\mathbf{curl\,F}$ which is easy to evaluate, just as the use of rectangular boxes in Subsection 3.1 led to the expression

$$\operatorname{div} \mathbf{F} = \frac{\partial F_1}{\partial x} + \frac{\partial F_2}{\partial y} + \frac{\partial F_3}{\partial z}$$

for the divergence of a vector field. The result is as follows.

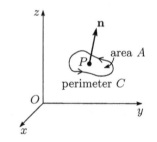

Figure 4.1

In Cartesian coordinates,

$$\mathbf{curl\,F} = \left(\frac{\partial F_3}{\partial y} - \frac{\partial F_2}{\partial z} \right) \mathbf{i} + \left(\frac{\partial F_1}{\partial z} - \frac{\partial F_3}{\partial x} \right) \mathbf{j} + \left(\frac{\partial F_2}{\partial x} - \frac{\partial F_1}{\partial y} \right) \mathbf{k}.$$

This complicated formula can be remembered by using determinants:

$$\mathbf{curl\,F} = \begin{vmatrix} \mathbf{i} & \mathbf{j} & \mathbf{k} \\ \partial/\partial x & \partial/\partial y & \partial/\partial z \\ F_1 & F_2 & F_3 \end{vmatrix}.$$

The formal expansion of this determinant gives the above expression for $\mathbf{curl\,F}$.

Exercise 4.1

Evaluate **curl F** for the vector field

$$\mathbf{F} = x\,\mathbf{i} + x^2 y^2\,\mathbf{j} + x^3 y^3 z^3\,\mathbf{k}$$

at the point $(1,1,1)$.

We can find expressions for **curl F** in cylindrical and spherical polar coordinates by similar methods. For example, in cylindrical polar coordinates, to find the z-component of **curl F** we should evaluate the line integral $\oint_C \mathbf{F} \cdot d\mathbf{r}$ around a curve whose sides consist of curve segments $r = $ constant and $\theta = $ constant (see Figure 4.2). We shall just quote the results.

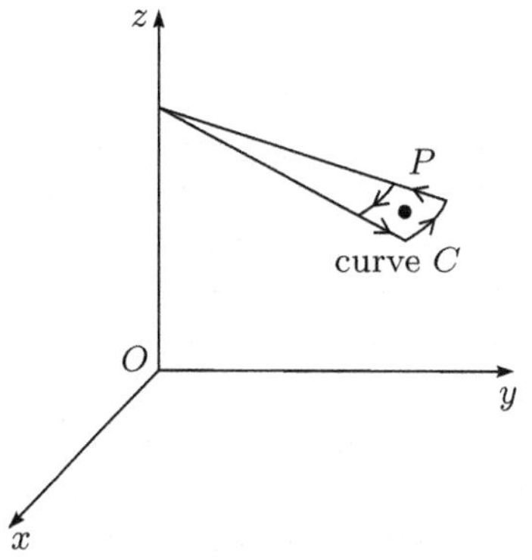

Figure 4.2

In cylindrical polar coordinates,

$$\mathbf{curl\,F} = \left(\frac{1}{r}\frac{\partial F_z}{\partial \theta} - \frac{\partial F_\theta}{\partial z} \right) \mathbf{e}_r + \left(\frac{\partial F_r}{\partial z} - \frac{\partial F_z}{\partial r} \right) \mathbf{e}_\theta$$

$$+ \left(\frac{1}{r}\frac{\partial}{\partial r}(rF_\theta) - \frac{1}{r}\frac{\partial F_r}{\partial \theta} \right) \mathbf{e}_z.$$

In spherical polar coordinates,

$$\mathbf{curl\,F} = \left(\frac{1}{r\sin\theta}\frac{\partial}{\partial \theta}(\sin\theta\, F_\phi) - \frac{1}{r\sin\theta}\frac{\partial F_\theta}{\partial \phi} \right) \mathbf{e}_r$$

$$+ \left(\frac{1}{r\sin\theta}\frac{\partial F_r}{\partial \phi} - \frac{1}{r}\frac{\partial}{\partial r}(rF_\phi) \right) \mathbf{e}_\theta + \left(\frac{1}{r}\frac{\partial}{\partial r}(rF_\theta) - \frac{1}{r}\frac{\partial F_r}{\partial \theta} \right) \mathbf{e}_\phi.$$

Just as the expression for **curl F** in Cartesian coordinates is most simply remembered in terms of a determinant, there are similar expressions for **curl F** in cylindrical and spherical polar coordinates.

In cylindrical polar coordinates,

$$\mathbf{curl\,F} = \frac{1}{r}\begin{vmatrix} \mathbf{e}_r & r\,\mathbf{e}_\theta & \mathbf{e}_z \\ \partial/\partial r & \partial/\partial \theta & \partial/\partial z \\ F_r & r\,F_\theta & F_z \end{vmatrix}.$$

Be careful with these expressions. Note the factors multiplying the components of **F** in the third rows.

In spherical polar coordinates,

$$\mathbf{curl\,F} = \frac{1}{r^2 \sin\theta}\begin{vmatrix} \mathbf{e}_r & r\,\mathbf{e}_\theta & r\sin\theta\,\mathbf{e}_\phi \\ \partial/\partial r & \partial/\partial \theta & \partial/\partial \phi \\ F_r & r\,F_\theta & r\sin\theta\,F_\phi \end{vmatrix}.$$

Exercise 4.2

Find **curl F** for the vector field defined in cylindrical polar coordinates by

$$\mathbf{F}(r, \theta, z) = \omega r\,\mathbf{e}_\theta, \qquad \text{where } \omega \text{ is a constant.}$$

4.2 Stokes' Theorem

Gauss' Theorem links a volume integral over a region to a surface integral over the bounding surface of that region. There is a corresponding theorem which links a surface integral over a surface to a line integral around the perimeter of that surface. We shall now derive that theorem.

If you wish to skip this derivation, go to Theorem 4.1 on page 189.

In Subsection 4.1, the curl of a vector field $\mathbf{F}$ at a point P was defined, in terms of the line integral of $\mathbf{F}$ around the perimeter, C, of a plane surface of area A containing P. Specifically,

$$(\mathbf{curl\,F}) \cdot \mathbf{n} = \lim_{A \to 0} \left(\frac{1}{A} \oint_C \mathbf{F} \cdot d\mathbf{r} \right),$$

where $\mathbf{n}$ is the unit normal to the surface, whose direction is connected to the sense of traversing the perimeter C by the right-hand screw rule (see Figure 4.3). For a small planar surface of area δA whose perimeter is δC, this definition leads to the approximation

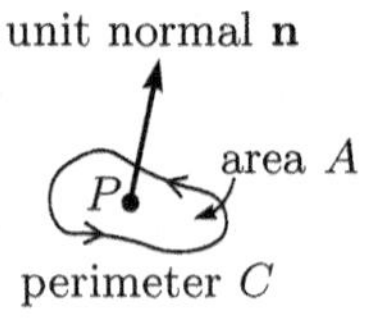

$$(\mathbf{curl\,F}) \cdot \mathbf{n} \simeq \frac{1}{\delta A} \oint_{\delta C} \mathbf{F} \cdot d\mathbf{r}. \qquad (4.1)$$

The error in this approximation tends to zero as the area δA tends to zero.

Figure 4.3

Now consider a *finite* open surface S with perimeter C (see Figure 4.4). We can divide the surface S into N surface elements labelled $1, 2, \ldots, N$, where the ith element δS_i has area δA_i and perimeter δC_i (see Figure 4.5). In the ith element, choose a point P_i, at which the unit normal to the surface is $\mathbf{n}_i$. Then Equation (4.1) gives the approximation

$$(\mathbf{curl\,F}(P_i)) \cdot \mathbf{n}_i \, \delta A_i \simeq \oint_{\delta C_i} \mathbf{F} \cdot d\mathbf{r}.$$

Adding these approximations for every surface element, we obtain

$$\sum_{i=1}^{N} (\mathbf{curl\,F}(P_i)) \cdot \mathbf{n}_i \, \delta A_i \simeq \sum_{i=1}^{N} \oint_{\delta C_i} \mathbf{F} \cdot d\mathbf{r}. \qquad (4.2)$$

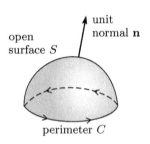

Figure 4.4

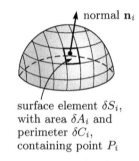

surface element δS_i, with area δA_i and perimeter δC_i, containing point P_i

Figure 4.5

The sum on the right includes contributions from the perimeters of all the surface elements, whether these edges are 'interior' or 'exterior' to the whole surface S. However, for two adjacent surface elements, the line integrals of $\mathbf{F}$ over the coincident portions of their edges cancel, because the edges are traversed in opposite directions (see Figure 4.6, in which the coincident curve segments AB and $A'B'$ have opposite directions). So the only remaining contributions to the line integrals arise from *exterior* edges, and hence the sum of the line integrals is equal to the line integral over C, the perimeter of the whole surface S; that is,

$$\sum_{i=1}^{N} \oint_{\delta C_i} \mathbf{F} \cdot d\mathbf{r} = \oint_C \mathbf{F} \cdot d\mathbf{r}.$$

So Equation (4.2) becomes

$$\sum_{i=1}^{N} (\mathbf{curl\,F}(P_i)) \cdot \mathbf{n}_i \, \delta A_i \simeq \oint_C \mathbf{F} \cdot d\mathbf{r}. \qquad (4.3)$$

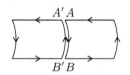

Figure 4.6

The number of terms, N, in this sum is inversely proportional to the mean area, δA, of the surface elements. Now, Equation (4.3) was obtained from Equation (4.1) by multiplying it by δA_i and summing from 1 to N, which is inversely proportional to δA. So the error in approximation (4.3) is of

The mean area is

$$\delta A = \frac{1}{N} \sum_{i=1}^{N} \delta A_i.$$

the same order as the error in approximation (4.1), and therefore tends to zero as $N \to \infty$. It follows that

$$\lim_{N \to \infty} \left(\sum_{i=1}^{N} (\mathbf{curl\,F}(P_i)) \cdot \mathbf{n}_i \, \delta A_i \right) = \oint_C \mathbf{F} \cdot d\mathbf{r}.$$

The line integral $\oint_C \mathbf{F} \cdot d\mathbf{r}$ is independent of N.

Finally, the limit on the left of this equation is, by definition, the surface integral of $(\mathbf{curl\,F}) \cdot \mathbf{n}$ over the whole surface S. So we conclude that

$$\int_S (\mathbf{curl\,F}) \cdot \mathbf{n} \, dA = \oint_C \mathbf{F} \cdot d\mathbf{r},$$

which is called *Stokes' Theorem*.

Theorem 4.1   Stokes' Theorem

Let $\mathbf{F}$ be a vector field defined on an open surface S and on its perimeter curve, C. Then

$$\int_S (\mathbf{curl\,F}) \cdot \mathbf{n} \, dA = \oint_C \mathbf{F} \cdot d\mathbf{r},$$

where the direction of the unit normal $\mathbf{n}$ to the surface S is connected to the sense of traversing the curve C by the right-hand screw rule.

Exercise 4.3

Verify Stokes' Theorem for the vector field

$$\mathbf{F} = -y\,\mathbf{i} + x\,\mathbf{j}$$

and for the surface S consisting of the upper half-surface of the unit sphere

$$x^2 + y^2 + z^2 = 1, \qquad z \geq 0.$$

4.3   Irrotational fields

In fluid mechanics, the curl of the velocity vector field $\mathbf{u}$ is called the *vorticity*, and it is a measure of how much the fluid is rotating at each point. A common property of fluid motion is that $\mathbf{curl\,u} = \mathbf{0}$ throughout the fluid. A vector field which satisfies this condition is said to be *irrotational*.

In Newtonian mechanics, force fields with this property are called 'conservative'. See MST209 *Unit 24*.

Definition

A vector field $\mathbf{F}$ is **irrotational** if, at every point,

$$\mathbf{curl\,F} = \mathbf{0}.$$

The terms 'irrotational' and 'conservative' mean the same, mathematically, but the first is usually applied to fluid velocity fields and the second to force fields.

Irrotational flows are particularly important because it can be shown that the flow of an inviscid fluid which is irrotational at a particular instant in time remains irrotational for all subsequent times. This means, for instance, that the motion of an inviscid fluid which is started from rest is always irrotational. This result is known as *Kelvin's Theorem*; we shall derive it and discuss the topic of vorticity in more detail in *Unit 7*.

'Irrotational flows' are those for which the velocity field is irrotational.

The mathematical results to be derived for irrotational vector fields in this subsection apply also, of course, to *conservative* fields.

Exercise 4.4

Show that the vector field

$$\mathbf{F}(x, y, z) = y^2 z^3\,\mathbf{i} + 2xyz^3\,\mathbf{j} + 3xy^2 z^2\,\mathbf{k}$$

is irrotational.

We have defined an irrotational field $\mathbf{F}$ to be one whose curl is zero. There are three alternative definitions of an irrotational vector field which are equivalent to this definition. The first of these is in terms of the line integral of $\mathbf{F}$ around a closed curve C. You are asked to establish this equivalence in the next two exercises.

Exercise 4.5

If $\mathbf{F}$ is an irrotational field, use Stokes' Theorem to show that the line integral of $\mathbf{F}$ around any closed path C is zero; that is,

$$\oint_C \mathbf{F} \cdot d\mathbf{r} = 0.$$

Exercise 4.6

If the line integral of the vector field $\mathbf{F}$ around any closed path C is zero, that is,

$$\oint_C \mathbf{F} \cdot d\mathbf{r} = 0,$$

use the definition of the curl,

$$(\mathbf{curl\,F}) \cdot \mathbf{n} = \lim_{A \to 0} \left(\frac{1}{A} \oint_C \mathbf{F} \cdot d\mathbf{r} \right),$$

to show that $\mathbf{F}$ is irrotational.

In the previous two exercises, you showed that if $\mathbf{curl\,F} = \mathbf{0}$, then $\oint_C \mathbf{F} \cdot d\mathbf{r} = 0$; and conversely, that if $\oint_C \mathbf{F} \cdot d\mathbf{r} = 0$ then $\mathbf{curl\,F} = \mathbf{0}$. This means that the two statements '$\mathbf{curl\,F} = \mathbf{0}$' and '$\oint_C \mathbf{F} \cdot d\mathbf{r} = 0$ for any closed path C' are equivalent, and so we could alternatively have defined an irrotational field as:

$\mathbf{F}$ is irrotational if $\oint_C \mathbf{F} \cdot d\mathbf{r} = 0$ for any closed path C.

The value of the line integral of a vector field will depend not only on the endpoints A and B of the integration, but usually also on the particular path of integration C from A to B (see Figure 4.7). However, we can show that if $\mathbf{F}$ is irrotational then this line integral is independent of the path.

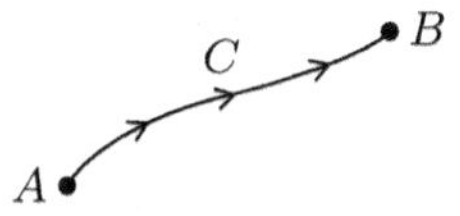

Figure 4.7

Example 4.1

Show that if the vector field $\mathbf{F}$ is irrotational, then the line integral

$$\int_C \mathbf{F} \cdot d\mathbf{r}$$

from a point A to a point B is independent of the path C from A to B.

Solution

Consider any two paths, ADB and AEB, from A to B, as shown in Figure 4.8. In order to prove that the line integral from A to B is independent of the path of integration, we need to show that

$$\int_{ADB} \mathbf{F} \cdot d\mathbf{r} = \int_{AEB} \mathbf{F} \cdot d\mathbf{r}.$$

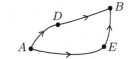

Figure 4.8

As $\mathbf{F}$ is irrotational, the line integral of $\mathbf{F}$ around any closed path must be zero. In particular, its integral around the path $ADBEA$ must be zero, that is,

$$\oint_{ADBEA} \mathbf{F} \cdot d\mathbf{r} = 0.$$

We can split the path of integration here into two segments, ADB and BEA, and so obtain

$$\int_{ADB} \mathbf{F} \cdot d\mathbf{r} + \int_{BEA} \mathbf{F} \cdot d\mathbf{r} = 0.$$

If we now reverse the direction of integration along the path BEA, this will change the sign of the line integral. Hence

$$\int_{ADB} \mathbf{F} \cdot d\mathbf{r} - \int_{AEB} \mathbf{F} \cdot d\mathbf{r} = 0.$$

Therefore,

$$\int_{ADB} \mathbf{F} \cdot d\mathbf{r} = \int_{AEB} \mathbf{F} \cdot d\mathbf{r},$$

which is the result we need in order to conclude that the line integral of an irrotational field is independent of the path of integration between the two endpoints, A and B. ◼

Exercise 4.7

Prove that if the line integral $\int_C \mathbf{F} \cdot d\mathbf{r}$ of a vector field $\mathbf{F}$ from any point A to any point B is independent of the path of integration C from A to B, then the vector field $\mathbf{F}$ is irrotational.

Example 4.1 and Exercise 4.7 show that a second equivalent definition of an irrotational field is:

$\mathbf{F}$ is irrotational if $\int_C \mathbf{F} \cdot d\mathbf{r}$ is independent of the path of integration C from the point A to the point B.

Finally, we derive one very important property of any irrotational vector field: it can always be expressed as the gradient of a scalar field.

Example 4.2

Show that if **F** is an irrotational vector field, then there exists a scalar field ϕ such that

$$\mathbf{F} = \operatorname{\mathbf{grad}} \phi.$$

Solution

As **F** is irrotational, the line integral $\int_{OP} \mathbf{F} \cdot d\mathbf{r}$, from any fixed reference point O to the point P (see Figure 4.9), is independent of the path of integration from O to P, and depends only on the position of the point P. Denote the value of this line integral by

Figure 4.9

$$\phi(P) = \int_{OP} \mathbf{F} \cdot d\mathbf{r}. \tag{4.4}$$

To evaluate a line integral, we usually parametrise the path. Suppose that we express the path from O to P in terms of a parameter s, as

$$x = x(s), \qquad y = y(s), \qquad z = z(s).$$

For convenience, choose the parameter s to be the distance along the path from the point O (any other parametrisation is equally good). So $s = 0$ at O, and if $s = s_1$ at P, then P has coordinates $(x(s_1), y(s_1), z(s_1))$. If we write $\phi(s_1)$ for $\phi(P)$, Equation (4.4) becomes

$$\phi(s_1) = \int_{s=0}^{s=s_1} \mathbf{F} \cdot \frac{d\mathbf{r}}{ds} \, ds. \tag{4.5}$$

Now, the Fundamental Theorem of Calculus states that if

$$G(s_1) = \int_{s=s_0}^{s=s_1} g(s) \, ds,$$

then

$$g(s) = \frac{dG}{ds}(s), \qquad \text{for any } s \text{ between } s_0 \text{ and } s_1.$$

Applying this theorem to Equation (4.5), we obtain

$$\mathbf{F} \cdot \frac{d\mathbf{r}}{ds} = \frac{d\phi}{ds}.$$

By the Chain Rule for partial derivatives, this becomes

$$\mathbf{F} \cdot \frac{d\mathbf{r}}{ds} = \frac{\partial \phi}{\partial x} \frac{dx}{ds} + \frac{\partial \phi}{\partial y} \frac{dy}{ds} + \frac{\partial \phi}{\partial z} \frac{dz}{ds} = \operatorname{\mathbf{grad}} \phi \cdot \frac{d\mathbf{r}}{ds}.$$

Since
$$\mathbf{r} = x(s)\,\mathbf{i} + y(s)\,\mathbf{j} + z(s)\,\mathbf{k},$$
we have
$$\frac{d\mathbf{r}}{ds} = \frac{dx}{ds}\,\mathbf{i} + \frac{dy}{ds}\,\mathbf{j} + \frac{dz}{ds}\,\mathbf{k}.$$
See MST209 *Unit 6*.

Hence

$$(\mathbf{F} - \operatorname{\mathbf{grad}} \phi) \cdot \frac{d\mathbf{r}}{ds} = 0.$$

From Figure 4.10, it can be seen that

$$\frac{d\mathbf{r}}{ds} = \lim_{\delta s \to 0} \frac{\delta \mathbf{r}}{\delta s} = \mathbf{t},$$

where **t** is the unit vector tangential to the path at the point under consideration. Therefore

$$(\mathbf{F} - \operatorname{\mathbf{grad}} \phi) \cdot \mathbf{t} = 0.$$

For this dot product to be zero, either $\mathbf{F} - \operatorname{\mathbf{grad}} \phi = \mathbf{0}$ or the vector $\mathbf{F} - \operatorname{\mathbf{grad}} \phi$ is perpendicular to the unit vector **t**. But we can choose the path of integration through the point under consideration so that it has a tangent **t** in any direction. So the only possibility is that

$$\mathbf{F} = \operatorname{\mathbf{grad}} \phi. \quad \blacksquare$$

If a parameter other than distance along the path were chosen for s, then $d\mathbf{r}/ds$ would still be tangential to the path, but it would not (in general) be of unit length.

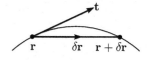

Figure 4.10

Exercise 4.8

(a) Show that, for any scalar field ϕ,

$$\mathbf{curl}\,(\mathbf{grad}\,\phi) = \mathbf{0}.$$

(b) Hence prove that, for any scalar field ϕ,

$$\mathbf{F} = \mathbf{grad}\,\phi$$

is an irrotational vector field.

Example 4.2 and Exercise 4.8 show that the third alternative definition of an irrotational vector field is:

F is irrotational if $\mathbf{F} = \mathbf{grad}\,\phi$ for some scalar field ϕ.

For an irrotational vector field **F**, the scalar field ϕ for which $\mathbf{grad}\,\phi = \mathbf{F}$ is called the *scalar potential* of **F**. It is unique to within a constant, which corresponds to the choice of reference point O in the definition $\phi(P) = \int_{OP} \mathbf{F} \cdot d\mathbf{r}$ (Equation (4.4)). Given any irrotational field **F**, rather than evaluate this line integral to find the corresponding scalar potential ϕ, it is usually easier to solve the three partial differential equations

$$\frac{\partial \phi}{\partial x} = F_1(x,y,z), \qquad \frac{\partial \phi}{\partial y} = F_2(x,y,z), \qquad \frac{\partial \phi}{\partial z} = F_3(x,y,z),$$

which arise from the equation $\mathbf{F} = \mathbf{grad}\,\phi$.

You saw how to solve such a system of partial differential equations in *Unit 3* Subsection 1.2.

Exercise 4.9

Find the vector field **F** whose scalar potential is

$$\phi(x,y,z) = xy^2 z^3.$$

Exercise 4.10

Find the scalar potential ϕ corresponding to the irrotational vector field

$$\mathbf{F} = yz\,\mathbf{i} + (xz + 2yz)\,\mathbf{j} + (y^2 + xy)\,\mathbf{k}.$$

This subsection has defined the term 'irrotational' for a vector field and introduced three alternative equivalent definitions. These definitive properties of an irrotational field are listed below. Note that we can use any one of them to prove that a vector field is irrotational, and then immediately deduce that the other properties hold.

Properties of an irrotational vector field F

(a) $\mathbf{curl}\,\mathbf{F} = \mathbf{0}$ (definition).

(b) The line integral $\oint_C \mathbf{F} \cdot d\mathbf{r}$ around any closed path C is zero.

(c) The line integral $\int_{AB} \mathbf{F} \cdot d\mathbf{r}$ is independent of the path of integration from the point A to the point B.

(d) There exists a scalar field ϕ such that $\mathbf{F} = \mathbf{grad}\,\phi$.

Recall that 'irrotational' means the same as 'conservative', so all of these properties apply also to conservative fields, as shown in MST209 *Unit 24*.

As you will see in *Unit 11*, the scalar potential, ϕ, is a very useful tool when discussing irrotational fields in general, and the flow of inviscid fluids in particular. This is because it is a single function rather than the three functions (the three components) needed to specify the vector field **F**.

Exercise 4.11

From the expression $\mathbf{F} = \mathbf{grad}\,\phi$, defining the scalar potential ϕ of an irrotational field $\mathbf{F}$, show that

$$\int_{AB} \mathbf{F} \cdot d\mathbf{r} = \phi(B) - \phi(A).$$

The scalar potential

Given an irrotational vector field $\mathbf{F}$, a scalar field ϕ can be defined by

$$\phi(P) = \int_{OP} \mathbf{F} \cdot d\mathbf{r},$$

where O is a fixed reference point. This scalar field ϕ is such that

$$\mathbf{F} = \mathbf{grad}\,\phi,$$

and is called the **scalar potential** of $\mathbf{F}$. The scalar potential can be used to evaluate line integrals of the irrotational field $\mathbf{F}$; that is,

$$\int_{AB} \mathbf{F} \cdot d\mathbf{r} = \phi(B) - \phi(A).$$

In MST209 *Unit 24*, the *potential* or *potential field* U of a vector field $\mathbf{F}$ was defined so that

$$\mathbf{F} = -\,\mathbf{grad}\,U.$$

In this course we refer to $\phi = -U$ as the scalar potential, since this choice is usual where the velocity field of a fluid is involved.

Exercise 4.12

For the vector field of Exercise 4.10, find the value of the line integral $\int_{AB} \mathbf{F} \cdot d\mathbf{r}$ along any path from the point A $(1,0,0)$ to the point B $(2,1,3)$.

End-of-section exercises

Exercise 4.13

Use Stokes' Theorem to evaluate the flux of the curl of the vector field

$$\mathbf{F} = (xz - y)\,\mathbf{i} + (x + y^2 z^2)\,\mathbf{j} + (x^3 + y^3)\,\mathbf{k}$$

through the portion S of the paraboloidal surface

$$x^2 + y^2 + z = 4$$

that lies above the plane $z = 0$ (shown in Figure 4.11).

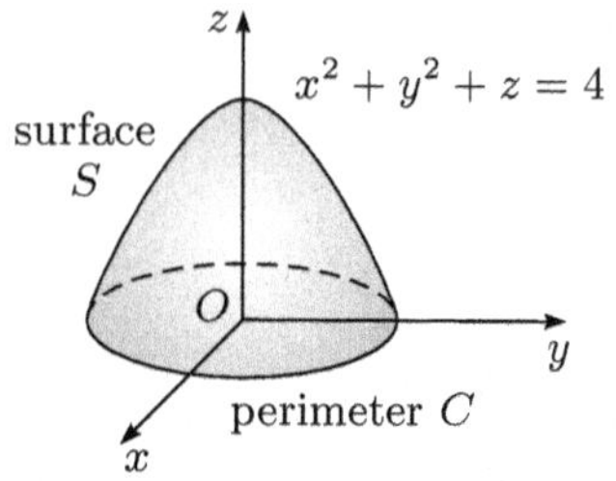

Figure 4.11

Exercise 4.14

(a) Show that the vector field $\mathbf{F}$, defined in cylindrical polar coordinates by

$$\mathbf{F} = 2r \sin\theta\,\mathbf{e}_r + r \cos\theta\,\mathbf{e}_\theta + 3z^2\,\mathbf{e}_z,$$

is irrotational.

(b) Find a scalar potential for this irrotational vector field.

(c) Hence evaluate the line integral $\int_{OA} \mathbf{F} \cdot d\mathbf{r}$ along the path defined parametrically by

$$r = t^2, \quad \theta = \pi t^3, \quad z = t^4 \qquad (0 \leq t \leq 1),$$

from the origin, O, to the point A with coordinates $r = 1$, $\theta = \pi$, $z = 1$.

5 Differential operators and identities

5.1 The vector differential operator ∇

We now introduce a special notation for the concepts of gradient, divergence and curl, which will enable us to express each of them in terms of one symbol. We start by considering the gradient of a scalar field f,

$$\operatorname{grad} f = \frac{\partial f}{\partial x}\mathbf{i} + \frac{\partial f}{\partial y}\mathbf{j} + \frac{\partial f}{\partial z}\mathbf{k},$$

which can be written in the symbolic form

$$\operatorname{grad} f = \left(\mathbf{i}\frac{\partial}{\partial x} + \mathbf{j}\frac{\partial}{\partial y} + \mathbf{k}\frac{\partial}{\partial z}\right) f,$$

where the suggested 'multiplication' actually leads to a differentation. The expression in the brackets is denoted by the symbol ∇ (which is pronounced 'del', or sometimes 'nabla'), so that

$$\nabla = \mathbf{i}\frac{\partial}{\partial x} + \mathbf{j}\frac{\partial}{\partial y} + \mathbf{k}\frac{\partial}{\partial z}.$$

The symbol ∇, and its use in writing expressions for div, **grad** and **curl**, were introduced in MST209 *Units 23* and *24*.

Using the symbol ∇, we have an alternative notation for the gradient of a scalar field f as ∇f, rather than $\operatorname{grad} f$. These two notations will be used quite interchangeably, depending on which is more convenient for particular needs.

The gradient of a scalar field f can be written as

$$\operatorname{grad} f \qquad \text{or} \qquad \nabla f.$$

Note that ∇f is usually pronounced 'grad eff' rather than 'del eff'.

The symbol ∇ is called a *vector differential operator*. It has no physical significance by itself, and takes on such significance only when applied to a function. Note that the operator is not actually a vector, although in many situations it is helpful to regard it as a vector. For example, when we apply the *vector* operator ∇ to the *scalar* field f, the outcome is a *vector* field, namely $\operatorname{grad} f = \nabla f$. That is why we call ∇ a *vector* differential operator, and print it in bold-face type, just as for normal vectors. In writing, you should underline the del symbol, just as for symbols which represent conventional vectors.

Vector times scalar gives a vector.

Similarly, **grad** and **curl** are printed in bold-face type, since the outcome for each of these is a vector quantity, whereas div appears in normal type, since its outcome is a scalar quantity. However, this is not a distinction that you need to worry about in handwritten work.

Having regarded ∇f as a 'multiplication' of a vector and a scalar, it is natural to consider the other possible multiplications involving vectors, namely, the dot product and the cross product. We look first at the dot product of the vector operator ∇ and the vector field $\mathbf{F}$. Applying the dot product formally, we have

$$\nabla \cdot \mathbf{F} = \left(\mathbf{i}\frac{\partial}{\partial x} + \mathbf{j}\frac{\partial}{\partial y} + \mathbf{k}\frac{\partial}{\partial z}\right) \cdot (F_1\mathbf{i} + F_2\mathbf{j} + F_3\mathbf{k})$$

$$= \frac{\partial}{\partial x}(F_1) + \frac{\partial}{\partial y}(F_2) + \frac{\partial}{\partial z}(F_3)$$

$$= \frac{\partial F_1}{\partial x} + \frac{\partial F_2}{\partial y} + \frac{\partial F_3}{\partial z}$$

$$= \operatorname{div} \mathbf{F}.$$

So the *dot product* of the *vector* operator ∇ and the *vector* field $\mathbf{F}$ gives the *scalar* field div $\mathbf{F}$.

Vector dot vector gives a scalar.

The divergence of a vector field $\mathbf{F}$ can be written as

    div $\mathbf{F}$ or $\nabla \cdot \mathbf{F}$.

Note that $\nabla \cdot \mathbf{F}$ is usually pronounced 'div eff' rather than 'del dot eff'.

Now look at the cross product involving the del operator and a vector field.

Exercise 5.1

By formally applying the definition of the cross product to the del operator ∇ and the vector field $\mathbf{F}$, show that

$$\nabla \times \mathbf{F} = \mathbf{curl}\, \mathbf{F}.$$

Recall that
$$\mathbf{a} \times \mathbf{b} = \begin{vmatrix} \mathbf{i} & \mathbf{j} & \mathbf{k} \\ a_1 & a_2 & a_3 \\ b_1 & b_2 & b_3 \end{vmatrix}.$$

By writing $\mathbf{curl}\, \mathbf{F}$ as the 'vector product' between ∇ and $\mathbf{F}$, we have an easy method of remembering the complicated expression for $\mathbf{curl}\, \mathbf{F}$ in terms of its Cartesian coordinates.

The curl of a vector field $\mathbf{F}$ can be written as

    $\mathbf{curl}\, \mathbf{F}$ or $\nabla \times \mathbf{F}$.

Note that $\nabla \times \mathbf{F}$ is usually pronounced 'curl eff' rather than 'del cross eff'.

Apart from the del operator, ∇, there is one further differential operator which has wide application in fluid mechanics, as well as in other branches of mathematical physics, such as electromagnetism, quantum mechanics, elasticity and waves. This operator is called the *Laplacian operator* and is denoted by ∇^2. It can be derived by formally taking the dot product of the del operator with itself:

Here ∇^2 is pronounced 'del squared'.

$$\begin{aligned} \nabla^2 &= \nabla \cdot \nabla \\ &= \left(\mathbf{i}\frac{\partial}{\partial x} + \mathbf{j}\frac{\partial}{\partial y} + \mathbf{k}\frac{\partial}{\partial z} \right) \cdot \left(\mathbf{i}\frac{\partial}{\partial x} + \mathbf{j}\frac{\partial}{\partial y} + \mathbf{k}\frac{\partial}{\partial z} \right) \\ &= \frac{\partial}{\partial x}\left(\frac{\partial}{\partial x} \right) + \frac{\partial}{\partial y}\left(\frac{\partial}{\partial y} \right) + \frac{\partial}{\partial z}\left(\frac{\partial}{\partial z} \right) \\ &= \frac{\partial^2}{\partial x^2} + \frac{\partial^2}{\partial y^2} + \frac{\partial^2}{\partial z^2}. \end{aligned}$$

The Laplacian operator ∇^2 is a *scalar differential operator* and can act on either a scalar field f or a vector field $\mathbf{F}$.

Here ∇^2 is a *scalar* operator, and so is printed in normal type.

Definition

The **Laplacian operator** ∇^2 is defined by

$$\nabla^2 = \frac{\partial^2}{\partial x^2} + \frac{\partial^2}{\partial y^2} + \frac{\partial^2}{\partial z^2}.$$

For a scalar field f,

$$\nabla^2 f = \left(\frac{\partial^2}{\partial x^2} + \frac{\partial^2}{\partial y^2} + \frac{\partial^2}{\partial z^2}\right) f = \frac{\partial^2 f}{\partial x^2} + \frac{\partial^2 f}{\partial y^2} + \frac{\partial^2 f}{\partial z^2}.$$

Here $\nabla^2 f$ is a scalar.

For a vector field $\mathbf{F}$,

$$\nabla^2 \mathbf{F} = \left(\frac{\partial^2}{\partial x^2} + \frac{\partial^2}{\partial y^2} + \frac{\partial^2}{\partial z^2}\right)(F_1\,\mathbf{i} + F_2\,\mathbf{j} + F_3\,\mathbf{k})$$

Here $\nabla^2 \mathbf{F}$ is a vector.

$$= \left(\frac{\partial^2 F_1}{\partial x^2} + \frac{\partial^2 F_1}{\partial y^2} + \frac{\partial^2 F_1}{\partial z^2}\right)\mathbf{i} + \left(\frac{\partial^2 F_2}{\partial x^2} + \frac{\partial^2 F_2}{\partial y^2} + \frac{\partial^2 F_2}{\partial z^2}\right)\mathbf{j}$$

$$+ \left(\frac{\partial^2 F_3}{\partial x^2} + \frac{\partial^2 F_3}{\partial y^2} + \frac{\partial^2 F_3}{\partial z^2}\right)\mathbf{k}$$

$$= (\nabla^2 F_1)\,\mathbf{i} + (\nabla^2 F_2)\,\mathbf{j} + (\nabla^2 F_3)\,\mathbf{k}.$$

Exercise 5.2

Evaluate $\nabla^2 f$ for the scalar field

$$f(x, y, z) = 2x^2 - y^2 - z^2 + 3xz.$$

In Exercise 5.2, the scalar field satisfies the equation $\nabla^2 f = 0$. This equation is called *Laplace's equation*. In fluid mechanics, an irrotational flow of an incompressible fluid is determined by Laplace's equation, $\nabla^2 f = 0$, where the function f is the scalar potential of the velocity field. This important type of fluid motion will be discussed in *Unit 11*.

All of the operations that have been constructed from ∇ are *linear* operations, because differentiation is itself a linear operation. This means, for example, that if f, g are scalar fields and a, b are constants, then

$$\nabla(af + bg) = a\nabla f + b\nabla g.$$

Alternatively, this can be written as

$$\mathbf{grad}\,(af + bg) = a\,\mathbf{grad}\,f + b\,\mathbf{grad}\,g.$$

At this point a word of caution is in order: although it is useful to think of ∇ as a vector, *it is also a differential operator*, and therefore must not be treated blindly as a vector. For example, if $\mathbf{F}$ and $\mathbf{G}$ are vector fields and h is a scalar field, then

$$\mathbf{F} \cdot (h\,\mathbf{G}) = h\,(\mathbf{F} \cdot \mathbf{G}),$$

but

$$\nabla \cdot (h\,\mathbf{G}) \neq h\,(\nabla \cdot \mathbf{G}).$$

The correct expression for $\nabla \cdot (h\,\mathbf{G})$ appears shortly.

Exercise 5.3

By considering the scalar field $h = x$ and the vector field $\mathbf{G} = \mathbf{i}$, show that

$$\nabla \cdot (h\,\mathbf{G}) \neq h\,(\nabla \cdot \mathbf{G}).$$

The reason for this result is that ∇ is a *differential* operator, and as such differentiates any field in the expression immediately to the right of it. For instance, in the above example, the expression $\nabla \cdot (h\,\mathbf{G})$ involves a differentiation of the scalar field h as well as of the vector field $\mathbf{G}$, whereas the expression $h\,(\nabla \cdot \mathbf{G})$ involves only a differentiation of the vector field $\mathbf{G}$. This means that you must be very careful when changing the position of the del operator in an expression. The formulas for simplifying expressions such as $\nabla \cdot (h\,\mathbf{G})$ are given in the next subsection.

5.2 Some vector identities

In Exercise 4.8(a) you showed that, for any scalar field ϕ,

$$\mathbf{curl}\,(\mathbf{grad}\,\phi) = \mathbf{0}.$$

In terms of the operator ∇, this becomes

$$\nabla \times (\nabla\phi) = \mathbf{0}.$$

Here there are two successive applications of ∇; the result is an identity, which is to say that it holds for all scalar fields ϕ.

There are many useful identities which make it possible to simplify such composite expressions. The most common are listed below.

If f and g are scalar fields, and $\mathbf{F}$ and $\mathbf{G}$ are vector fields, then the following identities hold.

$$\mathbf{grad}\,(fg) = f\,\mathbf{grad}\,g + g\,\mathbf{grad}\,f \tag{5.1}$$

$$\mathrm{div}\,(f\,\mathbf{F}) = f\,\mathrm{div}\,\mathbf{F} + \mathbf{F}\cdot\mathbf{grad}\,f \tag{5.2}$$

$$\mathbf{curl}\,(f\,\mathbf{F}) = f\,\mathbf{curl}\,\mathbf{F} - \mathbf{F}\times\mathbf{grad}\,f \tag{5.3}$$

$$\mathbf{grad}\,(\mathbf{F}\cdot\mathbf{G}) = (\mathbf{G}\cdot\nabla)\,\mathbf{F} + (\mathbf{F}\cdot\nabla)\,\mathbf{G}$$
$$+\,\mathbf{G}\times\mathbf{curl}\,\mathbf{F} + \mathbf{F}\times\mathbf{curl}\,\mathbf{G} \tag{5.4}$$

$$\mathrm{div}\,(\mathbf{F}\times\mathbf{G}) = \mathbf{G}\cdot\mathbf{curl}\,\mathbf{F} - \mathbf{F}\cdot\mathbf{curl}\,\mathbf{G} \tag{5.5}$$

$$\mathbf{curl}\,(\mathbf{F}\times\mathbf{G}) = \mathbf{F}\,\mathrm{div}\,\mathbf{G} - \mathbf{G}\,\mathrm{div}\,\mathbf{F} + (\mathbf{G}\cdot\nabla)\,\mathbf{F} - (\mathbf{F}\cdot\nabla)\,\mathbf{G} \tag{5.6}$$

$$\mathrm{div}\,(\mathbf{grad}\,f) = \nabla^2 f \tag{5.7}$$

$$\mathbf{curl}\,(\mathbf{grad}\,f) = \mathbf{0} \tag{5.8}$$

$$\mathrm{div}\,(\mathbf{curl}\,\mathbf{F}) = 0 \tag{5.9}$$

$$\mathbf{curl}\,(\mathbf{curl}\,\mathbf{F}) = \mathbf{grad}\,(\mathrm{div}\,\mathbf{F}) - \nabla^2\mathbf{F} \tag{5.10}$$

Here the scalar differential operator $\mathbf{a}\cdot\nabla$ is

$$\mathbf{a}\cdot\nabla = a_1\frac{\partial}{\partial x} + a_2\frac{\partial}{\partial y} + a_3\frac{\partial}{\partial z}.$$

You will see it put to use in *Unit 5*.

You should not attempt to memorise these identities, but you should refer to the list above when you need them. For convenience, these formulas, together with other formulas derived in this unit which you may wish to refer to during your study of the course, are reproduced at the back of the *Handbook*.

You established Equation (5.8) in Exercise 4.8(a); two of the other identities are proved in the next example and exercise.

Example 5.1

Prove that

$$\operatorname{div}(f\,\mathbf{F}) = f\operatorname{div}\mathbf{F} + \mathbf{F}\cdot\operatorname{\mathbf{grad}} f.$$

This is Equation (5.2).

Solution

In Cartesian components,

$$f\,\mathbf{F} = fF_1\,\mathbf{i} + fF_2\,\mathbf{j} + fF_3\,\mathbf{k}.$$

Hence

$$\operatorname{div}(f\,\mathbf{F}) = \frac{\partial}{\partial x}(fF_1) + \frac{\partial}{\partial y}(fF_2) + \frac{\partial}{\partial z}(fF_3)$$

By the Product Rule,
$$\frac{\partial}{\partial x}(uv) = u\frac{\partial v}{\partial x} + v\frac{\partial u}{\partial x}.$$

$$= \left(f\frac{\partial F_1}{\partial x} + F_1\frac{\partial f}{\partial x}\right) + \left(f\frac{\partial F_2}{\partial y} + F_2\frac{\partial f}{\partial y}\right) + \left(f\frac{\partial F_3}{\partial z} + F_3\frac{\partial f}{\partial z}\right)$$

$$= f\left(\frac{\partial F_1}{\partial x} + \frac{\partial F_2}{\partial y} + \frac{\partial F_3}{\partial z}\right) + \left(F_1\frac{\partial f}{\partial x} + F_2\frac{\partial f}{\partial y} + F_3\frac{\partial f}{\partial z}\right)$$

$$= f\operatorname{div}\mathbf{F} + \mathbf{F}\cdot\operatorname{\mathbf{grad}} f. \quad\blacksquare$$

Exercise 5.4

Prove that

$$\operatorname{div}(\operatorname{\mathbf{curl}}\mathbf{F}) = 0.$$

This is Equation (5.9).

Exercise 5.5

By using Equation (5.4), show that

$$\operatorname{\mathbf{grad}}\left(\tfrac{1}{2}|\mathbf{u}|^2\right) = (\mathbf{u}\cdot\boldsymbol{\nabla})\,\mathbf{u} + \mathbf{u}\times(\operatorname{\mathbf{curl}}\mathbf{u}).$$

This result will be useful in *Unit 5.*

In Sections 1, 3 and 4, expressions were given for $\operatorname{\mathbf{grad}} f$, $\operatorname{div}\mathbf{F}$ and $\operatorname{\mathbf{curl}}\mathbf{F}$ in cylindrical and spherical polar coordinates. We can use these formulas to derive the expressions for $\nabla^2 f$ in cylindrical and spherical polar coordinates. These will be needed in *Unit 11* when investigating the irrotational flow of an incompressible fluid.

In cylindrical polar coordinates,

$$\operatorname{\mathbf{grad}} f = \frac{\partial f}{\partial r}\,\mathbf{e}_r + \frac{1}{r}\frac{\partial f}{\partial \theta}\,\mathbf{e}_\theta + \frac{\partial f}{\partial z}\,\mathbf{e}_z$$

See Subsection 1.3.

and

$$\operatorname{div}(F_r\,\mathbf{e}_r + F_\theta\,\mathbf{e}_\theta + F_z\,\mathbf{e}_z) = \frac{1}{r}\frac{\partial}{\partial r}(rF_r) + \frac{1}{r}\frac{\partial F_\theta}{\partial \theta} + \frac{\partial F_z}{\partial z}.$$

This is from Equation (3.2).

Now,

$$\nabla^2 f = \operatorname{div}(\operatorname{\mathbf{grad}} f),$$

This is Equation (5.7), which comes from $\nabla^2 = \boldsymbol{\nabla}\cdot\boldsymbol{\nabla}$.

so combining the above two expressions for the gradient and the divergence, we have

$$\nabla^2 f = \frac{1}{r}\frac{\partial}{\partial r}\left(r\frac{\partial f}{\partial r}\right) + \frac{1}{r}\frac{\partial}{\partial \theta}\left(\frac{1}{r}\frac{\partial f}{\partial \theta}\right) + \frac{\partial}{\partial z}\left(\frac{\partial f}{\partial z}\right)$$

$$= \frac{1}{r}\frac{\partial}{\partial r}\left(r\frac{\partial f}{\partial r}\right) + \frac{1}{r^2}\frac{\partial^2 f}{\partial \theta^2} + \frac{\partial^2 f}{\partial z^2}.$$

Exercise 5.6

Use the identity

$$\operatorname{div}(\mathbf{grad}\, f) = \nabla^2 f$$

This is Equation (5.7).

to find the expression for $\nabla^2 f$ in spherical polar coordinates.

In Cartesian coordinates,

$$\nabla^2 f = \frac{\partial^2 f}{\partial x^2} + \frac{\partial^2 f}{\partial y^2} + \frac{\partial^2 f}{\partial z^2}.$$

In cylindrical polar coordinates,

$$\nabla^2 f = \frac{1}{r}\frac{\partial}{\partial r}\left(r\frac{\partial f}{\partial r}\right) + \frac{1}{r^2}\frac{\partial^2 f}{\partial \theta^2} + \frac{\partial^2 f}{\partial z^2}.$$

As usual, $r \neq 0$ is required in each of these formulas.

In spherical polar coordinates,

$$\nabla^2 f = \frac{1}{r^2}\frac{\partial}{\partial r}\left(r^2\frac{\partial f}{\partial r}\right) + \frac{1}{r^2 \sin\theta}\frac{\partial}{\partial \theta}\left(\sin\theta\frac{\partial f}{\partial \theta}\right) + \frac{1}{r^2 \sin^2\theta}\frac{\partial^2 f}{\partial \phi^2}.$$

Exercise 5.7

By using the expression for $\nabla^2 f$ in spherical polar coordinates, show that the scalar field

$$f(r, \theta, \phi) = r\cos\theta \qquad (r \neq 0)$$

satisfies Laplace's equation, $\nabla^2 f = 0$.

Similarly, we could derive expressions for $\nabla^2 \mathbf{F}$ in cylindrical and spherical polar coordinates, by using the identity

$$\mathbf{curl}\,(\mathbf{curl}\,\mathbf{F}) = \mathbf{grad}\,(\operatorname{div}\mathbf{F}) - \nabla^2\mathbf{F},$$

This is Equation (5.10).

but these expressions are not very illuminating and will not be needed in this course.

5.3   Green's theorems

In Sections 3 and 4, Gauss' Theorem and Stokes' Theorem were proved. We can now use the identities of the previous subsection to derive various corollaries of these theorems.

Exercise 5.8

By applying Gauss' Theorem,

$$\int_B \operatorname{div}\mathbf{F}\, dV = \oint_S \mathbf{F}\cdot\mathbf{n}\, dA,$$

to the vector field

$$\mathbf{F} = f\,\mathbf{grad}\, g,$$

prove that

$$\int_B (f\,\nabla^2 g + \mathbf{grad}\, f \cdot \mathbf{grad}\, g)\, dV = \oint_S f\,(\mathbf{grad}\, g)\cdot\mathbf{n}\, dA.$$

The result obtained in the previous exercise,

$$\int_B (f\,\nabla^2 g + \mathbf{grad}\,f \cdot \mathbf{grad}\,g)\,dV = \oint_S f\,(\mathbf{grad}\,g)\cdot\mathbf{n}\,dA,$$

is called *Green's First Theorem*. On interchanging the symbols f and g in this formula, we have

$$\int_B (g\,\nabla^2 f + \mathbf{grad}\,g \cdot \mathbf{grad}\,f)\,dV = \oint_S g\,(\mathbf{grad}\,f)\cdot\mathbf{n}\,dA.$$

Subtracting these two results, we obtain *Green's Second Theorem*,

$$\int_B (f\,\nabla^2 g - g\,\nabla^2 f)\,dV = \oint_S (f\,\mathbf{grad}\,g - g\,\mathbf{grad}\,f)\cdot\mathbf{n}\,dA.$$

Rather confusingly, both of these theorems are often just referred to as *Green's Theorem*. They have wide application, particularly in the theory of partial differential equations.

George Green (1793–1841) was a pioneer in the mathematical theory of electromagnetism.

You will see an application of Green's First Theorem in *Unit 11*.

Exercise 5.9

By applying Stokes' Theorem to the vector field

$$\mathbf{F} = P(x,y)\,\mathbf{i} + Q(x,y)\,\mathbf{j}$$

and to a flat surface S in the (x,y)-plane, bounded by the curve C, show that

$$\int_S \left(\frac{\partial Q}{\partial x} - \frac{\partial P}{\partial y}\right)dx\,dy = \oint_C \left(P\frac{dx}{dt} + Q\frac{dy}{dt}\right)dt.$$

The result that you proved in Exercise 5.9 is often called *Green's Theorem in the Plane*. The three theorems bearing Green's name are stated below.

Theorem 5.1   Green's First Theorem

For a region B bounded by a surface S,

$$\int_B (f\,\nabla^2 g + \mathbf{grad}\,f \cdot \mathbf{grad}\,g)\,dV = \oint_S f\,(\mathbf{grad}\,g)\cdot\mathbf{n}\,dA.$$

Theorem 5.2   Green's Second Theorem

For a region B bounded by a surface S,

$$\int_B (f\,\nabla^2 g - g\,\nabla^2 f)\,dV = \oint_S (f\,\mathbf{grad}\,g - g\,\mathbf{grad}\,f)\cdot\mathbf{n}\,dA.$$

Theorem 5.3   Green's Theorem in the Plane

For a surface S in the (x,y)-plane, with perimeter C,

$$\int_S \left(\frac{\partial Q}{\partial x} - \frac{\partial P}{\partial y}\right)dx\,dy = \oint_C \left(P\frac{dx}{dt} + Q\frac{dy}{dt}\right)dt.$$

This completes the task of finding the expressions for the gradient, divergence and curl in Cartesian, cylindrical polar and spherical polar coordinates, and proving the integral theorems which connect them. Throughout the rest of the course, you will need to keep referring to these formulas, which are collected at the back of the *Handbook*.

End-of-section exercises

Exercise 5.10

For a scalar field f and a vector field $\mathbf{F}$, show that

$$\operatorname{div}(\mathbf{F} \times \operatorname{\mathbf{grad}} f) = \operatorname{\mathbf{grad}} f \cdot \operatorname{\mathbf{curl}} \mathbf{F}.$$

Hence prove that

$$\int_{B} \operatorname{\mathbf{grad}} f \cdot \operatorname{\mathbf{curl}} \mathbf{F} \, dV = \oint_{S} (\mathbf{F} \times \operatorname{\mathbf{grad}} f) \cdot \mathbf{n} \, dA,$$

where S is the bounding surface of a region B.

Exercise 5.11

Show that, for any two scalar fields f and g,

$$\operatorname{\mathbf{curl}}(f \operatorname{\mathbf{grad}} g) = \operatorname{\mathbf{grad}} f \times \operatorname{\mathbf{grad}} g.$$

Hence, show that

$$\int_{S} (\operatorname{\mathbf{grad}} f \times \operatorname{\mathbf{grad}} g) \cdot \mathbf{n} \, dA = \oint_{C} f \, (\operatorname{\mathbf{grad}} g) \cdot d\mathbf{r},$$

where C is the perimeter of an open surface S.

Outcomes

After studying this unit you should be able to:

- work with scalar and vector fields expressed in any of the Cartesian, cylindrical polar or spherical polar coordinate systems (referred to below as 'the standard coordinate systems'), and change from one of these systems to another as necessary;
- apply the important properties of the gradient of a scalar field;
- calculate the gradient of a scalar field in each of the standard coordinate systems;
- evaluate volume integrals of a scalar or vector field in each of the standard coordinate systems;
- evaluate surface integrals of a scalar or vector field in each of the standard coordinate systems;
- calculate the divergence of a vector field in each of the standard coordinate systems;
- apply Gauss' Divergence Theorem where appropriate;
- apply the continuity equation to verify that a given vector field and density field can represent a possible fluid flow;
- calculate the curl of a vector field in each of the standard coordinate systems;
- apply Stokes' Theorem where appropriate;
- apply the properties of an irrotational vector field;
- make use of the scalar potential of an irrotational vector field to evaluate line integrals of the vector field;
- interpret and use the vector differential operator ∇ and the Laplacian operator ∇^2 as appropriate, in each of the standard coordinate systems;
- apply as appropriate the various identities, involving div, **grad**, **curl**, $\mathbf{a} \cdot \nabla$ and ∇^2, given on page 198;
- follow the derivations of Green's theorems.

Solutions to the exercises

Section 1

Solution 1.1

(a) We have
$$x = r\cos\theta = 4\cos(\tfrac{2}{3}\pi) = -4\cos(\tfrac{1}{3}\pi) = -2,$$
$$y = r\sin\theta = 4\sin(\tfrac{2}{3}\pi) = 4\sin(\tfrac{1}{3}\pi) = 2\sqrt{3},$$
$$z = z = -3.$$
So the Cartesian coordinates of the point are
$$(-2, 2\sqrt{3}, -3).$$

(b) We have
$$r = \sqrt{x^2 + y^2} = \sqrt{(-3)^2 + (-3)^2} = 3\sqrt{2}.$$
As $y < 0$,
$$\theta = -\arccos\left(\frac{x}{r}\right) = -\arccos\left(\frac{-3}{3\sqrt{2}}\right) = -\tfrac{3}{4}\pi.$$
(Alternatively, $\tan\theta = -3/(-3) = 1$ and $(-3, -3)$ is in the third quadrant, so $\theta = -\tfrac{3}{4}\pi$.) Also $z = z = -5$.
So the cylindrical polar coordinates of the point are
$$(3\sqrt{2}, -\tfrac{3}{4}\pi, -5).$$

Solution 1.2

We have
$$\begin{aligned}
\mathbf{r} &= x\,\mathbf{i} + y\,\mathbf{j} + z\,\mathbf{k} \\
&= (r\cos\theta)(\cos\theta\,\mathbf{e}_r - \sin\theta\,\mathbf{e}_\theta) \\
&\quad + (r\sin\theta)(\sin\theta\,\mathbf{e}_r + \cos\theta\,\mathbf{e}_\theta) + (z)(\mathbf{e}_z) \\
&= (r\cos^2\theta + r\sin^2\theta)\mathbf{e}_r + z\,\mathbf{e}_z \\
&= r\,\mathbf{e}_r + z\,\mathbf{e}_z.
\end{aligned}$$
(Alternatively, a short cut is possible by spotting that
$$r\cos\theta\,\mathbf{i} + r\sin\theta\,\mathbf{j} = r(\cos\theta\,\mathbf{i} + \sin\theta\,\mathbf{j}) = r\,\mathbf{e}_r.)$$

Solution 1.3

(a) By using $\mathbf{e}_r \cdot \mathbf{e}_r = 1$, $\mathbf{e}_\theta \cdot \mathbf{e}_\theta = 1$, $\mathbf{e}_z \cdot \mathbf{e}_z = 1$ and $\mathbf{e}_r \cdot \mathbf{e}_\theta = 0$, $\mathbf{e}_\theta \cdot \mathbf{e}_z = 0$, $\mathbf{e}_z \cdot \mathbf{e}_r = 0$, we have
$$\begin{aligned}
\mathbf{a} \cdot \mathbf{b} &= (a_r\mathbf{e}_r + a_\theta\mathbf{e}_\theta + a_z\mathbf{e}_z) \cdot (b_r\mathbf{e}_r + b_\theta\mathbf{e}_\theta + b_z\mathbf{e}_z) \\
&= a_r b_r\,\mathbf{e}_r \cdot \mathbf{e}_r + a_r b_\theta\,\mathbf{e}_r \cdot \mathbf{e}_\theta + a_r b_z\,\mathbf{e}_r \cdot \mathbf{e}_z \\
&\quad + a_\theta b_r\,\mathbf{e}_\theta \cdot \mathbf{e}_r + a_\theta b_\theta\,\mathbf{e}_\theta \cdot \mathbf{e}_\theta + a_\theta b_z\,\mathbf{e}_\theta \cdot \mathbf{e}_z \\
&\quad + a_z b_r\,\mathbf{e}_z \cdot \mathbf{e}_r + a_z b_\theta\,\mathbf{e}_z \cdot \mathbf{e}_\theta + a_z b_z\,\mathbf{e}_z \cdot \mathbf{e}_z \\
&= a_r b_r + a_\theta b_\theta + a_z b_z.
\end{aligned}$$

(b) By using $\mathbf{e}_r \times \mathbf{e}_r = 0$, $\mathbf{e}_\theta \times \mathbf{e}_\theta = 0$, $\mathbf{e}_z \times \mathbf{e}_z = 0$ and $\mathbf{e}_r \times \mathbf{e}_\theta = \mathbf{e}_z$, $\mathbf{e}_\theta \times \mathbf{e}_z = \mathbf{e}_r$, $\mathbf{e}_z \times \mathbf{e}_r = \mathbf{e}_\theta$, we have
$$\begin{aligned}
\mathbf{a} \times \mathbf{b} &= (a_r\mathbf{e}_r + a_\theta\mathbf{e}_\theta + a_z\mathbf{e}_z) \times (b_r\mathbf{e}_r + b_\theta\mathbf{e}_\theta + b_z\mathbf{e}_z) \\
&= a_r b_r\,\mathbf{e}_r \times \mathbf{e}_r + a_r b_\theta\,\mathbf{e}_r \times \mathbf{e}_\theta + a_r b_z\,\mathbf{e}_r \times \mathbf{e}_z \\
&\quad + a_\theta b_r\,\mathbf{e}_\theta \times \mathbf{e}_r + a_\theta b_\theta\,\mathbf{e}_\theta \times \mathbf{e}_\theta + a_\theta b_z\,\mathbf{e}_\theta \times \mathbf{e}_z \\
&\quad + a_z b_r\,\mathbf{e}_z \times \mathbf{e}_r + a_z b_\theta\,\mathbf{e}_z \times \mathbf{e}_\theta + a_z b_z\,\mathbf{e}_z \times \mathbf{e}_z \\
&= (a_\theta b_z - a_z b_\theta)\,\mathbf{e}_r + (a_z b_r - a_r b_z)\,\mathbf{e}_\theta \\
&\quad + (a_r b_\theta - a_\theta b_r)\,\mathbf{e}_z.
\end{aligned}$$

This expression for the vector product can be remembered (as in the Cartesian case) by writing it as a determinant:
$$\mathbf{a} \times \mathbf{b} = \begin{vmatrix} \mathbf{e}_r & \mathbf{e}_\theta & \mathbf{e}_z \\ a_r & a_\theta & a_z \\ b_r & b_\theta & b_z \end{vmatrix}.$$

Solution 1.4

With reference to the figure below, we have
$$x = OQ\cos\phi = (OP\sin\theta)\cos\phi = r\sin\theta\cos\phi,$$
$$y = OQ\sin\phi = (OP\sin\theta)\sin\phi = r\sin\theta\sin\phi,$$
$$z = OP\cos\theta = r\cos\theta.$$

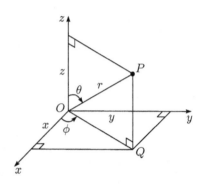

Solution 1.5

The partial derivatives of f are
$$\frac{\partial f}{\partial r} = 2r\sin\theta\,e^z, \qquad \frac{\partial f}{\partial\theta} = r^2\cos\theta\,e^z,$$
$$\frac{\partial f}{\partial z} = r^2\sin\theta\,e^z.$$
Therefore
$$\begin{aligned}
\operatorname{grad} f &= \frac{\partial f}{\partial r}\mathbf{e}_r + \frac{1}{r}\frac{\partial f}{\partial\theta}\mathbf{e}_\theta + \frac{\partial f}{\partial z}\mathbf{e}_z \\
&= 2r\sin\theta\,e^z\,\mathbf{e}_r + r\cos\theta\,e^z\,\mathbf{e}_\theta + r^2\sin\theta\,e^z\,\mathbf{e}_z.
\end{aligned}$$

Solution 1.6

The partial derivatives of f are
$$\frac{\partial f}{\partial r} = 2r\sin^2\theta\sin(2\phi),$$
$$\frac{\partial f}{\partial\theta} = 2r^2\sin\theta\cos\theta\sin(2\phi),$$
$$\frac{\partial f}{\partial\phi} = 2r^2\sin^2\theta\cos(2\phi).$$
Therefore
$$\begin{aligned}
\operatorname{grad} f &= \frac{\partial f}{\partial r}\mathbf{e}_r + \frac{1}{r}\frac{\partial f}{\partial\theta}\mathbf{e}_\theta + \frac{1}{r\sin\theta}\frac{\partial f}{\partial\phi}\mathbf{e}_\phi \\
&= 2r\sin^2\theta\sin(2\phi)\,\mathbf{e}_r \\
&\quad + 2r\sin\theta\cos\theta\sin(2\phi)\,\mathbf{e}_\theta \\
&\quad + 2r\sin\theta\cos(2\phi)\,\mathbf{e}_\phi.
\end{aligned}$$

Solution 1.7

The volume of the region is $V = \int_B dV$. Because of the rotational symmetry, we use cylindrical polar coordinates. So

$$V = \int_B r \, dr \, d\theta \, dz.$$

Begin with the θ integral. For fixed r and z, θ can take values between $\theta = -\pi$ and $\theta = \pi$. Next, take the r integral. For a fixed value of z, the variable r can take values between $r = 0$ and its value on the surface $x^2 + y^2 = z$. In cylindrical polar coordinates, this surface has equation $r^2 = z$, and so the upper limit for the r integral is $r = \sqrt{z}$ (see the figure below).

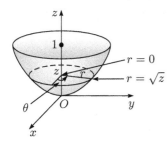

Finally, take the z integral. The minimum value of z is 0 and the maximum value is 1. (Any other order of integration is equally good.) Hence

$$V = \int_{z=0}^{z=1} \left(\int_{r=0}^{r=\sqrt{z}} \left(\int_{\theta=-\pi}^{\theta=\pi} r \, d\theta \right) dr \right) dz$$

$$= \int_{z=0}^{z=1} \left(\int_{r=0}^{r=\sqrt{z}} 2\pi r \, dr \right) dz$$

$$= \int_{z=0}^{z=1} \pi z \, dz = \tfrac{1}{2}\pi.$$

Solution 1.8

The volume of the sphere B is

$$V = \int_B dV = \int_B r^2 \sin\theta \, dr \, d\theta \, d\phi.$$

We integrate first with respect to ϕ, then with respect to θ, and finally with respect to r. (Any other order of integration is equally good.) For fixed θ and r, the variable ϕ can vary from $-\pi$ to π, so these are the limits for the ϕ integration. Secondly, for fixed r, the lower and upper values of θ are 0 and π. Finally, the lower limit of the r integral is the minimum value of r, which is 0, whereas the upper limit is the maximum value of r, which is R. Hence

$$V = \int_{r=0}^{r=R} \left(\int_{\theta=0}^{\theta=\pi} \left(\int_{\phi=-\pi}^{\phi=\pi} r^2 \sin\theta \, d\phi \right) d\theta \right) dr$$

$$= \int_{r=0}^{r=R} \left(\int_{\theta=0}^{\theta=\pi} 2\pi r^2 \sin\theta \, d\theta \right) dr$$

$$= \int_{r=0}^{r=R} 4\pi r^2 \, dr = \tfrac{4}{3}\pi R^3.$$

Solution 1.9

In spherical polar coordinates,

$$xyz = (r \sin\theta \cos\phi)(r \sin\theta \sin\phi)(r \cos\theta)$$
$$= r^3 \sin^2\theta \cos\theta \sin\phi \cos\phi,$$

and

$$\delta V \simeq r^2 \sin\theta \, \delta r \, \delta\theta \, \delta\phi.$$

Hence

$$\int_B xyz \, dV = \int_B r^5 \sin^3\theta \cos\theta \sin\phi \cos\phi \, dr \, d\theta \, d\phi.$$

The order of integration does not affect the limits of integration, which are: for r from 0 to 1, for θ from 0 to $\tfrac{1}{2}\pi$, and for ϕ from 0 to $\tfrac{1}{2}\pi$. So the volume integral reduces to

$$\int_{r=0}^{r=1} \left(\int_{\theta=0}^{\theta=\pi/2} \left(\int_{\phi=0}^{\phi=\pi/2} r^5 \sin^3\theta \cos\theta \sin\phi \cos\phi \, d\phi \right) d\theta \right) dr$$

$$= \int_{r=0}^{r=1} \left(\int_{\theta=0}^{\theta=\pi/2} \left[-\tfrac{1}{4} r^5 \sin^3\theta \cos\theta \cos(2\phi) \right]_{\phi=0}^{\phi=\pi/2} d\theta \right) dr$$

(having put $\sin\phi \cos\phi = \tfrac{1}{2}\sin(2\phi)$)

$$= \int_{r=0}^{r=1} \left(\int_{\theta=0}^{\theta=\pi/2} \tfrac{1}{2} r^5 \sin^3\theta \cos\theta \, d\theta \right) dr$$

$$= \int_{r=0}^{r=1} \left[\tfrac{1}{8} r^5 \sin^4\theta \right]_{\theta=0}^{\theta=\pi/2} dr$$

(using the substitution $u = \sin\theta$)

$$= \int_{r=0}^{r=1} \tfrac{1}{8} r^5 \, dr = \tfrac{1}{48}.$$

Solution 1.10

(a) In cylindrical polar coordinates,

$$\mathbf{grad} \, f = \frac{\partial f}{\partial r} \mathbf{e}_r + \frac{1}{r} \frac{\partial f}{\partial \theta} \mathbf{e}_\theta + \frac{\partial f}{\partial z} \mathbf{e}_z.$$

So

$$\mathbf{grad} \, f_1 = 3r^2 \sin^2\theta \, z^5 \, \mathbf{e}_r + 2r^2 \sin\theta \cos\theta \, z^5 \, \mathbf{e}_\theta$$
$$+ 5r^3 \sin^2\theta \, z^4 \, \mathbf{e}_z;$$
$$\mathbf{grad} \, f_2 = 4r^3 \cos^6\theta \, \mathbf{e}_r - 6r^3 \cos^5\theta \sin\theta \, \mathbf{e}_\theta.$$

(b) For two surfaces to be orthogonal, their normals must be orthogonal at each point. The normals to the surfaces are in the directions of $\mathbf{grad} \, f_1$ and $\mathbf{grad} \, f_2$ (by Property (c) on page 161), and for these to be perpendicular, we require $\mathbf{grad} \, f_1 \cdot \mathbf{grad} \, f_2 = 0$. Now, at the point (r, θ, z),

$$\mathbf{grad} \, f_1 \cdot \mathbf{grad} \, f_2$$
$$= 12r^5 \sin^2\theta \cos^6\theta \, z^5 - 12r^5 \sin^2\theta \cos^6\theta \, z^5 = 0.$$

Therefore the surfaces are orthogonal.

Section 2

Solution 2.1

The flux of fluid through the surface S is

$$\int_S \mathbf{u} \cdot \mathbf{n} \, dA.$$

Now, on the surface $r = R$, we have

$$\mathbf{u} = \frac{1}{R} \mathbf{e}_r.$$

The surface element is $\delta A = R \, \delta\theta \, \delta z$, and $\mathbf{n} = \mathbf{e}_r$.

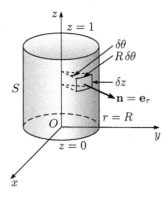

Hence, the flux of fluid through the surface is

$$\int_S \mathbf{u} \cdot \mathbf{n} \, dA = \int_S \frac{1}{R} \mathbf{e}_r \cdot \mathbf{e}_r \, R \, d\theta \, dz = \int_S d\theta \, dz$$

$$= \int_{z=0}^{z=1} \left(\int_{\theta=-\pi}^{\theta=\pi} d\theta \right) dz = 2\pi.$$

Solution 2.2

The surface area of the sphere S is

$$A = \int_S dA.$$

In terms of spherical polar coordinates, S is the surface $r = R$, and $\delta A \simeq R^2 \sin\theta \, \delta\theta \, \delta\phi$. Thus

$$A = \int_S R^2 \sin\theta \, d\theta \, d\phi.$$

This integral is equally easy to address with either of the two possible orders of integration. We elect to integrate first over ϕ and then over θ. For fixed θ, the variable ϕ can vary from $-\pi$ to π, and so these are the limits of the ϕ integration. The limits of the θ integration are the minimum and maximum values of θ, which are 0 and π, respectively. Hence, incorporating these limits, we obtain

$$A = \int_{\theta=0}^{\theta=\pi} \left(\int_{\phi=-\pi}^{\phi=\pi} R^2 \sin\theta \, d\phi \right) d\theta$$

$$= \int_{\theta=0}^{\theta=\pi} 2\pi R^2 \sin\theta \, d\theta = 4\pi R^2.$$

Solution 2.3

Using spherical polar coordinates, we have $\delta A \simeq R^2 \sin\theta \, \delta\theta \, \delta\phi$. Also, $\mathbf{n} = \mathbf{e}_r$.

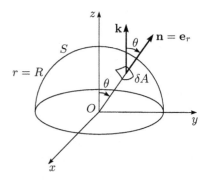

On the surface $r = R$, the vector field $\mathbf{F}$ becomes

$$\mathbf{F}(R, \theta, \phi) = R \cos\theta \, \mathbf{k}.$$

Hence

$$\mathbf{F} \cdot \mathbf{n} \, \delta A \simeq R^3 \sin\theta \cos\theta \, \delta\theta \, \delta\phi \, \mathbf{k} \cdot \mathbf{e}_r$$
$$= R^3 \sin\theta \cos^2\theta \, \delta\theta \, \delta\phi,$$

since $\mathbf{e}_r$ and $\mathbf{k}$ are unit vectors at an angle of θ to each other. Hence

$$\int_S \mathbf{F} \cdot \mathbf{n} \, dA = \int_S R^3 \sin\theta \cos^2\theta \, d\theta \, d\phi.$$

We integrate first with respect to ϕ and then with respect to θ. For fixed θ, the variable ϕ can vary from $-\pi$ to π. The minimum value of θ on the hemisphere is 0, and its maximum value is $\frac{1}{2}\pi$. Incorporating these limits, we obtain

$$\int_S \mathbf{F} \cdot \mathbf{n} \, dA = \int_{\theta=0}^{\theta=\pi/2} \left(\int_{\phi=-\pi}^{\phi=\pi} R^3 \sin\theta \cos^2\theta \, d\phi \right) d\theta$$

$$= \int_{\theta=0}^{\theta=\pi/2} 2\pi R^3 \sin\theta \cos^2\theta \, d\theta$$

$$= \left[-\tfrac{2}{3}\pi R^3 \cos^3\theta \right]_{\theta=0}^{\theta=\pi/2} = \tfrac{2}{3}\pi R^3.$$

Solution 2.4

The area is

$$A = \int_S dA,$$

where S is the curved surface of the cone. Now, in spherical polar coordinates, the cone has equation $\theta = \alpha$, and so we shall evaluate the surface integral by using spherical polar coordinates.

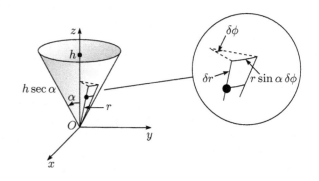

The surface element is approximately a rectangle (see the figure) with sides δr and $r \sin \alpha \, \delta \phi$. Hence

$$\delta A \simeq r \sin \alpha \, \delta r \, \delta \phi.$$

Therefore

$$A = \int_S r \sin \alpha \, dr \, d\phi.$$

We first integrate with respect to ϕ. For fixed r, the variable ϕ can vary from $-\pi$ to π. Then we integrate with respect to r. (Remember that, in spherical polar coordinates, r is the distance from the origin.) The minimum value of r is 0 and the maximum value is $h \sec \alpha$. Incorporating these limits, we obtain

$$A = \int_{r=0}^{r=h \sec \alpha} \left(\int_{\phi=-\pi}^{\phi=\pi} r \sin \alpha \, d\phi \right) dr$$

$$= \int_{r=0}^{r=h \sec \alpha} 2\pi r \sin \alpha \, dr = \pi h^2 \sin \alpha \sec^2 \alpha.$$

Solution 2.5

Because of the rotational symmetry of the surface of integration, we use cylindrical polar coordinates. The position vector is

$$\mathbf{r} \ (= x\mathbf{i} + y\mathbf{j} + z\mathbf{k}) = r\,\mathbf{e}_r + z\,\mathbf{e}_z \quad \text{(see Solution 1.2)},$$

and $|\mathbf{r}|^2 = r^2 + z^2$. Hence, the vector field is

$$\mathbf{F}(r, \theta, z) = (r^2 + z^2)(r\,\mathbf{e}_r + z\,\mathbf{e}_z).$$

On the surface of integration, $r = R$, we have

$$\mathbf{F} = (R^2 + z^2)(R\,\mathbf{e}_r + z\,\mathbf{e}_z).$$

The unit normal to the surface is $\mathbf{n} = \mathbf{e}_r$, and the surface element has area $\delta A = R \, \delta\theta \, \delta z$. Hence the flux of the vector field is

$$\int_S \mathbf{F} \cdot \mathbf{n} \, dA = \int_S R^2 (R^2 + z^2) \, d\theta \, dz.$$

The order of integration does not affect the limits of integration, which are: for θ from $-\pi$ to π, and for z from 0 to h. So we have

$$\int_S \mathbf{F} \cdot \mathbf{n} \, dA = \int_{z=0}^{z=h} \left(\int_{\theta=-\pi}^{\theta=\pi} R^2 (R^2 + z^2) \, d\theta \right) dz$$

$$= \int_{z=0}^{z=h} 2\pi R^2 (R^2 + z^2) \, dz$$

$$= 2\pi R^2 h (R^2 + \tfrac{1}{3} h^2).$$

Section 3

Solution 3.1

(a) Here $F_1 = x$, $F_2 = x^2 y^2$, $F_3 = x^3 y^3 z^3$, so

$$\frac{\partial F_1}{\partial x} = 1, \qquad \frac{\partial F_2}{\partial y} = 2x^2 y, \qquad \frac{\partial F_3}{\partial z} = 3x^3 y^3 z^2.$$

Hence

$$\text{div}\,\mathbf{F} = \frac{\partial F_1}{\partial x} + \frac{\partial F_2}{\partial y} + \frac{\partial F_3}{\partial z}$$

$$= 1 + 2x^2 y + 3x^3 y^3 z^2.$$

(b) At the point $(1, 2, 3)$, we have

$$\text{div}\,\mathbf{F}(1, 2, 3) = 1 + (2 \times 1^2 \times 2) + (3 \times 1^3 \times 2^3 \times 3^2)$$

$$= 1 + 4 + 216 = 221.$$

Solution 3.2

(a) Here $F_r = r^n$, $F_\theta = r \sin \theta$, $F_\phi = 0$; so, using Equation (3.3), we have

$$\text{div}\,\mathbf{F} = \frac{1}{r^2} \frac{\partial}{\partial r}(r^2 \times r^n) + \frac{1}{r \sin \theta} \frac{\partial}{\partial \theta}(r \sin^2 \theta)$$

$$= (n+2)r^{n-1} + 2\cos \theta.$$

(b) Now $F_r = 1/r$, $F_\theta = 0$, $F_z = z^2 - 1$; so using Equation (3.2), we have

$$\text{div}\,\mathbf{F} = \frac{1}{r} \frac{\partial}{\partial r}(1) + \frac{\partial}{\partial z}(z^2 - 1) = 2z.$$

Solution 3.3

The solution to this exercise is given in the audio session.

Solution 3.4

The surface integral has contributions from the top, the bottom and the curved surface of the cylinder.

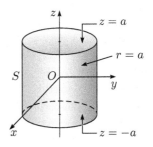

On the top face, $z = a$, we have

$$\mathbf{n} = \mathbf{e}_z \qquad \text{and} \qquad \mathbf{u} = r\,\mathbf{e}_r + a\,\mathbf{e}_z,$$

so $\mathbf{u} \cdot \mathbf{n} = a$. Hence

$$\int_{\text{top}} \mathbf{u} \cdot \mathbf{n} \, dA = a \int_{\text{top}} dA = \pi a^3,$$

since $\int_{\text{top}} dA$ is equal to the area of the top face of the cylinder, πa^2. Similarly, on the bottom face, $z = -a$, we have

$$\mathbf{n} = -\mathbf{e}_z \qquad \text{and} \qquad \mathbf{u} = r\,\mathbf{e}_r - a\,\mathbf{e}_z,$$

so $\mathbf{u} \cdot \mathbf{n} = a$, and

$$\int_{\text{bottom}} \mathbf{u} \cdot \mathbf{n} \, dA = \pi a^3.$$

On the curved surface, $r = a$, we have

$$\mathbf{n} = \mathbf{e}_r \qquad \text{and} \qquad \mathbf{u} = a\,\mathbf{e}_r + z\,\mathbf{e}_z,$$

so $\mathbf{u} \cdot \mathbf{n} = a$. Hence

$$\int_{\text{curved}} \mathbf{u} \cdot \mathbf{n} \, dA = a \int_{\text{curved}} dA = 4\pi a^3,$$

since $\int_{\text{curved}} dA$ is equal to the area of the curved surface of the cylinder, $2\pi a \times 2a = 4\pi a^2$.

Adding these three contributions, we obtain

$$\oint_S \mathbf{u} \cdot \mathbf{n} \, dA = 6\pi a^3.$$

Now, the volume of the cylinder is $\pi a^2 \times 2a = 2\pi a^3$, and so

$$\operatorname{div} \mathbf{u} = \lim_{V \to 0} \left(\frac{1}{V} \oint_S \mathbf{u} \cdot \mathbf{n}\, dA \right)$$

$$= \lim_{a \to 0} \left(\frac{6\pi a^3}{2\pi a^3} \right) = 3.$$

Solution 3.5

We have $u_r = r$, $u_\theta = 0$, $u_z = z$, so

$$\operatorname{div} \mathbf{u} = \frac{1}{r} \frac{\partial}{\partial r}(r^2) + \frac{\partial}{\partial z}(z) = 2 + 1 = 3.$$

Solution 3.6

We have

$$\operatorname{div} \mathbf{F} = \frac{\partial}{\partial x}(x^2 yz) + \frac{\partial}{\partial y}(xy^2 z) + \frac{\partial}{\partial z}(xyz^2) = 6xyz.$$

Hence

$$\int_B \operatorname{div} \mathbf{F}\, dV = \int_{z=0}^{z=c} \left(\int_{y=0}^{y=b} \left(\int_{x=0}^{x=a} 6xyz\, dx \right) dy \right) dz$$

$$= \int_{z=0}^{z=c} \left(\int_{y=0}^{y=b} 3a^2 yz\, dy \right) dz$$

$$= \int_{z=0}^{z=c} \tfrac{3}{2} a^2 b^2 z\, dz = \tfrac{3}{4} a^2 b^2 c^2.$$

The surface integral $\oint_S \mathbf{F} \cdot \mathbf{n}\, dA$ has contributions from all six faces. On the face $x = 0$, the outward normal is $\mathbf{n} = -\mathbf{i}$, and $\mathbf{F} = \mathbf{0}$. Hence $\mathbf{F} \cdot \mathbf{n} = 0$, and

$$\int_{\text{face } x=0} \mathbf{F} \cdot \mathbf{n}\, dA = 0.$$

On the face $x = a$, the outward normal is $\mathbf{n} = \mathbf{i}$, and $\mathbf{F} = a^2 yz\,\mathbf{i} + ay^2 z\,\mathbf{j} + ayz^2\,\mathbf{k}$. Hence, $\mathbf{F} \cdot \mathbf{n} = a^2 yz$.

Now, for the face $x = a$, $\delta A = \delta y\, \delta z$, and

$$\int_{\text{face } x=a} \mathbf{F} \cdot \mathbf{n}\, dA = \int_{z=0}^{z=c} \left(\int_{y=0}^{y=b} a^2 yz\, dy \right) dz$$

$$= \int_{z=0}^{z=c} \tfrac{1}{2} a^2 b^2 z\, dz = \tfrac{1}{4} a^2 b^2 c^2.$$

Similarly,

$$\int_{\text{face } y=0} \mathbf{F} \cdot \mathbf{n}\, dA = 0, \quad \int_{\text{face } y=b} \mathbf{F} \cdot \mathbf{n}\, dA = \tfrac{1}{4} a^2 b^2 c^2,$$

$$\int_{\text{face } z=0} \mathbf{F} \cdot \mathbf{n}\, dA = 0, \quad \int_{\text{face } z=c} \mathbf{F} \cdot \mathbf{n}\, dA = \tfrac{1}{4} a^2 b^2 c^2.$$

Adding the contributions from all six faces, we obtain

$$\oint_S \mathbf{F} \cdot \mathbf{n}\, dA = \tfrac{3}{4} a^2 b^2 c^2.$$

Hence

$$\int_B \operatorname{div} \mathbf{F}\, dV = \oint_S \mathbf{F} \cdot \mathbf{n}\, dA,$$

which confirms Gauss' Theorem for this case.

Solution 3.7

By Gauss' Theorem,

$$\oint_S \mathbf{r} \cdot \mathbf{n}\, dA = \int_B \operatorname{div} \mathbf{r}\, dV.$$

Now

$$\operatorname{div} \mathbf{r} = \operatorname{div} (x\,\mathbf{i} + y\,\mathbf{j} + z\,\mathbf{k})$$

$$= \frac{\partial}{\partial x}(x) + \frac{\partial}{\partial y}(y) + \frac{\partial}{\partial z}(z) = 3.$$

Therefore,

$$\oint_S \mathbf{r} \cdot \mathbf{n}\, dA = \int_B 3\, dV = 3 \int_B dV = 3V.$$

Solution 3.8

(a) As ρ is constant,

$$\frac{\partial \rho}{\partial t} = 0 \quad \text{and} \quad \operatorname{div} (\rho\, \mathbf{u}) = \rho \operatorname{div} \mathbf{u}.$$

Since $\rho > 0$, the continuity equation reduces to

$$\operatorname{div} \mathbf{u} = 0.$$

(b) For $\mathbf{u} = cx\,\mathbf{i} + cy\,\mathbf{j} - 2cz\,\mathbf{k}$,

$$\operatorname{div} \mathbf{u} = \frac{\partial}{\partial x}(cx) + \frac{\partial}{\partial y}(cy) + \frac{\partial}{\partial z}(-2cz)$$

$$= c + c - 2c = 0.$$

So $\mathbf{u}$ satisfies the continuity equation for an incompressible fluid of uniform constant density.

Solution 3.9

By Gauss' Theorem,

$$\oint_S (\operatorname{\mathbf{grad}} f) \cdot \mathbf{n}\, dA = \int_B \operatorname{div} (\operatorname{\mathbf{grad}} f)\, dV,$$

where B is the interior of the sphere bounded by S. Now $\operatorname{\mathbf{grad}} f = 4x^3\,\mathbf{i} + 4y^3\,\mathbf{j} + 4z^3\,\mathbf{k}$, so

$$\operatorname{div} (\operatorname{\mathbf{grad}} f) = 12(x^2 + y^2 + z^2).$$

Therefore

$$\oint_S (\operatorname{\mathbf{grad}} f) \cdot \mathbf{n}\, dA = \int_B 12(x^2 + y^2 + z^2)\, dV.$$

This integral can most easily be evaluated by using spherical polar coordinates, for which

$$x^2 + y^2 + z^2 = r^2 \quad \text{and} \quad \delta V \simeq r^2 \sin \theta\, \delta r\, \delta \theta\, \delta \phi.$$

Hence

$$\oint_S (\operatorname{\mathbf{grad}} f) \cdot \mathbf{n}\, dA = \int_B 12(x^2 + y^2 + z^2)\, dV$$

$$= \int_{r=0}^{r=a} \left(\int_{\theta=0}^{\theta=\pi} \left(\int_{\phi=-\pi}^{\phi=\pi} 12 r^4 \sin \theta\, d\phi \right) d\theta \right) dr$$

$$= \int_{r=0}^{r=a} \left(\int_{\theta=0}^{\theta=\pi} 24\pi r^4 \sin \theta\, d\theta \right) dr$$

$$= \int_{r=0}^{r=a} 48\pi r^4\, dr = \tfrac{48}{5} \pi a^5.$$

Solution 3.10

By Gauss' Theorem,
$$\oint_S \frac{\mathbf{r} \cdot \mathbf{n}}{r^2} \, dA = \int_B \operatorname{div}\left(\frac{\mathbf{r}}{r^2}\right) dV.$$
Now, since $\mathbf{r} = x\,\mathbf{i} + y\,\mathbf{j} + z\,\mathbf{k}$,
$$\operatorname{div}\left(\frac{\mathbf{r}}{r^2}\right) = \operatorname{div}\left(\frac{x}{x^2+y^2+z^2}\,\mathbf{i} + \frac{y}{x^2+y^2+z^2}\,\mathbf{j}\right.$$
$$\left. + \frac{z}{x^2+y^2+z^2}\,\mathbf{k}\right)$$
$$= \left(\frac{1}{x^2+y^2+z^2} - \frac{2x^2}{(x^2+y^2+z^2)^2}\right)$$
$$+ \left(\frac{1}{x^2+y^2+z^2} - \frac{2y^2}{(x^2+y^2+z^2)^2}\right)$$
$$+ \left(\frac{1}{x^2+y^2+z^2} - \frac{2z^2}{(x^2+y^2+z^2)^2}\right)$$
$$= \frac{3}{x^2+y^2+z^2} - \frac{2(x^2+y^2+z^2)}{(x^2+y^2+z^2)^2}$$
$$= \frac{1}{x^2+y^2+z^2} = \frac{1}{r^2}.$$
(Note: It would have been easier to evaluate $\operatorname{div}\left(\mathbf{r}/r^2\right)$ using spherical polar coordinates, since $\mathbf{r} = r\,\mathbf{e}_r$.)
Hence
$$\oint_S \frac{\mathbf{r} \cdot \mathbf{n}}{r^2} \, dA = \int_B \frac{1}{r^2} \, dV,$$
as required.

Section 4

Solution 4.1

We have
$$F_1 = x, \quad \text{so} \quad \frac{\partial F_1}{\partial y} = 0, \quad \frac{\partial F_1}{\partial z} = 0;$$
$$F_2 = x^2 y^2, \quad \text{so} \quad \frac{\partial F_2}{\partial z} = 0, \quad \frac{\partial F_2}{\partial x} = 2xy^2;$$
$$F_3 = x^3 y^3 z^3, \quad \text{so} \quad \frac{\partial F_3}{\partial x} = 3x^2 y^3 z^3, \quad \frac{\partial F_3}{\partial y} = 3x^3 y^2 z^3.$$
Therefore
$$\mathbf{curl\,F} = \left(\frac{\partial F_3}{\partial y} - \frac{\partial F_2}{\partial z}\right)\mathbf{i} + \left(\frac{\partial F_1}{\partial z} - \frac{\partial F_3}{\partial x}\right)\mathbf{j}$$
$$+ \left(\frac{\partial F_2}{\partial x} - \frac{\partial F_1}{\partial y}\right)\mathbf{k}$$
$$= 3x^3 y^2 z^3\,\mathbf{i} - 3x^2 y^3 z^3\,\mathbf{j} + 2xy^2\,\mathbf{k}.$$
At the point $(1, 1, 1)$, this gives
$$\mathbf{curl\,F}(1,1,1) = 3\,\mathbf{i} - 3\,\mathbf{j} + 2\,\mathbf{k}.$$

Solution 4.2

Here $F_r = 0$, $F_\theta = \omega r$, $F_z = 0$. Therefore
$$\mathbf{curl\,F} = -\frac{1}{r}\frac{\partial}{\partial z}\left(\omega r^2\right)\mathbf{e}_r + \frac{1}{r}\frac{\partial}{\partial r}\left(\omega r^2\right)\mathbf{e}_z = 2\omega\,\mathbf{e}_z.$$

Solution 4.3

Here $\mathbf{curl\,F}$ is equal to
$$\left(\frac{\partial}{\partial y}(0) - \frac{\partial}{\partial z}(x)\right)\mathbf{i} + \left(\frac{\partial}{\partial z}(-y) - \frac{\partial}{\partial x}(0)\right)\mathbf{j}$$
$$+ \left(\frac{\partial}{\partial x}(x) - \frac{\partial}{\partial y}(-y)\right)\mathbf{k} = 2\,\mathbf{k}, \quad \text{so}$$
$$\int_S (\mathbf{curl\,F}) \cdot \mathbf{n} \, dA = \int_S 2\,\mathbf{k} \cdot \mathbf{n} \, dA.$$
Using spherical polar coordinates, on the surface $r = 1$, $z \geq 0$, we have
$$\mathbf{k} \cdot \mathbf{n} = \cos\theta \qquad \text{(see the figure below)},$$
and
$$\delta A \simeq \sin\theta\,\delta\theta\,\delta\phi.$$

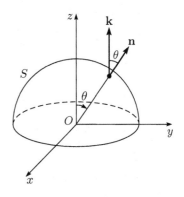

Therefore
$$\int_S 2\,\mathbf{k} \cdot \mathbf{n} \, dA = \int_{\theta=0}^{\theta=\pi/2} \left(\int_{\phi=-\pi}^{\phi=\pi} 2\sin\theta\cos\theta \, d\phi\right) d\theta$$
$$= \int_{\theta=0}^{\theta=\pi/2} 2\pi \sin(2\theta) \, d\theta$$
$$= \left[-\pi\cos(2\theta)\right]_{\theta=0}^{\theta=\pi/2} = 2\pi.$$
The perimeter of the hemisphere is the circle
$$x^2 + y^2 = 1, \quad z = 0,$$
which is expressed parametrically by
$$x = \cos\phi, \quad y = \sin\phi, \quad z = 0 \quad (-\pi < \phi \leq \pi).$$
Hence $\mathbf{F} = -\sin\phi\,\mathbf{i} + \cos\phi\,\mathbf{j}$ and
$$\frac{dx}{d\phi} = -\sin\phi, \quad \frac{dy}{d\phi} = \cos\phi, \quad \frac{dz}{d\phi} = 0.$$
So $\mathbf{F} \cdot d\mathbf{r}/d\phi = \sin^2\phi + \cos^2\phi = 1$, and
$$\oint_C \mathbf{F} \cdot d\mathbf{r} = \int_{\phi=-\pi}^{\phi=\pi} \mathbf{F} \cdot \frac{d\mathbf{r}}{d\phi} \, d\phi$$
$$= \int_{\phi=-\pi}^{\phi=\pi} d\phi = 2\pi.$$
Hence
$$\int_S (\mathbf{curl\,F}) \cdot \mathbf{n} \, dA = \oint_C \mathbf{F} \cdot d\mathbf{r},$$
as predicted by Stokes' Theorem.

Solution 4.4

We have

$$\mathbf{curl\,F} = \left(\frac{\partial F_3}{\partial y} - \frac{\partial F_2}{\partial z}\right)\mathbf{i} + \left(\frac{\partial F_1}{\partial z} - \frac{\partial F_3}{\partial x}\right)\mathbf{j}$$

$$+ \left(\frac{\partial F_2}{\partial x} - \frac{\partial F_1}{\partial y}\right)\mathbf{k}$$

$$= (6xyz^2 - 6xyz^2)\mathbf{i} + (3y^2z^2 - 3y^2z^2)\mathbf{j}$$
$$+ (2yz^3 - 2yz^3)\mathbf{k}$$

$$= \mathbf{0},$$

so $\mathbf{F}$ is an irrotational field.

Solution 4.5

As $\mathbf{F}$ is irrotational, $\mathbf{curl\,F} = \mathbf{0}$.

Now, by Stokes' Theorem, if S is any open surface whose perimeter is C, then

$$\oint_C \mathbf{F} \cdot d\mathbf{r} = \int_S (\mathbf{curl\,F}) \cdot \mathbf{n}\, dA = 0.$$

Solution 4.6

As $\oint_C \mathbf{F} \cdot d\mathbf{r} = 0$ for *every* closed path C,

$$(\mathbf{curl\,F}) \cdot \mathbf{n} = \lim_{A \to 0}\left(\frac{1}{A}\oint_C \mathbf{F} \cdot d\mathbf{r}\right) = 0,$$

where $\mathbf{n}$ is the unit normal to the plane surface S with perimeter C and area A. For this dot product to be zero, either $\mathbf{curl\,F} = \mathbf{0}$, or $\mathbf{curl\,F}$ is perpendicular to $\mathbf{n}$. (Note that $\mathbf{n} \neq \mathbf{0}$ because $\mathbf{n}$ is a unit vector.) But the dot product is zero for *any* unit vector $\mathbf{n}$, and so the first possibility must be true; that is,

$$\mathbf{curl\,F} = \mathbf{0},$$

which means that $\mathbf{F}$ is irrotational.

Solution 4.7

Choose any arbitrary closed curve C, and on it select points A, D, B, E as shown below.

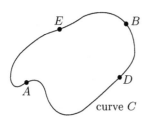

curve C

As the line integral is independent of the path from A to B,

$$\int_{ADB} \mathbf{F} \cdot d\mathbf{r} = \int_{AEB} \mathbf{F} \cdot d\mathbf{r}.$$

If we reverse the direction of integration along the path AEB, we change the sign of the integral. Hence

$$\int_{ADB} \mathbf{F} \cdot d\mathbf{r} = -\int_{BEA} \mathbf{F} \cdot d\mathbf{r}.$$

Therefore

$$\int_{ADB} \mathbf{F} \cdot d\mathbf{r} + \int_{BEA} \mathbf{F} \cdot d\mathbf{r} = 0,$$

that is,

$$\oint_{ADBEA} \mathbf{F} \cdot d\mathbf{r} = 0, \quad \text{or} \quad \oint_C \mathbf{F} \cdot d\mathbf{r} = 0,$$

where we have combined the segments ADB and BEA to form the closed path C. As this is true for every closed path C, the vector field $\mathbf{F}$ is irrotational.

Solution 4.8

(a) Now

$$\mathbf{grad}\,\phi = \frac{\partial \phi}{\partial x}\mathbf{i} + \frac{\partial \phi}{\partial y}\mathbf{j} + \frac{\partial \phi}{\partial z}\mathbf{k}, \quad \text{and}$$

$$\mathbf{curl}\,(F_1\,\mathbf{i} + F_2\,\mathbf{j} + F_3\,\mathbf{k})$$

$$= \left(\frac{\partial F_3}{\partial y} - \frac{\partial F_2}{\partial z}\right)\mathbf{i} + \left(\frac{\partial F_1}{\partial z} - \frac{\partial F_3}{\partial x}\right)\mathbf{j}$$

$$+ \left(\frac{\partial F_2}{\partial x} - \frac{\partial F_1}{\partial y}\right)\mathbf{k}.$$

Therefore $\mathbf{curl}\,(\mathbf{grad}\,\phi)$ is equal to

$$\left(\frac{\partial}{\partial y}\left(\frac{\partial \phi}{\partial z}\right) - \frac{\partial}{\partial z}\left(\frac{\partial \phi}{\partial y}\right)\right)\mathbf{i}$$

$$+ \left(\frac{\partial}{\partial z}\left(\frac{\partial \phi}{\partial x}\right) - \frac{\partial}{\partial x}\left(\frac{\partial \phi}{\partial z}\right)\right)\mathbf{j}$$

$$+ \left(\frac{\partial}{\partial x}\left(\frac{\partial \phi}{\partial y}\right) - \frac{\partial}{\partial y}\left(\frac{\partial \phi}{\partial x}\right)\right)\mathbf{k}$$

$$= \left(\frac{\partial^2 \phi}{\partial y \partial z} - \frac{\partial^2 \phi}{\partial z \partial y}\right)\mathbf{i} + \left(\frac{\partial^2 \phi}{\partial z \partial x} - \frac{\partial^2 \phi}{\partial x \partial z}\right)\mathbf{j}$$

$$+ \left(\frac{\partial^2 \phi}{\partial x \partial y} - \frac{\partial^2 \phi}{\partial y \partial x}\right)\mathbf{k}$$

$$= \mathbf{0}.$$

(b) If $\mathbf{F} = \mathbf{grad}\,\phi$, then

$$\mathbf{curl\,F} = \mathbf{curl}\,(\mathbf{grad}\,\phi) = \mathbf{0}, \quad \text{by part (a).}$$

So $\mathbf{F}$ is irrotational.

Solution 4.9

We have

$$\mathbf{F} = \mathbf{grad}\,\phi = \frac{\partial \phi}{\partial x}\mathbf{i} + \frac{\partial \phi}{\partial y}\mathbf{j} + \frac{\partial \phi}{\partial z}\mathbf{k}$$

$$= y^2z^3\,\mathbf{i} + 2xyz^3\,\mathbf{j} + 3xy^2z^2\,\mathbf{k}.$$

Solution 4.10

Since $\mathbf{F}$ is irrotational, $\mathbf{F} = \mathbf{grad}\,\phi$, that is,

$$F_1\,\mathbf{i} + F_2\,\mathbf{j} + F_3\,\mathbf{k} = \frac{\partial \phi}{\partial x}\mathbf{i} + \frac{\partial \phi}{\partial y}\mathbf{j} + \frac{\partial \phi}{\partial z}\mathbf{k}.$$

So

$$\frac{\partial \phi}{\partial x} = F_1 = yz, \tag{S.1}$$

$$\frac{\partial \phi}{\partial y} = F_2 = xz + 2yz, \tag{S.2}$$

$$\frac{\partial \phi}{\partial z} = F_3 = y^2 + xy. \tag{S.3}$$

Integrating Equation (S.1), we obtain

$$\phi(x, y, z) = xyz + f_1(y, z),$$

where f_1 is an arbitrary function. Hence

$$\frac{\partial \phi}{\partial y} = xz + \frac{\partial f_1}{\partial y}(y, z).$$

Comparing this with Equation (S.2), we have

$$\frac{\partial f_1}{\partial y}(y, z) = 2yz, \qquad \text{and so}$$

$$f_1(y, z) = y^2 z + f_2(z),$$

where f_2 is an arbitrary function. Now

$$\phi(x, y, z) = xyz + y^2 z + f_2(z), \qquad \text{so that}$$

$$\frac{\partial \phi}{\partial z} = xy + y^2 + \frac{df_2}{dz}.$$

Comparing this with Equation (S.3), we have

$$\frac{df_2}{dz} = 0, \qquad \text{that is,} \qquad f_2(z) = c,$$

where c is an arbitrary constant. Therefore

$$\phi(x, y, z) = xyz + y^2 z + c.$$

Solution 4.11

We have

$$\int_{AB} \mathbf{F} \cdot d\mathbf{r} = \int_{AB} \mathbf{grad}\, \phi \cdot d\mathbf{r}.$$

Now parametrise the path AB by

$$x = x(t), \qquad y = y(t), \qquad z = z(t),$$

with $t = t_A$ and $t = t_B$ at the endpoints A and B. Then

$$\int_{AB} \mathbf{F} \cdot d\mathbf{r} = \int_{t_A}^{t_B} \left(\mathbf{grad}\, \phi \cdot \frac{d\mathbf{r}}{dt} \right) dt$$

$$= \int_{t_A}^{t_B} \left(\frac{\partial \phi}{\partial x}\frac{dx}{dt} + \frac{\partial \phi}{\partial y}\frac{dy}{dt} + \frac{\partial \phi}{\partial z}\frac{dz}{dt} \right) dt$$

$$= \int_{t_A}^{t_B} \frac{d\phi}{dt}\, dt,$$

by using the Chain Rule. Hence

$$\int_{AB} \mathbf{F} \cdot d\mathbf{r} = [\phi(t)]_{t_A}^{t_B} = \phi(B) - \phi(A).$$

Solution 4.12

From Solution 4.10, the scalar potential for the given vector field is $\phi(x, y, z) = xyz + y^2 z + c$. Hence

$$\int_{AB} \mathbf{F} \cdot d\mathbf{r} = \phi(B) - \phi(A) = (6 + 3 + c) - c = 9.$$

Solution 4.13

The flux of $\mathbf{curl}\,\mathbf{F}$ through the surface S is

$$\int_S (\mathbf{curl}\,\mathbf{F}) \cdot \mathbf{n}\, dA = \oint_C \mathbf{F} \cdot d\mathbf{r},$$

by Stokes' Theorem. The perimeter, C, is

$$x^2 + y^2 = 4,$$

which is a circle of radius 2. Parametrically, this can be expressed as

$$x = 2\cos t, \qquad y = 2\sin t, \qquad z = 0 \quad (-\pi < t \le \pi).$$

Hence, on the perimeter C, we have

$$\mathbf{F} = -2\sin t\, \mathbf{i} + 2\cos t\, \mathbf{j} + (8\cos^3 t + 8\sin^3 t)\, \mathbf{k},$$

$$\mathbf{r} = 2\cos t\, \mathbf{i} + 2\sin t\, \mathbf{j},$$

$$\frac{d\mathbf{r}}{dt} = -2\sin t\, \mathbf{i} + 2\cos t\, \mathbf{j}.$$

So, on C,

$$\mathbf{F} \cdot \frac{d\mathbf{r}}{dt} = 4\sin^2 t + 4\cos^2 t = 4.$$

Therefore, the flux of $\mathbf{curl}\,\mathbf{F}$ through the surface S is

$$\int_S (\mathbf{curl}\,\mathbf{F}) \cdot \mathbf{n}\, dA = \oint_C \mathbf{F} \cdot \frac{d\mathbf{r}}{dt}\, dt = \int_{t=-\pi}^{t=\pi} 4\, dt = 8\pi.$$

Solution 4.14

(a) The vector field $\mathbf{F}$ is irrotational if $\mathbf{curl}\,\mathbf{F} = \mathbf{0}$. Now

$$\mathbf{curl}\,\mathbf{F} = \left(\frac{1}{r}\frac{\partial F_z}{\partial \theta} - \frac{\partial F_\theta}{\partial z} \right) \mathbf{e}_r + \left(\frac{\partial F_r}{\partial z} - \frac{\partial F_z}{\partial r} \right) \mathbf{e}_\theta$$

$$+ \left(\frac{1}{r}\frac{\partial}{\partial r}(r F_\theta) - \frac{1}{r}\frac{\partial F_r}{\partial \theta} \right) \mathbf{e}_z$$

$$= (0-0)\, \mathbf{e}_r + (0-0)\, \mathbf{e}_\theta + (2\cos\theta - 2\cos\theta)\, \mathbf{e}_z$$

$$= \mathbf{0}.$$

So the vector field $\mathbf{F}$ is irrotational.

(b) The scalar potential ϕ satisfies $\mathbf{F} = \mathbf{grad}\, \phi$. The three components of this equation in cylindrical polar coordinates are

$$\frac{\partial \phi}{\partial r} = 2r\sin\theta, \tag{S.4}$$

$$\frac{1}{r}\frac{\partial \phi}{\partial \theta} = r\cos\theta, \tag{S.5}$$

$$\frac{\partial \phi}{\partial z} = 3z^2. \tag{S.6}$$

From Equation (S.4),

$$\phi(r, \theta, z) = r^2 \sin\theta + f_1(\theta, z),$$

where f_1 is an arbitrary function. Substituting this into Equation (S.5), we obtain

$$r\cos\theta + \frac{1}{r}\frac{\partial f_1}{\partial \theta} = r\cos\theta, \qquad \text{that is,} \qquad \frac{\partial f_1}{\partial \theta} = 0.$$

So $f_1(\theta, z) = f_2(z)$, where f_2 is an arbitrary function, and

$$\phi(r, \theta, z) = r^2 \sin\theta + f_2(z).$$

Substituting this into Equation (S.6), we obtain

$$\frac{df_2}{dz} = 3z^2, \qquad \text{so} \qquad f_2(z) = z^3 + c,$$

where c is an arbitrary constant. Hence

$$\phi(r, \theta, z) = r^2 \sin\theta + z^3 + c.$$

(c) As $\mathbf{F}$ is irrotational, the line integral is independent of the path of integration. Its value is

$$\int_{OA} \mathbf{F} \cdot d\mathbf{r} = \phi(A) - \phi(O)$$

$$= (1^2 \times \sin\pi + 1^3) - (0^2 \times \sin 0 + 0^3) = 1.$$

211

Section 5

Solution 5.1

Formally, we have

$$\nabla \times \mathbf{F} = \left(\mathbf{i} \frac{\partial}{\partial x} + \mathbf{j} \frac{\partial}{\partial y} + \mathbf{k} \frac{\partial}{\partial z} \right) \times (F_1 \mathbf{i} + F_2 \mathbf{j} + F_3 \mathbf{k})$$

$$= \begin{vmatrix} \mathbf{i} & \mathbf{j} & \mathbf{k} \\ \partial/\partial x & \partial/\partial y & \partial/\partial z \\ F_1 & F_2 & F_3 \end{vmatrix}$$

$$= \left(\frac{\partial F_3}{\partial y} - \frac{\partial F_2}{\partial z} \right) \mathbf{i} + \left(\frac{\partial F_1}{\partial z} - \frac{\partial F_3}{\partial x} \right) \mathbf{j}$$

$$+ \left(\frac{\partial F_2}{\partial x} - \frac{\partial F_1}{\partial y} \right) \mathbf{k}$$

$$= \operatorname{curl} \mathbf{F}.$$

(Indeed, the determinant expression above for **curl F** was given in Subsection 4.1.)

Solution 5.2

We have

$$\frac{\partial f}{\partial x} = 4x + 3z, \qquad \frac{\partial f}{\partial y} = -2y, \qquad \frac{\partial f}{\partial z} = -2z + 3x,$$

$$\frac{\partial^2 f}{\partial x^2} = 4, \qquad \frac{\partial^2 f}{\partial y^2} = -2, \qquad \frac{\partial^2 f}{\partial z^2} = -2.$$

Hence

$$\nabla^2 f = \frac{\partial^2 f}{\partial x^2} + \frac{\partial^2 f}{\partial y^2} + \frac{\partial^2 f}{\partial z^2} = 4 - 2 - 2 = 0.$$

Solution 5.3

We have $h\,\mathbf{G} = x\,\mathbf{i}$. Therefore

$$\nabla \cdot (h\,\mathbf{G}) = \frac{\partial}{\partial x}(x) + \frac{\partial}{\partial y}(0) + \frac{\partial}{\partial z}(0) = 1.$$

But

$$\nabla \cdot \mathbf{G} = \frac{\partial}{\partial x}(1) + \frac{\partial}{\partial y}(0) + \frac{\partial}{\partial z}(0) = 0,$$

and so $h\,(\nabla \cdot \mathbf{G}) = 0$. Hence

$$\nabla \cdot (h\,\mathbf{G}) \neq h\,(\nabla \cdot \mathbf{G}).$$

Solution 5.4

We have

$$\operatorname{curl} \mathbf{F} = \left(\frac{\partial F_3}{\partial y} - \frac{\partial F_2}{\partial z} \right) \mathbf{i} + \left(\frac{\partial F_1}{\partial z} - \frac{\partial F_3}{\partial x} \right) \mathbf{j}$$

$$+ \left(\frac{\partial F_2}{\partial x} - \frac{\partial F_1}{\partial y} \right) \mathbf{k},$$

so div (**curl F**) is equal to

$$\frac{\partial}{\partial x}\left(\frac{\partial F_3}{\partial y} - \frac{\partial F_2}{\partial z} \right) + \frac{\partial}{\partial y}\left(\frac{\partial F_1}{\partial z} - \frac{\partial F_3}{\partial x} \right)$$

$$+ \frac{\partial}{\partial z}\left(\frac{\partial F_2}{\partial x} - \frac{\partial F_1}{\partial y} \right)$$

$$= \frac{\partial^2 F_3}{\partial x \partial y} - \frac{\partial^2 F_2}{\partial x \partial z} + \frac{\partial^2 F_1}{\partial y \partial z} - \frac{\partial^2 F_3}{\partial y \partial x}$$

$$+ \frac{\partial^2 F_2}{\partial z \partial x} - \frac{\partial^2 F_1}{\partial z \partial y} = 0.$$

Solution 5.5

Now,

$$\operatorname{grad}\left(\tfrac{1}{2}|\mathbf{u}|^2 \right) = \operatorname{grad}\left(\tfrac{1}{2}\mathbf{u} \cdot \mathbf{u} \right) = \tfrac{1}{2}\operatorname{grad}\left(\mathbf{u} \cdot \mathbf{u} \right).$$

Equation (5.4) is

$$\operatorname{grad}(\mathbf{F} \cdot \mathbf{G}) = (\mathbf{G} \cdot \nabla)\mathbf{F} + (\mathbf{F} \cdot \nabla)\mathbf{G}$$

$$+ \mathbf{G} \times \operatorname{curl}\mathbf{F} + \mathbf{F} \times \operatorname{curl}\mathbf{G}.$$

Hence

$$\operatorname{grad}(\mathbf{u} \cdot \mathbf{u}) = (\mathbf{u} \cdot \nabla)\mathbf{u} + (\mathbf{u} \cdot \nabla)\mathbf{u}$$

$$+ \mathbf{u} \times \operatorname{curl}\mathbf{u} + \mathbf{u} \times \operatorname{curl}\mathbf{u}$$

$$= 2(\mathbf{u} \cdot \nabla)\mathbf{u} + 2\mathbf{u} \times \operatorname{curl}\mathbf{u}.$$

Therefore

$$\operatorname{grad}\left(\tfrac{1}{2}|\mathbf{u}|^2 \right) = (\mathbf{u} \cdot \nabla)\mathbf{u} + \mathbf{u} \times \operatorname{curl}\mathbf{u}.$$

Solution 5.6

In spherical polar coordinates (from Subsection 1.3),

$$\operatorname{grad} f = \frac{\partial f}{\partial r}\mathbf{e}_r + \frac{1}{r}\frac{\partial f}{\partial \theta}\mathbf{e}_\theta + \frac{1}{r\sin\theta}\frac{\partial f}{\partial \phi}\mathbf{e}_\phi$$

and (from Equation (3.3))

$$\operatorname{div}(F_r\,\mathbf{e}_r + F_\theta\,\mathbf{e}_\theta + F_\phi\,\mathbf{e}_\phi)$$

$$= \frac{1}{r^2}\frac{\partial}{\partial r}(r^2 F_r) + \frac{1}{r\sin\theta}\frac{\partial}{\partial \theta}(\sin\theta\,F_\theta) + \frac{1}{r\sin\theta}\frac{\partial F_\phi}{\partial \phi}.$$

Combining these two expressions, we have

$$\nabla^2 f = \operatorname{div}(\operatorname{grad} f)$$

$$= \frac{1}{r^2}\frac{\partial}{\partial r}\left(r^2 \frac{\partial f}{\partial r} \right) + \frac{1}{r\sin\theta}\frac{\partial}{\partial \theta}\left(\frac{\sin\theta}{r}\frac{\partial f}{\partial \theta} \right)$$

$$+ \frac{1}{r\sin\theta}\frac{\partial}{\partial \phi}\left(\frac{1}{r\sin\theta}\frac{\partial f}{\partial \phi} \right)$$

$$= \frac{1}{r^2}\frac{\partial}{\partial r}\left(r^2 \frac{\partial f}{\partial r} \right) + \frac{1}{r^2\sin\theta}\frac{\partial}{\partial \theta}\left(\sin\theta\frac{\partial f}{\partial \theta} \right)$$

$$+ \frac{1}{r^2\sin^2\theta}\frac{\partial^2 f}{\partial \phi^2}.$$

Solution 5.7

The partial derivatives of f are

$$\frac{\partial f}{\partial r} = \cos\theta, \qquad \frac{\partial f}{\partial \theta} = -r\sin\theta, \qquad \frac{\partial f}{\partial \phi} = 0, \qquad \text{so}$$

$$\frac{\partial}{\partial r}\left(r^2 \frac{\partial f}{\partial r} \right) = \frac{\partial}{\partial r}(r^2 \cos\theta) = 2r\cos\theta,$$

$$\frac{\partial}{\partial \theta}\left(\sin\theta\frac{\partial f}{\partial \theta} \right) = \frac{\partial}{\partial \theta}(-r\sin^2\theta) = -2r\sin\theta\cos\theta,$$

$$\frac{\partial^2 f}{\partial \phi^2} = 0.$$

Hence, using the expression for $\nabla^2 f$ at the end of Solution 5.6 (or above the statement of Exercise 5.7), we have

$$\nabla^2 f = \frac{1}{r^2}(2r\cos\theta) + \frac{1}{r^2\sin\theta}(-2r\sin\theta\cos\theta)$$

$$= \frac{2\cos\theta}{r} - \frac{2\cos\theta}{r} = 0 \qquad (r \neq 0).$$

Solution 5.8

With $\mathbf{F} = f\,\mathbf{grad}\,g$, we have

$$\begin{aligned}
\operatorname{div}\mathbf{F} &= \operatorname{div}(f\,\mathbf{grad}\,g) \\
&= f\operatorname{div}(\mathbf{grad}\,g) + \mathbf{grad}\,g\cdot\mathbf{grad}\,f \\
&\qquad\qquad\text{(using Equation (5.2))} \\
&= f\,\nabla^2 g + \mathbf{grad}\,f\cdot\mathbf{grad}\,g \\
&\qquad\qquad\text{(using Equation (5.7))}
\end{aligned}$$

Substituting this into Gauss' Theorem, we obtain

$$\int_B (f\,\nabla^2 g + \mathbf{grad}\,f\cdot\mathbf{grad}\,g)\,dV = \oint_S f\,(\mathbf{grad}\,g)\cdot\mathbf{n}\,dA.$$

Solution 5.9

For a surface in the (x,y)-plane,

$$\delta A = \delta x\,\delta y \qquad\text{and}\qquad \mathbf{n} = \mathbf{k}.$$

Therefore

$$\int_S (\mathbf{curl}\,\mathbf{F})\cdot\mathbf{n}\,dA = \int_S (\mathbf{curl}\,\mathbf{F})\cdot\mathbf{k}\,dx\,dy$$

$$= \int_S \left(\frac{\partial Q}{\partial x} - \frac{\partial P}{\partial y}\right)dx\,dy.$$

For the perimeter C in the (x,y)-plane, with parameter t, we have

$$\frac{d\mathbf{r}}{dt} = \frac{dx}{dt}\,\mathbf{i} + \frac{dy}{dt}\,\mathbf{j}.$$

Therefore

$$\oint_C \mathbf{F}\cdot d\mathbf{r} = \oint_C \left(F_1\frac{dx}{dt} + F_2\frac{dy}{dt}\right)dt$$

$$= \oint_C \left(P\frac{dx}{dt} + Q\frac{dy}{dt}\right)dt.$$

So, by Stokes' Theorem,

$$\int_S \left(\frac{\partial Q}{\partial x} - \frac{\partial P}{\partial y}\right)dx\,dy = \oint_C \left(P\frac{dx}{dt} + Q\frac{dy}{dt}\right)dt.$$

Solution 5.10

Using the vector identities (5.5) and (5.8), we have

$$\begin{aligned}
\operatorname{div}(\mathbf{F}\times\mathbf{grad}\,f) &= \mathbf{grad}\,f\cdot\mathbf{curl}\,\mathbf{F} - \mathbf{F}\cdot\mathbf{curl}(\mathbf{grad}\,f) \\
&= \mathbf{grad}\,f\cdot\mathbf{curl}\,\mathbf{F}.
\end{aligned}$$

Now by Gauss' Theorem,

$$\oint_S (\mathbf{F}\times\mathbf{grad}\,f)\cdot\mathbf{n}\,dA = \int_B \operatorname{div}(\mathbf{F}\times\mathbf{grad}\,f)\,dV$$

$$= \int_B \mathbf{grad}\,f\cdot\mathbf{curl}\,\mathbf{F}\,dV.$$

Solution 5.11

Using the vector identities (5.3) and (5.8), we have

$$\begin{aligned}
\mathbf{curl}(f\,\mathbf{grad}\,g) &= f\,\mathbf{curl}(\mathbf{grad}\,g) - \mathbf{grad}\,g\times\mathbf{grad}\,f \\
&= \mathbf{grad}\,f\times\mathbf{grad}\,g.
\end{aligned}$$

By Stokes' Theorem,

$$\oint_C f\,(\mathbf{grad}\,g)\cdot d\mathbf{r} = \int_S \mathbf{curl}(f\,\mathbf{grad}\,g)\cdot\mathbf{n}\,dA$$

$$= \int_S (\mathbf{grad}\,f\times\mathbf{grad}\,g)\cdot\mathbf{n}\,dA.$$

Index